Foreword

Successful marketing is vital to the retention and expansion of markets for U.S. agricultural products. The ability to produce agricultural goods efficiently is not enough. We must be aware of the desires of those who buy our products, and recognize how our qualities can be tailored to this demand.

In many instances, marketing means merely getting out the word on the attractive characteristics of our goods. USDA sponsored a conference this summer on "Agricultural Products Quality and Competitiveness," at which the quality of many of our products was discussed. Quality is developed at every stage of agricultural production, from the use of proper fertilizers and modern cultivation techniques, to the use of new technologies in processing, storage, and transportation.

Consumers are becoming increasingly conscious of the health and nutritional aspects of their food. Understandably, they would like to avoid sacrificing taste, texture, and color as they improve their diets. Also, they would like greater convenience in their meals—whether it be shorter preparation time, or longer storage without losing freshness.

We have it in our power to meet this demand for higher quality. With each passing day, new technology is invented and adapted that can produce value-added agricultural products that are congruous with the values sought by our potential customers. To capitalize on our opportunities, a concerted effort must be made to identify these desired qualities, and to match the research and technology needs of the industry with our growing body of knowledge.

Opportunities for aggressive marketing should become even greater in the years ahead. Our proposal in the current Uruguay round of the General Agreement on Tariffs and Trade, when adopted, will remove government distortions from the agricultural marketplace. All of our trading partners will benefit from such an open trading environment, particularly because it will eliminate the great economic cost of inefficiently allocated resources, the inevitable byproduct of government interference in the marketplace. Greater economic growth should result, providing an even greater demand for higher quality food products. Freer trade means more trade, and consumers will be even more discriminating in response to the greater variety provided by increased market access.

The marketing efforts of our farm sector will determine whether or not we can meet this challenge and compete successfully in expanding world markets.

This volume of the Yearbook of Agriculture should prove of help to the individuals and firms whose job it is to meet the changing demands of our buyers, innovating and modifying our high-quality raw materials to give people the types of products they want.

American ingenuity, creativity, and resourcefulness—the distinguishing characteristics of our capitalist democracy—take a back seat to no one. This particularly holds true for U.S. agriculture.

Richard E. Lyng
Secretary of Agriculture

Preface

Have you shopped for food lately? Have you eaten out? Marketing of food and other agricultural products touches us all—farmers, consumers, and everyone between.

1988 has seen striking changes in the food marketplace. There are new products, new packaging, new departments in retail outlets—aimed at giving us high-quality, fresh, convenient, and safe food the way we want it. There is more food-to-go in stores and restaurants. The American agricultural sector—farmers, food processors, manufacturers, packagers, distributors, foodservice outlets, and others—have researched what we want and need, and then they have developed, produced, and distributed it for us, and sometimes convinced us to buy it.

That is marketing.

Agricultural industries follow a similar process to sell more U.S. exports, which are crucial to our farm sector and the U.S. balance of trade, and also important to people in other countries who, like us, want good and fairly priced agricultural products.

If you want to sell something, you need a buyer. If you want to buy something, you need a seller. The market is what brings buyers and sellers together—whether at the corner store or across the globe.

This Yearbook on "Marketing U.S. Agriculture" will help readers better understand the agricultural marketing system and the need for a strong marketing orientation. It is also a marketplace of marketing ideas. Experts from the private sector as well as Government and universities offer successful marketing strategies that have worked for firms and farmers.

Readers can shop here for ideas that may help them solve their own marketing problems.

Part I highlights how the U.S. marketing system for food and fiber works, and identifies major changes affecting that system.

Part II shows how to develop a successful marketing strategy—whether for an individual farmer, a group of farmers, an agribusiness firm, or U.S. agriculture as a whole.

In Parts III, IV, V, and VI, agricultural marketers tell their own success stories, focusing on four key aspects of the marketing process:

• Discovering what buyers want,
• Developing new or better products to meet demand,
• Delivering quality goods, and
• Promoting agricultural products.

Part VII offers Government and other resources for farmers and firms who want more information and help in marketing agricultural products.

The book treats marketing in the broadest sense, as a total orientation toward business enterprise—one which involves identifying demand and, to the extent possible, offering products that are responsive to that demand in quality and price. This broad sense of marketing includes marketing in the sense of the functions of processing, transferring, and delivering goods, as well as marketing in the sense of promoting and advertising them.

U.S. agriculture does respond to changes in demand; for example, many new food products contain less fat and salt, because that's what health-conscious consumers want.

The 1988 Yearbook of Agriculture is the latest in a series that predates USDA. I am honored and challenged

to be Editor of a Yearbook with these highlights in its publishing history:
- The first edition, 1849, was published by the U.S. Patent Office—before the tractor was invented,
- The 1862 edition was the first published by the newly created U.S. Department of Agriculture—before the first farmers' interest group, the Grange, was formed, and
- The 1894 edition was the first published with the name "Yearbook of the United States Department of Agriculture"—before radio was invented.

Just as there are many players in getting food to people, a large number of people work together to produce the Yearbook of Agriculture. The team includes the authors who write the chapters; the Yearbook Committee members, who help shape the book, identify topics and authors, and work with those authors and their chapters; the copy editor and photo editor, who get the words and pictures right; and the production team of designers and printers, who take a ragged, scribbled manuscript and turn it into the beautiful and solid object you have in hand.

Deborah Takiff Smith
Yearbook Editor

Contents

Foreword
Richard E. Lyng, Secretary of Agriculture i

Preface
Deborah Takiff Smith, Yearbook Editor ii

Part I. Marketing in a Changing World

1. Marketing Challenges in a Dynamic World 2
   Ewen M. Wilson

2. Food Marketing Industry Responds to Social Forces 6
   Alden C. Manchester

3. U.S. Food Marketing—A Specialized System 12
   Milton C. Hallberg

4. A Global Agribusiness Market Revolution 18
   Ray A. Goldberg

5. How Markets Communicate Information About
   Quality 25
   V. James Rhodes

Part II. Marketing Strategies

6. How To Develop a Successful Marketing Strategy 32
   James C. Cornelius

7. Marketing Strategies and Alternatives for Individual
   Farmers 37
   John (Jake) N. Ferris

8. Generic Advertising: A Marketing Strategy for Farmer
   Groups 44
   Olan D. Forker and Ronald W. Ward

9. Food Marketing Strategies for Firms 50
   Emerson M. Babb

10. Impact of Global Market Changes on U.S. Agricultural
    Producers 58
    Jerry Siebert

11. International Marketing Strategies 64
    Leo V. Mayer

Part III. Discovering What Buyers Want

12. What Do American Women Eat? 70
    Laura S. Sims and Alanna J. Moshfegh

13. Challenges Ahead for Supermarkets 76
    William T. Boehm

14. Do Your Own Market Research .80
    Judy Green and Nancy Grudens Schuck

15. U.S. Foodservice Industry: Responsive and Growing . . .86
    Steven D. Mayer

16. Tailoring U.S. Pork to Japanese Style 91
    C. Lynn Knipe

17. Florida Citrus Industry Sets High Standards 95
    Robert M. Behr

18. Keeping the Consumer in Mind .99
    Arnold E. Denton and Ginny Marcin

19. Inventing and Testing New Products 105
    Sylvia Schur

Part IV. New or Better Products To Meet Demand

20. ADAPT—Agricultural Diversification Spells Profit 112
    Richard Krumme

21. Oklahoma Farmers Try Alternatives 116
    Janet Kim Kaplan

22. Revolution on Supermarket Shelves: The Value Added
    Is Convenience 120
    Allen Bildner

23. Turkey Anytime 125
    Barbara A. Schuelke

24. How To Grow in a Maturing Foodservice Market 128
    Kristin S. Ferguson

25. Beef Makes a Comeback—by Listening to
    Consumers 133
    William G. Fielding

26. Frieda's Finest—Promoting Specialty Produce 137
    Karen Caplan

27. Fruit and Vegetable Varieties: New and More
    Marketable 141
    Howard J. Brooks

28. Marketing Ben & Jerry's Equals Fun 145
    Jeff Durstewitz

29. New Product Development: The Ocean Spray Way . . .149
    Tom Bullock

30. Commercializing Promising Technologies 153
    Paul F. O'Connell

31. Commodity Boards Help Develop New Products 159
    J. Patrick Boyle

Part V. Delivering Quality Goods

32. Productivity in the Food Industry 166
    John R. Block

33. A Jewel of a Market for Blue Diamond 169
    Walt Payne

34. They Chose to Fight 173
    Tom Jurchak

35. Marketing on a Central Illinois Cash-Grain Farm 179
    Darrel Good and Bob Sampson

36. Quality in Marketing Grain 182
    Mack N. Leath

37. Value-Added Packaging: An Edge in the
    Marketplace 187
    Susan B. Bassin

38. Moving the Farm Harvest 191
    Martin F. Fitzpatrick, Jr.

39. Convenience and Competition in Food Marketing and
    Distribution 196
    Drayton McLane, Jr.

40. Electronic Marketing Energizes Agricultural Trading . . . 199
    Wayne D. Purcell and James B. Bell

41. Scanning the Future 203
    Harold S. Ricker and Oral Capps, Jr.

42. Farmers' Marketing Businesses Will Surprise You 208
    Randall E. Torgerson and Gene Ingalsbe

43. Research To Make U.S. Products More Competitive . . . 213
    Gordon Rasmussen and R. Tom Hinsch

44. Technologies for Maintaining Food Quality 217
    Robert Davis

Part VI. Promoting Agricultural Products

45. Marketing Products to Foreign Customers 222
    William L. Davis

46. Building Foreign Markets in a Competitive
    Environment 226
    Kevin Rackstraw

47. Opening New Markets for U.S. Soybeans 230
    Wayne Bennett

48. Promoting High Quality U.S. Foods Through Regional
    Trade Associations 234
    James Youde

49. Exporting With Foreign Sales Agents 240
    Bruce J. Reynolds

50. Bringing Buyer and Seller Together 244
    Lisa Jager

51. Marketing Food Products Internationally—The Global
    Challenge 249
    John C. Lenker

52. Video Merchandising at Point of Sale 253
    Roger J. Stroh

53. "Jersey Fresh": A Fresh Idea in Farm Products
    Marketing 256
    Arthur R. Brown, Jr.

54. Potatoes—Turnaround in Consumer Attitudes 261
    Robert L. Mercer

55. Consumers Want Leaner Beef—and Get It 265
    John J. Francis

56. The Other White Meat® 268
    Charles R. Harness

57. Dairy Farmers Are Pioneers in Promotion 271
    Joseph J. Westwater

58. Problems in Evaluating Generic Dairy Promotion
    Programs 276
    Tom Cox and Bob Wills

59. Consumers "Take Comfort in Cotton" 281
    J. Nicholas Hahn

60. Louisiana, We're Really Cookin' Cajun 286
    Larry Michaud

Part VII. Where To Get More Marketing Information

61. U.S. Export Assistance Programs 294
    Melvin E. Sims

62. Getting the Facts and Figures for Farming 299
    Charles E. Caudill

63. From NAL: Everything You Want To Know About
    Agricultural Marketing 306
    Robert W. Butler

64. Agricultural Marketing Service—Its Programs and
    Services 311
    Information staff, Agricultural Marketing Service

65. How To Find Marketing Information You Can Use 314
    Ovid Bay

Index 319

Marketing Challenges
in a Dynamic World

Ewen M. Wilson, Assistant Secretary for Economics

Marketing the Nation's food and fiber is a huge undertaking. It embodies a variety of functions, employs about 10 percent of the total work force, contributes about 10 percent of the total gross national product, and is changing fast.

At one time, marketing consisted largely of transferring commodities between producers and consumers with little product change. Textbooks on marketing stressed how to bring buyers and sellers together, develop price information systems, establish consistent grades and product quality standards, and transport the product. Many firms viewed marketing as simply "order taking," rather than a complex set of activities designed to produce and distribute a product in the form and place desired by consumers. Farmers produced a given amount, and they faced a given demand in the marketplace. If production exceeded demand at an initial bargaining price, price declined until the market cleared. Prices were bid up when production fell short. Responses to lower or higher prices occurred in the next production cycle.

The marketing efforts of farmers were largely confined to discovering the "best" place and time to market their commodities. Institutional schemes were developed, such as forward contracting and futures markets, in an attempt to transfer price risk to others in the marketing system, and some firms became vertically integrated to manage risk. But producers paid little attention to influencing demand, or developing new products to satisfy changing needs.

Today, modern food stores and delicatessens and a dazzling array of restaurants ranging from fast food to exotic white tablecloth establishments demonstrate the complicated, dynamic nature of food marketing. Markets now offer a wide choice of products, various systems of distribution, and many built-in services such as precooked meats or microwave meals. Much of the present market diversity results from the keen awareness by food processors, manufacturers, and retailers that the market is consumer driven. Consumers vote every day in the marketplace with their dollars, and the market hears what consumers are saying.

Finding out what consumers want and how they feel about various product characteristics has become big business. Management practices now involve studying changes in consumer lifestyles and preferences, and adjusting businesses to capitalize on those changes. The food marketing industry spends billions of dollars each year on market research, new product development, and advertising.

Modern marketing involves product development, pricing strategies, efficient distribution, and product promotion. Marketing strategies integrate these components into an overall plan. Firms develop new products with desirable characteristics revealed through consumer research. Marketing managers are concerned with optimum pricing of products and efficient systems of distribution. Aggressive firms try to influence consumer tastes and preferences by advertising and other promotional activities.

Since farmers do not retain ownership of commodities through the marketing process, they usually are not involved in promoting their products. In recent years, however, many commodity organizations have assumed a greater role in promotional activities, with generic advertising programs funded by producer assessments. Such activities are informing consumers of the desirable characteristics of various foods, while, at the same time, helping producers understand the importance of responding to changing consumer demands.

Adapting to the 1980's

Lifestyles are changing rapidly. Today, many households have both spouses working outside the home. Over one-half of all American women over the age of 15 are in the work force, leaving less time to prepare food. This has increased the demand for highly prepared foods and for meals at restaurants. Product requirements in the prepared food and foodservice markets are different from the requirements of retail grocery stores. The rising proportion of food sold through foodservice outlets, or in a highly prepared form, is creating demands for new food characteristics. Furthermore, the growing internationalization of food processing has accelerated product innovation, heightened competition, and forced companies to adjust to the changing market environment.

Importance of Successful Marketing

The 1988 Yearbook of Agriculture explains why successful marketing is critically important to producers, marketing firms, and consumers in today's changing world. The changing market environment affects the food processing and marketing system. Some of the changes are external to the industry, such as population demographics, changing lifestyles, health concerns, and economic conditions. Others are internal, such as the technological advances in packaging and product preparation, use of electronic scanners in foodstores, and new product development and promotion.

Determining the sources of change and how consumers alter their buying habits and perceptions helps explain the marketing environment.

Once they have evaluated the characteristics of consumer demand, firms must develop desired products and pursue appropriate marketing techniques. Successful firms have strategies for accomplishing these tasks. Most new products fail in the marketplace within the first year after introduction, despite huge investments. In 1987, over 10,000 new products or product variations were put on grocery store shelves.

A good, well-researched product will not necessarily ensure success. A product must be widely distributed, always available, and visibly displayed. Food manufacturers attest to the fact that dollar and volume sales relate directly to the amount of shelf space devoted to the product, the location of display in the store, and the number of outlets carrying the product.

Securing shelf space in major retail chain stores is not easy. Food retailers increasingly have the ability to use information provided by electronic scanners to evaluate the profitability of every single product they sell. Food processors must manufacture products that generate adequate profits per square foot of retail display space or else lose the space to competitors.

An efficient and extensive distribution system is essential. One of the motivations for mergers between large marketing firms is the potential benefit gained from the other company's established distribution system.

A key to successful marketing is promotion, which may involve one or more of the following activities:

Advertising distributes messages about a product on television, radio, billboards, newspapers and newspaper supplements, and magazines. It aims to shape consumer perceptions and attitudes about the product or commodity, and to establish a long-term market base.

Markets offer a wide choice of products. This supermarket offers more than 100 food items in bulk to help consumers save money. (Giant Foods, Inc.)

Price promotion is used to stimulate quick sales response. Using "dealer price incentives," for example, manufacturers allow retailers and wholesalers to purchase products for limited periods of time at discounts. Retailers may decide to pass all, part, or none of the incentive on to consumers. Price incentives are often aimed directly at consumers through cents-off coupons and rebates.

Merchandising promotions focus on the point of sale at the retail foodstore, restaurant, or fast food outlet. Merchandising techniques include end-of-aisle displays, additional shelf facings, banners and signs, and in-store demonstrations. These are used to introduce new products and stimulate quick sales response.

Public relations activities include support for local and national civic projects or sports events, support of public television and radio, educational programs and materials, meetings with food editors, and periodic news releases. The goal is to stimulate sales by accomplishing one or more of three objectives: 1) present the company in a favorable light, 2) present the product in a favorable light, 3) foster activities that call attention to the product.

Food marketing firms and commodity groups spend more than $10 billion annually to advertise and promote food.

Developing Overseas Markets

The overseas market is increasingly important for U.S. farm products. A knowledge of consumer tastes, preferences, and habits that vary among countries or cultures is critical to successful product marketing. Also, a well-developed distribution system must be in place. Many U.S. firms enter new foreign markets via joint ventures with firms in the host country to take advantage of the marketing expertise and distribution systems already in place. U.S. producers also are increasingly looking to foodservice firms and hotels that already have a foothold in a foreign country as a vehicle for entering export markets.

U.S. producers can receive Government help in developing export markets through cooperator programs run by the U.S. Department of Agriculture's Foreign Agricultural Service (FAS). Under these programs, the domestic producer, the foreign distributor or retailer, and FAS share the costs of promoting U.S. products in overseas markets.

This Yearbook provides a wealth of information on today's agricultural marketing system and the innovative strategies pursued by some companies and commodity organizations as they strive to respond to the sovereignty of the consumer in the marketplace.

Food Marketing Industry Responds to Social Forces

Alden C. Manchester, senior economist, Economic Research Service

Successful marketing takes into account changes at all levels of the food and fiber system. We know about the big changes in recent decades in the size and profile of the U.S. population—age, household size, race, working wives, regional distribution—and in incomes. Another major change is that markets for agricultural products and processed foods have become global and highly competitive.

Many other influential changes have occurred outside the food industry. Consider:

- Consumer lifestyles
- Economic conditions, such as inflation and unemployment
- Technological advances
- World financial conditions that alter the competitiveness between U.S. and foreign firms
- Supply costs, especially the two tremendous jumps in petroleum prices in the 1970's
- Farm policies and programs

Marketers of food and other agricultural products must adjust to these changes, sometimes defensively, making the best of a poor situation. At times, such external changes create opportunities for new marketing methods and organizational structures. Changes under the control of the firm include:

- Use of new technology—for example, scanners in retail stores, bulk transport of orange juice, fats with reduced cholesterol or calories, artificial sweeteners
- Advertising and promotion techniques
- Layout of stores and their services
- Mergers and acquisitions

Let us look at how some of the changes that occur outside the food industry trigger changes within it.

Population and Income Changes

For most food products, long-term market growth within the United States is heavily dependent on U.S. population growth. After a period of slow increase during the depression, population growth took off after World War II. The baby boom years of 1946-64 raised growth rates sharply into the early 1960's; growth rates slowed in the 1970's and 1980's. Though the population grew younger in the 1950's and 1960's, it has grown older since then.

Growth rates have been higher in the South and the West than in the North, due partly to migration between regions but also to more migration by younger people who have more babies. The movement of the elderly to sunbelt retirement homes in States like Florida and Arizona adds to their population, while decreasing birth rates.

The racial distribution of the population also has changed. Immigration is one reason, but more important is the higher growth rate of black and Hispanic groups.

Average household and family size have been declining with later marriages, more divorces, smaller families, and less doubling-up (two families in one household). With more young and old people maintaining their own residences, the proportion of single-person households went up from 11 percent in 1950 to 13 percent in 1960, 17 percent in 1970, and 23 percent in the 1980's.

The proportion of families with more than one earner began to increase sharply after World War II—from 39 percent in 1950 to 46 percent in 1960, 54 percent in 1970, and 56 percent in 1985. With the added effects of rising real income per wage earner (adjusted for inflation) and declining family and household size, average income per person in households rose 137 percent between 1950 and 1984.

Implications of Consumer Changes

Each population group eats different foods and at different places, and each buys somewhat differently. The young and higher income households eat out more. Their selections of foods differ from older and less prosperous people. Households with children spend more of their at-home food dollars on milk and sweets; the elderly spend more on fruits and vegetables. Higher income families spend more on fish, cheese, and butter. There are also differences between races and geographic regions. For example, people in the Northeast drink more milk than those in other regions of the United States.

The most striking change in food consumption and marketing has been in away-from-home eating. From 1948 to 1985, the share of total food dollars spent away from home increased from 24 to 43 percent, and the share of total food quantities from 21 to 29 percent. Over this period, prices of food eaten away from home rose 18 percent more than prices of food at home. The two most important factors affecting the choice between food at home and away from home are rising real incomes (which made increased away-from-home eating possible) and the increase in working women (which boosted family incomes and provided more incentives for eating out).

Industry Changes

These changes at the consumer level have forced marketing changes. Retailers have worked to identify and develop profitable market segments (groups of customers) within each of the home and away-from-home markets for food.

Eating Away from Home

Most of the growth in the away-from-home market has occurred in the fast food industry. Its share of the away-from-home market grew from 8 percent in 1948 to 30 percent in 1982. Over the same time span, the share of table-service restaurants, lunchrooms, cafeterias, and caterers—the more traditional eating places—declined from 48 to 40 percent.

Fast food restaurants were largely a creation of the 1950's. Their rapid penetration into every community led to market saturation by the late 1970's. Building additional outlets was no longer the profitable route for the major fast food organizations. Instead, many have tried other avenues of growth, such as salad bars and breakfasts. Hamburger chains added chicken nuggets. Pizza establishments that serve only the takeout trade became common, some with large delivery networks.

Kinds of Grocery Stores

The supermarket was the creation of the Great Depression. Depressed incomes created pressure to cut retail prices and compete for the available business. One way to cut costs and make lower prices profitable was to go to self-service instead

Foodservice as a share of all food

Percent

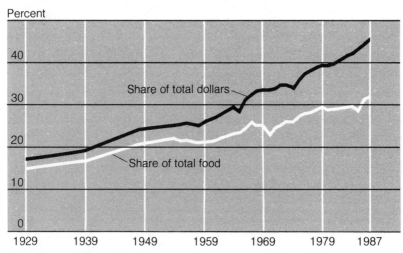

Source: Economic Research Service

of the prevalent clerk service. Also, by the 1930's, more and more families had automobiles and could travel several miles to supermarkets for one-stop shopping.

After a good start during the Depression and a pause during World War II (because of a shortage of construction materials and labor), the supermarket boom took off, with real food sales (adjusted for inflation) increasing 13-15 percent a year into the mid-1960's and nonfood sales increasing even faster. During the late 1960's, the rate of increase slowed to 4-5 percent a year, as potential supermarket sites and new customers became increasingly scarce. The 1970's brought a further slowing of the growth rate to less than 1 percent a year in sales of both food and nonfood products.

Rapid food price inflation in the mid-1970's created opportunities for supermarket operators. Many opened warehouse stores that emphasized fewer services, lower costs, lower prices, and a more limited product variety than conventional supermarkets. Since that time, there has been a flowering of varied store formats, each appealing to a different segment of the market.

The trend toward larger supermarkets continues, as indicated by the increasing importance of the superstore (which has a greater variety of products than conventional supermarkets), combination store (food and drugs and/or other products) and superwarehouse store (larger than a warehouse store, with greater food variety, including meat, deli, and seafood departments).

The number of superstores more than doubled between 1980 and 1986, while combination food and drug formats increased fivefold, although from a smaller base. The number of superwarehouse stores, including the new hypermarkets, nearly tripled over the 6 years. The hypermarket is a one-stop shopping supermarket that brings together a broad variety of food and nonfood products in a single store of about 120,000 square feet (conventional supermarkets typically have 20-30,000 square feet). The largest sales segment, conventional supermarkets, decreased from 73 percent of supermarket sales in 1980 to 50 percent in 1984.

Food retailers continue to experiment and synthesize successful elements of supermarket formats, so that distinctions among formats are becoming less clear. For example, the products and services offered by superstores and combination stores are often so similar that customers find no differences. The in-store pharmacy, a characteristic of the combination store, has been introduced to superwarehouse stores. And the low-margin strategy of warehouse stores has been applied to the grocery products of large combination stores with extensive service and specialty departments.

As warehouse stores have attempted to broaden their appeal through expanded product variety and service departments, they have become vulnerable to competitors that emphasize rockbottom prices, such as the wholesale club outlets. These stores originally served businesses and emphasized volume purchases, such as larger sized or case-lot products, on a cash-and-carry basis. In recent years, the wholesale club stores have extended participation to the public through membership fees or through affiliation with a credit union or similar consumer group. Although food products are the largest product category, variety is limited to about 4,000 nonperishable items, often sold in larger, institutional packages, multipacks, or by the case. Other product categories sold in wholesale club stores include clothing and linen, housewares and hardware, and electronics and appliances.

Wholesale club stores have grown considerably since their inception in 1976. Sales in 1986 probably exceeded $48 billion through 220 outlets.

Convenience stores were developed in the late 1950's starting in the South and West. To some extent, they filled the role in the expanding suburbs of the mom and pop grocery stores in older communities. A number of them started as dairy stores, with milk accounting for as much as 40-50 percent of sales. These helped to fill the niche of home delivery of milk, which was declining. With skyrocketing gasoline prices in the 1970's and 1980's, many convenience stores added self-service gasoline pumps. More recently, carryout foods, including hot sandwiches, and in-store eating have become staples of convenience stores.

Wholesaling

Food and grocery wholesaling has changed in response to changes at retail. Large supermarket chains have long done their own wholesaling through their own warehouses and still generally do, but smaller chains have increasingly relied on independent wholesalers for their supplies.

As foodservice grew to more than half the market for independent wholesalers, specialization into foodservice wholesaling became typical. Mergers among wholesalers in the 1970's and 1980's transformed grocery wholesaling from a local or regional enterprise into a near-national business, largely specialized either to foodservice or supermarket customers.

Food Manufacturing

As more specialized segments have been developed at retail and wholesale, food manufacturing has responded. Some companies that once supplied all segments of the market are now specializing in one segment such as branded consumer products, foodservice products, or ingredients for food manufacturers. In general, only large firms have the resources to supply a broad line of branded consumer foods. They engage in continuous product development and promotion, an expensive and risky process, since the majority of new products do not succeed.

Other manufacturers have chosen to emphasize products developed for foodservice or for particular segments of the foodservice market. Some specialize in products for particular hamburger chains. Several manufacturers have done extensive wholesaling to foodservice outlets, selling not only their own manufactured food products, but other items as well.

Since World War II, mergers have been a major force in changing the organization of food manufacturing and the kinds of business that companies do. Companies increasingly handle a broader line of products. Specialized canners of fruits and vegetables have broadened their lines to a wide array of food and nonfood products, as have dairy firms and meat packers. Increasingly, acquisitions are made with the explicit intent of retaining only a part of the acquired company. A striking example of this was Quaker's 1986 acquisition of Anderson Clayton solely to obtain its pet food segment, not the much larger oilseed processing and feed mill operations.

Food manufacturing, like many other lines, has gone international since World War II. Many large food companies are manufacturing and selling abroad—a few have greater sales abroad than in the United States. Exports of U.S.-made food products (not counting raw farm products like grain, or intermediate products like soybean oil and meal) have grown fairly slowly, partly because food product manufacturing by U.S. companies has moved offshore.

Just as American companies have moved into other countries (often by acquiring local firms), European, Canadian, and most recently Australian companies have acquired U.S. food firms. After decades of following a quiet course in the United States for fear of antitrust action, world companies such as Nestle and Uniliver have made major acquisitions in the United States.

More Change

The only certainty for the future is that change will continue. But beyond that, some changes are much more likely than others. For example, barring major disaster, the U.S. population will continue to grow older. Less certain but still with high probability, incomes will continue to rise, as they have in most years since the Great Depression. Changes in the makeup of the population, population growth, and rising incomes likely will mean that away-from-home eating will outpace at-home eating. If Americans continue to make similar choices among foods, at-home consumption of fish, cheese, fresh fruits, and vegetables will rise more than consumption of eggs and milk.

U.S. Food Marketing—
A Specialized System

Milton C. Hallberg, professor of agricultural economics,
Department of Agricultural Economics and Rural Sociology,
The Pennsylvania State University, University Park, PA

In the formative years of this Nation, most Americans were farmers producing food and fiber mainly for domestic consumption. And they did more than just produce it. They grew or fabricated most of the inputs needed to produce these products. They also processed farm products into a form that could be consumed: grain into flour, flour into bread, fibers into cloth, hides into leather. They packaged their produce to meet consumers' needs. They cured the meat and processed the milk so it could be stored for future consumption. They took their produce to the villages or to loading docks for export. They sought out buyers and saw to all of the financial matters involved in transferring ownership of their produce. All of these activities—beyond growing the basic raw materials— added value or utility to the farm products.

As farmers and nonfarmers alike developed and applied new technologies, and as people carved out areas of specialization, it became physically impossible for farmers to perform some of these functions, and economically infeasible for them to perform others.

Specialists evolved to provide building supplies, machinery, and tools; to process and package food; to transport the goods; and to buy and sell farm produce. They were not only more efficient at the tasks, but they could also capitalize on the economies of large-scale operations. Farmers also became better at producing the raw material, since they no longer had to divide their skills between farming and a host of other activities.

In the early days, farmers captured almost all of the consumer's food dollar, but the food was expensive because farmers were not efficient at providing all of the marketing functions in addition to producing the raw material. Today, farmers capture less than 30 cents of the consumer's food dollar, but collectively the price of food and all of the services that the marketing sector adds is less than it otherwise would be. Ironically, this lets farmers sell more produce at a higher price than they otherwise could.

In the end, everyone gains: Consumers have access to a greater quantity and variety of products at a lower unit cost; farmers can sell more produce at a higher unit price; and the marketing sector can employ more people, because the increased demand for food and fiber (and the services embodied in these products) requires more workers.

Specialized Functions

Even in a primitive economy, someone has to do several things to transform farm produce into consumable items. So a mature marketing system such as ours performs many specialized functions.

The first of these is *buying and assembling.* This function consists of seeking the sources of supply, assembling the products, and carrying out the necessary transactions. It can be seen at the farm level (buying and assembling raw farm products) and at the finished product level (getting finished products to those who must meet the demands of the consumer).

The *selling* function involves all those activities associated with merchandising: Setting prices. Displaying the goods. Advertising to make consumers more aware of the product and its special features. Establishing the proper unit of sale, the proper package, the best marketing channel, and the proper time and place to approach potential buyers.

The *storage* function makes the goods available when consumers want to purchase them. In general, farm goods are not produced steadily throughout the year; but of course consumers need to eat year-round. Thus the production glut must be stored and kept fresh until needed.

The *transportation* function makes food products available where consumers want to buy them. Transportation routes must be designed, alternative routes must be weighed, and the proper transport technology must be chosen. Crating and handling enroute also must be done.

Viewed broadly, the marketing system also performs a *processing* function—converting live animals into meat, fresh apples into canned or frozen slices, wheat into bread or noodles or pizza, and raw meat and vegetables into frozen packages that can quickly be popped into the microwave oven and served.

The process of converting farm products into food products would be much more complex without uniform standards for measurement and quality. Because of this standardization function, adequate production description is possible, the pricing system can reflect quantity and quality differences, and similar grades and quantities can be collected and moved more efficiently.

The *informational* function makes marketing intelligence available throughout the system. Efficient marketing cannot operate in an information vacuum. To make rational decisions, both buyers and sellers must be well informed about today's prices, likely future prices, appropriate grades and standards, and present and expected future quantities produced and consumed. They need to know that storage and transportation facilities are adequate at the right times, that proper product grades and standards exist, that market research is sufficient, and that appropriate marketing channels are available.

A *financing* function provides capital to carry out the various marketing functions. Also, risks are taken as the product changes in value from the time it is placed in storage until it is sold for consumption. Someone must be willing to fulfill the risk-bearing function, assuming these and many other kinds of marketing risks.

In general, farm commodities are seasonally produced and must be stored until they are needed. These cooperative grain bins make that storage possible. (Farmland Industries, Inc.)

Marketing Agents

A modern and efficient marketing system consists of several different types of business agents. The *retailer* buys products for resale directly to the consumer and manages thousands of products. Retailers are the most numerous of all the marketing agents.

The *wholesaler* sells to retailers, other wholesalers, and industrial users. Wholesalers collectively are highly heterogeneous, varying in size and products sold. Local buyers or country assemblers who buy goods directly from farmers and ship products forward to other wholesalers and processors are the most numerous wholesalers. Included here are grain elevator operators, fruit and vegetable packers, and local livestock buyers. Another group of wholesalers operate in large urban centers and offer a variety of services—writing orders and matching buyers and sellers, for example—in addition to the physical handling of goods. These businesses also are referred to as jobbers or car-lot receivers.

A second group of business firms are referred to as *brokers* or individuals who work on *commission.* They do not take title to the products they handle, but rather sell services on commission. For example, they sell market knowledge or know-how in bringing buyer and seller together or they do the actual bargaining on behalf of buyers or sellers. Those who work on commission normally arrange for the terms of sale, collect money, deduct the fee, and remit the balance to the principal. The broker, on the other hand, usually has less discretionary power in price negotiations, and usually does not handle the product.

Speculators (also called traders, scalpers, and spreaders) take title to products and absorb risks associated with price movements. Their reward for serving as the principal risk takers in the marketing system is profits made on price fluctuations over time. They usually operate at the same level in the marketing system, attempting to profit from short-run price fluctuations, for example, in grain buying.

Processors and manufacturers exist principally to change the product from raw farm output into consumer goods. Some act as their own buying agents and wholesale their products to retailers. Many also engage in advertising to help develop a market for their products.

Role Combinations and Helpers

Restaurants, fast food stores, and other *foodservice firms* serve a combination of the roles outlined and are a growing part of the food industry. This growth is in response to consumers' increasing demand for away-from-home meals, a demand stimulated by the trend to more dual-career households. These foodservice firms are part retailers, part wholesalers, and part processors.

In addition, others, such as stockyard companies, grain exchanges, fruit auctions, and a variety of trade associations, help these organizations work. In some cases, they may simply provide a place where buyers and sellers can transact business. In other cases, they make sure that information flows effectively throughout the marketing system.

Cost of Marketing Services

The cost of marketing food is the difference between what consumers pay for the final product and what farmers receive for the raw products. It is usually referred to as the marketing margin or food marketing bill.

In 1986, the farm value was only about one-fourth of consumer expenditures on food. Therefore, the marketing sector added considerable value to consumers' food purchases. As a result, price changes at the farm level are much less important in the final price of food than are wage rates and other cost items incurred in marketing (wages and salaries of workers in the food marketing sector far overshadow all other costs).

Farm Value of Food Products Consumed, and Distribution of Consumer's Food Dollar by Cost Component and by Marketing Function, 1986

Expenditures on Farm Food		$1.00
Food consumed at home	$.679	
Food consumed away from home	.311	
Farm Value		$.25
Marketing Costs		.75
By major cost component		
Wages and salaries	$.340	
Packaging	.075	
Intercity rail & trucking	.045	
Fuel & electricity	.040	
Depreciation	.040	
Advertising	.040	
Profits before taxes	.035	
Net rent	.030	
Net interest	.015	
Repairs	.015	
Other	.075	
By function		
Processing	$.261	
Foodservices	.193	
Retailing	.158	
Wholesaling	.088	
Transportation	.050	

Source: *National Food Review*. Economic Research Service, NFR-37. 1987

In addition, the processing, foodservice, and retailing sectors collectively account for more than 80 percent of the total food marketing bill.

Over the past several decades, marketing costs have moved steadily upward (while the farm value of consumer expenditures on food has moved downward) as consumers have demanded more and more services built into their food purchases. Another significant trend in the last few years is the growing importance of away-from-home eating and the rapid growth of the foodservice industry.

The marketing margin, and thus the farmer's share, differ widely among the various food products. For example, the farmer's share of the consumer's dollar spent on beef is more than three times the share for cereals and bakery products. There are four major reasons for this difference:

- Some food products require more processing to change the form of the product, and some require changes in packaging or size to satisfy consumers.
- Some products are more perishable than others, adding to the cost of providing refrigeration to prevent spoilage.
- Some products are bulky, requiring more space in transportation and storage and therefore incurring more marketing charges.
- Farm products that are highly seasonal in production require more storage facilities than others, and as a result, incur higher marketing costs.

Farmer's Share of the Consumer's Dollar Spent on Selected Foods, 1986

	Percent
Eggs	61.1
Beef, choice	54.0
Pork	46.0
Dairy products	43.7
Poultry	54.0
Cereal & bakery products	7.5
Fresh fruit	22.7
Fresh vegetables	24.0
Processed fruits & vegetables	19.1

Source: *Agricultural Outlook.* Economic Research Service, AO-138. Jan.-Feb. 1988.

Marketing Efficiency

Marketing encompasses a wide variety of functions involving many different firms and institutions. Although the marketing system must target its activities to consumers, salesmanship and consumer acceptance are not the *only* marketing issues. The entire system must operate to provide sufficient incentives for all participants. It must be innovative in developing and adopting new methods and practices to stay competitive in today's complex economic world. Participants in the marketing system also must continue to adapt to the changing desires of consumers by developing new products or by adding new or better services. Finally, the system must be continually monitored to ensure that it is operating as smoothly and efficiently as possible.

A Global Agribusiness
Market Revolution

Ray A. Goldberg, Moffett professor of agriculture and business,
Harvard Graduate School of Business Administration,
Boston, MA

In the last two decades, we have witnessed a revolution in the global agribusiness market. The U.S. agribusiness system has participated in this revolution at various levels, including the farm, farm supplier, processor, and retailer. The following trends are key aspects of the agribusiness revolution:
- Volatility of supplies, credit, and foreign exchange rates
- Increased globalization of markets and marketing
- Shift to retailer leadership
- Impact of biotechnology on products and productivity
- New packaging and store design
- Increasing awareness of the relationship between agribusiness and environmental and health concerns.

All of these trends are leading to a restructuring of industries, firms, and coordinating institutions and arrangements. The leaders are changemakers at every level of the vertical agribusiness system—from farm supplier to consumer—and market orientation is their principal focus. What follows is a summary of the impact of these trends on participants in the U.S. food and fiber system, and specific examples of firm strategies that respond to these trends.

Volatility of Supplies, Credit, Foreign Exchange Rates

Retailers and processors became conscious that they were part of a global agribusiness system as the market switched from a buyer's to a seller's market in the early 1970's.

The growth of the international grain market at an 11.7-percent annual rate in the 1970's was almost three times the 1950-70 annual growth rate. Even though the freeing up of foreign exchange rates and the rapid increase in interest rates occurred during this period, these increased cost factors and currency uncertainties were not considered burdensome in an expanding global food market.

As traditional agricultural commodity markets were expanding, an even greater expansion occurred in the nontraditional and value-added global food markets. Global transportation and information networks enabled both commodities and value-added products to be shipped by water and air between countries more economically than within countries. But it was easy for the United States to ignore the global value-added markets, especially when we had such a strong domestic U.S. food market.

The U.S. share of the global agricultural market by volume went from 25 percent in 1970 to 39 percent in 1980, but by value it dropped from 20 percent to 18 percent during the same period. Other countries with high unemployment levels were eager to add value to their food products for shipment abroad, especially countries that had surpluses. For example, Ireland exported more dairy products through Bailey's Irish Cream than through traditional commodity products. Similarly, Danish Butter Cookies, which contained 25-30 percent butter, moved more butter out of Denmark through cookies than through traditional commodity products.

The 1980's saw a sharp reversal. International growth in commodities declined as the price of oil declined, petrodollar loans were no longer available, and global food trade in absolute terms declined for the first time since World War II. The United States once again became a residual agricultural commodity supplier instead of the major order taker of the 1970's. All the national food policy programs that had been developed during a global food expansion period began to bump into each other. Market access became a political as well as an economic question.

U.S. agricultural trade volume in the first half of the 1980's declined an average of 6.6 percent per year. By 1986, the U.S. volume share of the world's agricultural trade market had declined to 24 percent. Even with the U.S. soft drink, processed foods, and fast food industries providing global value-added products, the U.S. share of the world agricultural market by value decreased to 12 percent.

Value-added products were being developed in all aspects of the food system, from New Zealand's lamb processing and its license with Matthew's of England to produce lamb roasts for the export market, to "cool wool" products from Australia for year-round clothes.

As a consequence, and because national governments—including the United States—no longer have the budgets to manage the financial and commodity volatilities of the world's food system, new global private and cooperative firms are emerging in the food system based on the market needs of their customers for commodities and value-added products.

Increased Globalization of Markets

1. Matrix Approach

The global coordination of the food system is exemplified by the emergence of companies and cooperatives that have a variety of strategies to respond to the changing demographics of a global food system. One type of firm is a company that wants to position the producer as part of a global matrix of commodity and finished product movements.

The grain being loaded on this Mississippi River barge is headed for New Orleans, LA, where it will be exported as a part of the global matrix of commodity movements. (William E. Carnahan)

These companies are creative in looking at the world as a matrix—a giant logistical system integrating processing, transportation, and financing so that all parts of the system mesh with one another. Typical of such companies is Cargill, Inc. Not only is it masterful at creating and using a matrix system, but it can also utilize futures markets in commodities, financial instruments, and transportation to minimize risk in the operations of such a matrix. Cargill also has developed joint ventures with farm cooperatives to enable farmers to have access to their matrix on a mutually profitable basis.

2. New Entrants into U.S. Market
In addition to locally based U.S. firms that have developed a global logistics system, a number of overseas firms such as Elders from Australia have entered the U.S. market to transfer their technologies (agricultural, research, natural resource, financing, satellite information network, and brewing) to U.S. agribusiness participants. They have enabled U.S. farmers, farm suppliers, processors, and distributors to become part of their global operation, thus offering new avenues of access to a global food system.

Other examples of new entrants include British Petroleum purchase of Ralston Purina's feed business and Funk Seeds, ICI purchase of Garst Seeds, and Dow Chemical purchase of United Agriseeds. These U.S. and overseas energy and pharmaceutical firms are bringing their technologies to the U.S. market and relating the U.S. perspective to their overseas feed, seed, chemical, and pharmaceutical operations.

3. Integration by Processors and Retailers
Other firms have looked to the U.S. market as a way of integrating U.S. processing, retailing, and fast food operations into
their off-shore operations. Similarly, U.S. food processors have
begun to lead in developing a global procurement network.
One such firm is ConAgra, which is developing a network for
protein-based foods such as fish, poultry, and meat, all with
value-added vertical systems from farm supply to ultimate consumer products.

Other leadership activities in the global food system are
occurring at the retail level. Businesses are creating their own
superbrands to compete with national and global premium-
priced brands in both quality and value, and creating low-cost
quality generic brands to compete primarily on price.

The food system all over the world, irrespective of commu-
nistic, socialistic, or capitalistic ideologies, is increasingly
driven by consumers in all of these interrelated societies.
Typical of this consumer-oriented trend is the shift in leadership of the agribusiness system to the retailer.

Shift to Retailer Leadership
The U.S. food distribution system is undergoing major change.
In the 1960's and 1970's, it was characterized by a highly fragmented series of components. Most geographic markets were
comprised of numerous retailers. They ranged from small
independent grocers, through regional chains that grossed
$100-750 million yearly, to the regional divisions of $3-4 billion
food retailers. Attaining market dominance came principally
through price wars or unique service and location. Marketing
was a brute force exercise characterized by selling high-volume
nationally branded products at retail prices that approached
cost. For the most part, retailers had neither the marketing
sophistication to clearly understand the tactics they used to
obtain and keep customers, not the tools to measure what was
occurring store by store and item by item.

From the perspective of the national brand manufacturers,
this situation kept them in their leadership role. Television
allowed the branded manufacturers to presell the ultimate
consumer. Other factors that contributed to leadership by
manufacturers included national television, radio, and print,
followed by customer coupons, sophisticated packaging, trial
sizes delivered to the home, research and development, and
product and brand managers. To many, the retailer was merely
a conduit through which the consumer was reached by the
manufacturer—"a seller of shelf space."

Product Standards
During this period, national manufacturers both developed and
defined the standards of products and their acceptability to the
U.S. consumer. Catsup was defined by the color and viscosity

of a brand standard. Toilet paper was defined by a standard of softness, and towels were expected to absorb certain volumes of water. Product recognition was a branded name, a distinctive package color. Consumer loyalty was assured by national manufacturers who invested heavily in media.

Product Positioning by Manufacturers

National manufacturers complemented their activities with the consumer by offering personnel and expertise to assist retailers in placing products on retail shelves. Marketplace strength was measured by the degree to which manufacturers could position their products—both in the number of packages of each type of item on the shelf, and in the shelf's position or location in the store. Positioning displays on the ends of aisles or in other high-sales-volume locations were the hallmarks of a manufacturer-led system. During this period, retailers found themselves in an adversarial position with their competition and with the brand manufacturer.

Information Technology Helps Retailers

In a retail industry made up of companies whose profit margin approaches only 1 percent of sales, and where hundreds of suppliers daily ship tens of millions of units through warehouses and stores, information is critical. The universal product code, which took years to develop and implement, has been the forerunner of retailer systems to measure the profitability of each of the store categories. (Profitability can be measured in terms of a pricing structure for a category, a newspaper ad, or an individual item.) It can be tracked and coded, and counted and measured by store, by item, by consumer.

The principal players in the shift of retailing power are computer specialists, managers trained in analytical techniques, and managers of companies whose primary purpose is to gather and study warehouse and store movement figures. Now a retailer can determine the importance of shelf position, the number of items each brand should have on the shelf, and the amount of display space to utilize efficiently.

As with most changes, only a few firms have taken a leadership role by adapting and using the enormous amount of information that became available. The larger chains that invested in information technology obtained excellent feedback that affected their profitable operations. As results of their activities became publicly acknowledged and reflected in improved profit, other firms began to become part of the new information-based retailer revolution. The use of information by the retailer in determining market strategy is still at an early stage of adoption.

Store Consolidation

Concurrently, consolidation is in full swing at the foodstores. Most major metropolitan markets have food retailers that are either well in excess of $1 billion in sales, or have more than

25 percent market share, or both. Wholesalers also have been consolidating.

Less Media Influence

Because media costs are increasing and the three major television networks are becoming less and less effective in reaching segmented audiences, manufacturers each year are spending less on media and more on promotions at the store and consumer level.

At the consumer level, far greater market segmentation is represented by the wide variety in size and composition of households and in lifestyles. Promotions are more effective than media in reaching these many segments.

Retailers can also add value by improving a formula over the brand standard, adjusting and developing products to the needs of its special consumers. Those manufacturers, farmers, and farm suppliers who participate with retailers to develop these new value-added products also enhance the profitability of their own operations.

All of these elements—information technology, retailer management skills, store consolidation by market, and diminished power of the media—have set the stage for the retailer to take a leadership role.

Impact of Biotechnology on Products and Productivity

Leading the agribusiness market revolution is biotechnology and its impact on global agribusiness. Biotechnology, which can engineer the component parts of plants and animals, has the potential to help customize products for nutritional and taste appeal. Through growth proteins, researchers can develop lean beef, pork, and lamb products that have a low cholesterol count. The same type of growth protein can yield more milk with less feed. In essence, the technology enables the natural system of plants and animals to work more effectively. It enables the end product to have different types of food values.

The technology also helps to create natural defenses against disease and pests; to overcome climatic conditions, permitting a greater variety of crops to be grown in the same location; and to produce crops for industrial uses such as fuel and pharmaceuticals.

This biotechnological revolution will encourage even greater coordination between retailer and manufacturer product innovators and producers who will cooperate in developing these new products.

New Packaging and Store Design

Another major focus in the global agribusiness market revolution is the importance of packaging and store design. Educating the consumer and attracting attention to good values in the food system require attractive, informative packaging design and a creative shopping environment and experience. Similarly, store design in relation to product design and display influences where people shop and what they buy. The service features at retail stores (from providing the physically handicapped with motor scooters to offering motorists undercover parking) indicate a growing awareness that food shopping can and should be enjoyable. At the same time, the consumer is able to choose where to shop: From a low-cost no-frills warehouse store to a 60,000-square foot combination food store and garden center, to a 100,000-square-foot supercenter.

This type of creative-competition also has led to new breeds of product and store designers who are engaged in working with food manufacturers and distributors throughout the world. Consumer satisfaction requires a bundle of services, information, and packaging that recognizes the uniqueness of markets and market segments, as well as the shared expectations of people worldwide for consistency in the global food system.

Environmental and Health Concerns

In 1986, the National Institutes of Health released a study indicating that more than 50 percent of the increase in longevity in the United States was due to a change in diet. Consumers want safer chemicals or alternatives to chemicals at the farm and in the home. At the same time, biotechnology is helping to develop products that can use waste and byproducts in a productive, profitable, and environmentally sound manner. The social and environmental priorities of society are being noted in the food system, along with improvements in products and processes.

Restructuring of Agribusiness

All of the trends have required agribusinesses to change and restructure their operations. The new breed of men and women who participate in all the functions of agribusiness have to be proactive in creating new products and processes that are desired and nutritionally sound for global food consumers. In some cases, they may have to be small-scale scientific, product, process, and market innovators. In other cases, they may work with many parts of the vertical food system in joint ventures to satisfy the consumer. In all cases, the agribusiness system is consumer driven on a global basis. If those inside the system do not become part of the restructuring process and help the system adjust to change, others outside the system will restructure the U.S. agribusiness sector.

How Markets Communicate Information About Quality

V. James Rhodes, professor of agricultural economics, University of Missouri-Columbia, MO

Market communication costs like the dickens, but most folks think it's worth it.

Producers, processors, and other marketers expend much money and effort to inform existing and potential customers about their products and services. Increased sales and profits are the expected rewards for this type of communication from sellers to buyers.

A reverse flow of information from buyers to sellers, however, is just as important. The purchase of any item carries a powerful message to the seller when placed in the context of expected and past sales. Growing sales spell buyer satisfaction, while falling sales suggest buyer dissatisfaction. In addition, various forms of explicit information—praise, complaints, and suggestions—may be communicated.

Message About Quality

What is meant by communication about quality? What is quality? Is it freshness, tenderness, color, appearance, or lack of defects? The economist would say that quality is what the consumer says it is. But consumers also have much assistance from producers, processors, and others in developing their various concepts of quality. Also, in this technological age, when changes in the techniques of production and marketing can affect the typical freshness, appearance, or palatability of a food, changes in commodities can occur alongside changes in consumer attitudes.

Consumers and even other buyers in the marketing system often delegate quality selection to someone else, because the actual sorting involves more expertise than the buyers possess or takes more time than they want to spend. Buyers often learn to rely upon Federal grades and variety names — such as No. 1 Jonathan apples—for quality selection in many commodities. The grade stamp and variety name assure consumers that they have No. 1 Jonathans. A retail buyer can order a truckload of apples without inspection by specifying No. 1 Jonathans. Likewise, buyers learn to rely on specific brands for most processed food and fiber products. The Food and Drug Administration standards of identity define numerous processed foods such as margarine. USDA standards of composition control meat and poultry ingredients, for example, the minimum amount of meat required in beef hash.

Buyers who have never heard of these standards still know that both margarine and beef hash have predictable characteristics.

Grades are important aids to communicating quality variations in commodities. Grading is the process of grouping continuous quality gradations of a commodity into a few grades or classes. The sorting is typically done by federally employed or supervised graders.

Very large buyers may insist on using their own specifications, but most smaller players in the market find it more convenient to rely on Federal grades and graders. Widely recognized and reliable grades enable trading without personal inspection by either buyer or seller. Thus, grades are an effective contributor to reduced costs of buying and selling numerous commodities. Because grading is typically voluntary, the use of grades is evidence of their value to marketers and sometimes to consumers.

Product Qualities Consumers Want

At times, certain product attributes seem to drive consumer behavior. For example, in recent years consumers have expressed a desire for convenience and variety in their foods and have preferred fats of vegetable, rather than animal, origin.

Processors and food distributors have worked overtime to provide the desired attribute of convenience. Examples are easy-to-open packages, wrappings that can also serve as the cooking or warming dish in a microwave oven, new precooked foods, salad bars in supermarkets, and double driveup

Food distributors have worked overtime to provide the desired conveniences, such as this salad bar in a supermarket where "salad fixin's" are sold by weight. (Giant Food, Inc.)

windows at fast food outlets, where customers place their orders at one window and immediately proceed to another to pick them up.

The surge in ethnic foods responds to the consumer's desire for more variety. A similar response is the great expansion in the produce departments of supermarkets to include many formerly exotic items.

The gradual shift from animal to vegetable fats has been motivated by various factors including handling characteristics, health concerns, and relative prices. The response at the farm level in the past quarter century has been to increase vegetable oil production and reduce animal fat production. Processors and distributors also have responded to these changing market demands by providing low-fat milks, close-trimmed meats, and new vegetable oil products.

Even plant and animal breeders have responded to changing consumer demands. Plant breeders have altered a variety of rapeseed to produce an edible oil. Animal breeders have increased the muscling and reduced the fat in hogs and cattle. The breeds of dairy cattle producing milk with lower butterfat such as Holstein have largely replaced the high butterfat breeds such as Jersey and Guernsey.

Sending and Receiving Messages

The process of sending and receiving messages within the market is imperfect and sometimes frustrating. Suppose consumers lose their zest for broccoli or for low-butterfat ice cream. When sellers of those items lower prices to move them, the progressively lower sales raise a warning flag that something is wrong. Declining sales data in themselves often do not indicate possible opportunities or cures—simply that a problem exists.

Something can be learned from consumer questions, comments, suggestions, praise, or criticism. Many agribusinesses and even producer groups have engaged in systematic consumer research to enhance this communication process. Problems can be defined more clearly. Potential marketing opportunities may be spotted. Frequently, the marketing research helps processors to sort among many new product ideas for those few that seem most likely to succeed.

The costs of developing, test marketing, and launching a new product range into the millions of dollars. Some new items are highly profitable, while others are failures that are soon withdrawn. Many big food companies offer a continuous flow of new products. Like baseball players, product innovations do not have to bat 1,000 to be successful.

Promotion and advertising are the most costly parts of launching a new product. They are also the means by which marketers keep communicating their messages for older products. Food-related advertising costs about $10 billion a year, and the sums for other kinds of promotion are probably even greater. Communication in the brand-name side of the market does not come cheap.

Marketers learn that there are frequently fascinating and profitable market niches outside the mainstream. For example, ice cream recipes were drastically modified toward less butterfat in the past quarter century in response to the general concern to reduce fat and calorie consumption and also to lower price. However, convinced that many consumers will occasionally forget their diets and splurge on a rich-tasting ice cream, several companies in recent years have revived the sales of high-butterfat, premium-priced products. (See *Marketing Ben & Jerry's Equals Fun* by Jeff Durstewitz.) Those innovators have undoubtedly reaped the rewards of market entrepreneurship.

Promoting Commodities

The marketing side of communicating about commodities is more subdued and less expensive than the process for branded products. Numerous commodity groups under the authority of State or Federal legislation of various sorts do substantial promotion and generic (commodity) advertising. Pork is touted as "the other white meat." Beef is advertised on TV by famous people. While substantial sums are being spent in this way, the total for all commodities is less than 10 percent of the $10 billion for branded products.

Changes in Consumer Perceptions

What happens when consumer ideas change about the desired quality of a specific commodity? Suppose affluent consumers become more willing to pay for the more expensive A grade rather than the once-favorite B grade? In this simple case, normal market actions communicate effectively. The inventory of the A grade group begins to sell out more frequently; the retail price of A probably rises relative to B, and messages travel through the system to produce more of grade A and less of B. Ordinarily the proportions produced of various qualities can be varied (within technical limits), so the market responds.

Eggs have been an example of this change process. As consumers became more willing in the past quarter century to pay for high quality, and as the egg production and handling system changed to make quality eggs easier to provide, we have seen grades B and C disappear from retail shelves. Only the premium A and AA eggs remain.

Also, some producers and packers have developed branded beef aimed at consumers who want tender but lean meat. Many breeding efforts have been directed toward producing a lean and palatable combination, and cattle feeding times have been shortened to reduce the external fat deposited on the muscling.

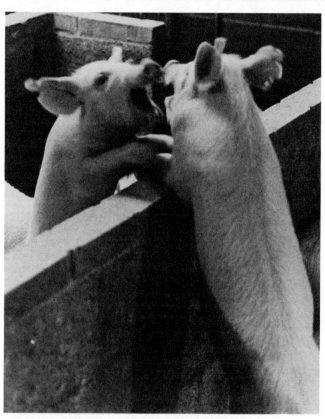

Most hog farmers have been convinced they must produce leaner hogs, even though the price premium usually has been zero or close to it. Consequently, the average hog today is much leaner than 25 years ago. (Norman E. Pruitt)

Not Getting the Message

Farmers have sometimes felt that the premiums paid at retail for quality seldom trickle back to them. There is evidence for some concern. In theory, if farmers produce quality A that is valued more by consumers than quality B, then market forces should reward farmers for the superior quality. The reasoning is that retailers receiving a premium for quality A will pay a premium to processors (handlers) to obtain more of A. In turn, other handlers will pay a premium in the system and eventually the first buyers from farmers will offer them a premium for A.

Even under the best of circumstances, the absolute size of the premium between retail and farm level will decline. The reason is that farm prices are reduced by the considerable marketing margins between the farm and the retail shelf. Suppose, for example, that quality A retails at $8 per unit while B sells at only $6. Suppose that the farm price is generally about 25 percent of the retail price. Then the farm prices are $2 for A and $1.50 for B; the retail difference of $2 between grades A and B has fallen to 50 cents even though the B price is three-fourths the A price at both farm and retail.

Under the worst of circumstances, a price premium at retail may disappear at farm level. Suppose the quality difference so prized at retail is not readily distinguishable until after processing. The quality difference is assumed to exist in the farm commodity, but it is not readily apparent to the producer nor to the processor buyer. The processor eventually learns that his average purchase consists of, say, half quality B and half quality A. Instead of paying $2 for A and $1.50 for B, as in the previous example, the commodity is purchased for $1.75. If each farmer does produce one-half quality A, then there are no complaints about the $1.75 average price. If some farmers produce two-thirds A while other farmers produce one-third A and the rest B, then the first group of farmers will be underpaid for quality if all farmers receive $1.75.

The hog industry bears some resemblance to the last example. Most hogs are purchased on a liveweight basis with little or no premium for leanness. Such hogs are typically bought on an "average value" basis. Many buyers will provide a certain premium for leanness if pricing is done after the degree of leanness is fully revealed by slaughter. Those farmers who suspect that their hogs are below average in leanness are understandably reluctant to sell on a carcass basis.

Fortunately for the hog industry, most producers have been convinced that they must move to leaner hogs, even though the price premiums usually have been zero or close to it. Consequently, the average hog today is much leaner than 25 years ago. Information has traveled through the market and stimulated producer response, despite the garbled price signals in the hog industry.

Part II

Marketing Strategies

How to Develop a Successful Marketing Strategy

James C. Cornelius, extension economist, Oregon State University, Corvallis, OR

Businesses at all levels have a need for marketing strategies to complement the strategies for production, financing, and input acquisition. Many of the principles are the same for an individual farmer as for a large corporation manufacturing a diverse assortment of food and nonfood products. Obviously, the large corporation can devote more resources to developing a strategy than can an individual farmer, but planning is equally important for both. And the elements of a strategy are the same.

Marketing agricultural commodities has always posed a challenge. Like the weather, the sales price and quantity demanded are largely beyond the control of the producer.

Uncertainties in market conditions over time create risks in sales decisions. For example, prices received for agricultural commodities often vary 10-20 percent or more over the marketing year, causing uncertainty for both farmer and marketer. Revenue changes of even a few percentage points can mean the difference between success and failure, so marketing considerations can be among the manager's most important decisions. The market cannot be controlled by an individual, but its consequences can be managed. Strategies are needed that both manage market risks and pursue the opportunities available in the marketplace.

Food manufacturers must decide which products to produce and which market to target. Retailers also plan which segment of the market to concentrate on—consumers interested in low prices and minimal services, those willing to pay for many services, or the quick-serve market.

Marketing Decisions

Marketing decisions in agriculture typically cover timing of sales, price level, volume, product form, delivery, and method of exchange. Institutional arrangements have evolved for many commodities that combine various sales considerations into distinct marketing alternatives such as auction sale, forward contracting, or direct private treaty sale.

The selection of a marketing alternative by itself, however, does not address all of the necessary sales decisions. For example, a producer's decision to hedge corn sales in the futures market does not answer questions about when to place the hedge, the contract month to use, how many contracts to sell, when to lift the hedge, and so forth. Selection of the appropriate marketing alternative is important, but it is just one component of decisionmaking.

Marketing Strategy Concept

Studies of agricultural marketing practices reveal that decisionmakers rely on a variety of approaches ranging from complex, computer-aided marketing plans to the simple logic that a producer was "going to town anyway." The means of arriving at marketing decisions, along with the logic for making these judgments, is called the marketing strategy. The strategy concept is an approach to agricultural marketing that employs systematic, coordinated decisionmaking. The strategy for an individual farm firm is tailored to the particular situation it faces. Developing a successful marketing strategy requires a combination of business skills, planning, analysis, and action.

Elements of a Marketing Strategy

The first ingredient in formulating a strategy is the successful organization of information. In other words, "plan before you act." You can provide some structure to decisionmaking by examining a few elementary principles of managerial science: 1) Where am I? 2) Where do I want to go? 3) How do I get there?

Answers to these questions form the elements of a marketing strategy. The activities necessary to develop this information are assessment, objectives, and action.

Assessment

The assessment—determining "where am I?"—often requires the most work. It covers three general areas that will influence the strategy: the market, your own financial situation, and the marketing alternatives available.

Market Assessment

A complete understanding of the workings of a particular agricultural market may require special training and years of experience. Even then, few market analysts are sufficiently skilled to consistently and accurately forecast commodity prices.

Market assessment is more than just forecasting prices. The purpose is to understand the fundamental supply and demand conditions that influence price. This understanding also is used to maintain a timely awareness of the current market situation. For example, knowledge of factors such as price trends, the supply or inventory situation, recent behavior of customers or consumers, and status of the current crop have a direct impact on an individual producer's marketing plan. A negative or "bearish" market environment characterized by weak demand, excess supplies, and falling prices may call for a much different strategy than an optimistic or "bullish" market with strong demand and rising prices.

Because many price determinants are uncertain, market assessment must also consider the sources and consequences of risk. Risk complicates marketing, but such uncertainty is an inescapable part of decisionmaking. Moreover, strategies can often be developed to help manage market risk.

Financial Situation

In addition to analyzing the market situation, you also must assess your own financial situation. A periodic assessment of financial health—liquidity, solvency, and profitability—including a careful examination of enterprise budgets and debt structure provides important insight into the cost variables associated with the sales plan. Managers cannot develop intelligent marketing strategies unless they first know the cost structure of producing a particular good. Additional information on the firm's financial condition allows for progressively more responsive and precise marketing plans.

Marketing Alternatives

Understanding the operation, advantages, and disadvantages of available marketing alternatives is the third component of the assessment process. Traditional alternatives may or may not reflect today's realities. As the world, agriculture, and farming have changed, so have markets. Innovations in sales opportunities involving futures markets, options markets, vertical integration, forward cash contracting, and electronic auction sales offer refinements in market planning.

Marketing alternatives vary with regard to their flexibility, riskiness, buyer and seller obligations, simplicity, and efficiency. As a result, the selection of an alternative should be tailored to the market assessment and financial capabilities of the individual. An optimistic market outlook might favor a speculative sales plan, whereas a conservative approach is more appropriate given a bearish market environment. Similarly, a marketing alternative that provided the most favorable returns one year might perform poorly the next if market conditions change.

Objectives

Assessment provides information on what exists, and objectives define what is desired. Objectives provide the guiding philosophy in developing the marketing strategy. Clarifying desirable and realistic marketing objectives can be difficult, particularly the conversion of personal values or quality-of-life concerns into explicit market goals.

Marketing decisions are enhanced by distinct objectives. In the absence of such guidance, you can drift aimlessly through sales opportunities, vaguely seeking the "highest price" or a "fair return." These standards rarely provide recognizable signals in the marketplace and, therefore, sales decisions become highly speculative or forced at the last minute.

The formulation of market objectives is enhanced by a careful evaluation of your own financial situation, backed by an inventory of personal attitudes toward risk, profits, growth, and lifestyle. A helpful approach is to link objectives to production costs. A breakeven price is calculated that will generate enough revenue at a given sales volume to cover specificed costs. Calculation of appropriate production costs will vary, depending on cash-flow requirements, production practices, and budgeting considerations. Actual price or market objectives may be set above or below the breakeven calculation, based on market expectations, risk attitudes, and other family or business goals.

Know the breakeven price. It provides a meaningful reference for evaluating the market at any time. Sales opportunities can be judged in terms of their direct financial impact on the firm. In some cases, production practices may be modified to adjust the breakeven price, if warranted by market or financial conditions.

The price objective is identified in advance of the sales decision, and when the market reaches this objective, it's time to act. Contingency price objectives are necessary in the event market prices never reach the objective, or continually exceed it. Further refinements in identifying a cost-based price objective may be necessary, depending on the market and financial assessment.

Another approach to establishing market objectives is based on general expectations about price levels. In this case, your objective might be to sell in the upper half or upper third of the seasonal price range of a given commodity. This goal is less objective than cost-based strategies and is inherently more speculative. However, in volatile markets the technique can be effective in determining when to sell. It is best when based on well-founded forecasts of future price levels combined with a recognition of cost considerations.

Action

The focus of a marketing strategy is a plan of action. To take action, the manager must 1) use your assessment results to analyze market outlook and price-determining factors, 2) evaluate the ability of various marketing alternatives to deal with market conditions and the outlook, 3) examine the financial status and requirements of the farm business, and 4) establish your market or price objectives.

The objective is to formulate a strategy that provides the greatest likelihood of achieving marketing objectives using appropriate sale alternatives. There is no single "best" strategy, however; the best plan might range from a simple one, such as selling everything at harvest on the local cash market, to a complex risk-management strategy using options markets. Once the basic logic of a marketing strategy has been worked out, write it down. Be specific; do not rely on vague generalities. Next, test your strategy. Does it provide sufficient guidelines to trigger sales? Work through several hypothetical market scenarios and evaluate your strategy's performance. Have your objectives been met? What are the key management variables to consider? Based on this test, revise your marketing strategy as necessary, and clarify, in advance, the conditions under which you will change the plan.

Then, once it's finalized and in place, follow the plan. Lack of management discipline is a common problem. Experience using a marketing strategy will improve both your confidence and market performance. Give your strategy time to work, refine and evaluate it periodically, and do not expect miracles. Many perceived marketing problems are actually rooted in production or financial issues unrelated to the market.

Marketing Management

Developing a successful marketing strategy is a major management obligation. The information requirements can be a large undertaking, particularly for multiple enterprises and large farming or agribusiness operations. This underlines the importance of committed, ongoing managerial attention. This is not just a decision on when to sell, but a coordinated planning effort required to support a strategy. Marketing management should start even before production begins, not as a forced decision late in the game when there are no other alternatives.

A marketing "decision calendar" may help in coordinating production, financing, and marketing plans. Plan, in advance, the timing of major production activities over the calendar year, and then add the associated marketing plans and decisions that are necessary over the same period. The calendar can remind you of marketing management tasks, as well as point out the need for coordination among the wide range of management obligations in farming and agribusiness.

Marketing Strategies and Alternatives for Individual Farmers

John (Jake) N. Ferris, Department of Agricultural Economics, Michigan State University, East Lansing, MI

By all means, look at marketing strategies for what they can do for you as a farmer. But in addition, recognize two additional challenges: appropriate marketing strategies by groups within the current system, and needed changes in the system itself. In many cases, what serves the individual farmer well in the short run may not benefit the industry—and may even hurt the farmer in the long run.

For example, a hog producer may profit by feeding to heavy weights when hog prices are high relative to corn prices. This may be good for the individual farmer whose goal is to maximize net income that year. Consumers, however, are sending signals to the marketplace that they do not want fat pork. The short-run market strategy of feeding to heavy weights may be detrimental to consumer demand and the hog industry in the long run.

What and How Much to Produce

The first step is to determine what customers want. This may seem like a trite statement, but many farmers and those who serve them tend to be production oriented. Farming is a way of life in addition to a business. Much satisfaction is gained from combining off-farm inputs with labor, management, soil, sun, and water to create a product. The problem is that the production orientation diverts attention from agriculture's most important role of serving consumers, and it can jeopardize an industry's future.

Decisions on which varieties of crops to plant and which type and breed of animal to raise are key elements of a marketing strategy for an individual farmer. These decisions should be based not only on what customers and consumers demand now, but with some anticipation of future demands. This is particularly important in producing fruit, beef, and dairy, because variety and type selection have long-range consequences. Crop cultural practices and livestock feeding programs can affect the quality of the product, and these too can be considered marketing decisions.

The subtle difference between production and marketing orientation is that farmers who are market oriented first contact market outlets and identify what consumers require before venturing into new programs. Ideally, contractual arrangements should be made in advance. Because of volume requirements of buyers, most individual farmers do not have the size to consider alternative enterprises independently.

Another marketing decision is how much of a commodity to produce. Since most farmers produce only a minute portion of total industry output, their scale of operation will have no impact on price. The decision, then, relates more to their cost structure and ability to handle risk. To maximize profits, they would operate at a scale where price is equal to the increase in costs of producing an additional unit.

Where to Sell

In addition to the marketing decisions of *what* to produce, *what quality* to produce, and *how much* to produce are decisions relating to *where* to sell, *how* to sell, and *when* to sell. A standard rule on where to sell is to contact two or more buyers or check prices at multiple markets. This has to be done regularly because circumstances that alter price differentials will change.

After checking the most relevant markets, determine transportation costs to each market to establish which destination would net the highest price at the farm gate. This is the key to maintaining competition. If commonly practiced by farmers, this would tend to keep prices in line over a geographic area. Whenever price differentials exceed transportation costs, such actions would tend to keep price differentials about equal to transportation costs. This activity is called "arbitrage." It does have flaws. For one, farmers must be certain that the quoted prices relate to the quality of the product they have to sell. This means that farmers should ask for discounts as well as base prices. Another flaw is that farmers are forced to take all transportation costs into account. For example, livestock lose weight in transit, making it difficult to obtain true measures of price differences between markets.

Farmers selling through their own cooperatives may find that, at times, they may net less that way than from other markets. Rather than abandon their cooperatives, they may appropriately continue to sell through this channel to perpetuate a competitive structure. But if the cooperative is repeatedly unable to meet competition, the farmer members may need to determine why and change the cooperative's program or discontinue it.

Increased size of farms and improved transportation facilities have opened up alternatives on where to sell. Also, expanded onfarm storage capacities on grains have provided farmers more flexibility. These developments have enabled producers to generate semi-truckloads which, in turn, expand their market area.

Charles and Anne Geyer display a sample of ARS-developed thornless blackberries grown on a pick-your-own farm they manage in Virginia.
(Tim McCabe)

How to Sell

The decision on *how* to sell can be quite involved. The alternatives are too numerous to discuss in detail. Most grains and soybeans are sold at local elevators and at terminals at posted cash prices derived from major futures markets. Livestock may be sold at terminals, or through local auction markets, or delivered directly to packers. Most milk is marketed through farmer cooperatives at prices established by a system of market orders and the Government price support program. Fresh produce is sold through several channels including cooperatives, brokers, terminal markets, direct delivery to wholesalers and retailers, and, sometimes, direct sales by producers to consumers at roadside stands, "pick-your-own," and farmers' markets. Most processed fruits and vegetables are sold under contract to processors. Some producers may use a combination of these outlets.

Basic to the question of how to sell is how much of the marketing function should farmers perform. The answer relates to the financial position of farmers, their managerial skills, and their personality traits. Farmers who enjoy dealing with people are more suited to marketing directly and negotiating prices and other terms of sale. Other farmers who could economically justify such activities would prefer to let someone else do them.

In many cases, farmers do not have the time and resources to acquire the necessary marketing skills. So they hire the professional services of an advisory firm, or they consign their product to commission firms, which perform the selling function.

In timing spot (current) or forward (contract for future delivery) sales, some farmers prefer to do their own analysis and follow charts and technical market signs. Others take advice from professional services or even turn the entire selling function over to such agencies. The appropriate procedure depends on the farmer's preferences. In many cases, however, the best approach may be a combination of farmer involvement in the marketing decision with the support of professional services. (See article *Marketing on a Central Illinois Cash-Grain Farm* by Darrel Good and Bob Sampson.)

Perhaps the most important step individual farmers have taken to perform marketing functions is the expansion in onfarm grain storage facilities in combination with more onfarm trucks. This has contributed to the demise of many local grain elevators.

The decision of whether or not to build onfarm storage facilities used to be much clearer than in recent years. Early on, there were strong economic incentives for building onfarm storage. As cash grain farms expanded and became more specialized, they could economically justify adding storage and drying facilities. They could also justify learning the skills needed to maintain the quality of grain in storage. Government programs subsidized the building of onfarm storage and provided storage payments for grain in the Farmer-Owned Reserve.

Farmers expanding onfarm storage also must consider the long-term outlook. What will Government programs be in the future? Will surpluses build or decline? What will be the future demands for quality? One of the problems related to exporting corn is the poor quality of U.S. grain. Broken kernels are attributed to onfarm drying practices, as well as handling in shipping and inappropriate grain standards. Will quality requirements change and, if so, how will onfarm storage practices be affected? These are all difficult but relevant questions for farmers developing marketing strategies on grain. (See article *Quality in Marketing Grain* by Mack N. Leath.)

When to Sell

Perhaps the most important marketing decision is *when to sell.* The volatility of many commodity markets is such that often the difference between profit and loss is the timing of the sale. With the many commodities traded on futures markets and the recent introduction of options, farmers have a broad array of forward pricing tools in addition to the current cash market.

In developing a marketing strategy on timing of sales and tools to use, the obvious objectives are to maximize average returns and minimize risks. Realistically, tradeoffs are involved. Strategies which result in the highest average returns over the years are usually the riskiest. The safest strategies usually generate lower average returns. The best strategy depends on the farmer's financial and emotional ability to handle risk.

Futures Markets

Agricultural futures markets date back to the mid-1800's in Chicago. Trading is carried out by open outcry in market facilities designed to foster competition and broad dissemination of information. The trading is over contracts called futures, which are legally binding commitments to deliver or take delivery of a given quantity and quality of a commodity at a specified price, during a specified future month and at specified locations. (A recent exception to this is "cash settlement" on feeder cattle.) While the contracts relate to physical goods, in reality few deliveries are made. Instead, buyers and sellers "offset" their purchases and sales by appropriate sales and purchases before the delivery date.

The reason deliveries are negligible is simply because delivering is usually less profitable than offsetting. Yet the fact that some deliveries are made and are profitable means that cash and futures markets generally parallel each other. This enables farmers to effectively use futures markets for an activity called "hedging."

It substantially reduces—but does not eliminate—the financial risks that result from price fluctuations. Hedging is simply betting against yourself by taking an opposite position in the futures market to that in the cash market. For example, farmers committed to producing a commodity or who are holding a commodity are said to be "long" in the cash market. The appropriate hedge is to take the opposite, "short," position in the futures market by selling futures.

Assume farmers have hedged at a profitable price. They could make this assessment by subtracting their delivery costs, including transportation, from the futures price. More appropriately, however, they would subtract the usual difference between futures and their local cash markets at delivery time in making this assessment. This difference is called "basis." Again, this approach is more appropriate because the net return is usually greater if farmers sell their product on their local cash markets and buy back (offset) their short position in futures.

If cash and futures prices decline after the hedge is placed, the value of the cash product declines, but farmers profit from the short position in futures. On the other hand, if the price level increases, farmers gain equity in the cash commodity, but lose in futures.

The key is the extent to which cash prices move relative to futures. If cash prices turn out to be high relative to futures (basis is "strong"), the farmer benefits, because returns from the hedge are higher than expected. If cash prices turn out to be low relative to futures (basis is "weak"), the farmer loses, because returns from the hedge are lower than expected. However, this "basis risk" is usually much less than the risk of losing money in a strictly cash market.

Futures markets are complex to use and understand. Partly for this reason, farmers have not hedged directly very much. However, they have hedged indirectly by forward contracting extensively with local elevators and livestock marketing agencies which hedge routinely. The only way buyers can give them guarantees on forward cash contracts is if the buyers themselves hedge.

A second reason farmers have not hedged directly is their distaste for "margin calls." To open an account with a broker, a farmer must put up "margin money." This is a good faith deposit to give the broker assurance of protection in case the market "goes against" the client. "Going against" means that a farmer who has hedged a product to be sold (futures are sold) experiences a rise in price. While a farmer would have to deposit only a small part of the value of the contract (usually 10 percent or less), a major rise in futures prices can involve substantial amounts of additional margin. This means that the farmer must maintain cash liquidity to meet these inevitable margin calls or have an understanding banker who realizes that the farmer's equity in the cash product is increasing in line with the loss in futures.

Another reason farmers have not made extensive use of futures markets is because they hate to miss out on "bull markets"—sharp rises in prices that are often unexpected and very profitable.

Commodity Options Market

An alternative forward pricing mechanism that addresses directly some of the drawbacks of hedging is the commodity option market. Options, a market institution that was banned for agricultural commodities in the 1930's, was reintroduced in 1984 on a pilot basis. Options provide farmers 1) downside price protection, 2) limited exposure to cash losses with brokers (there are no margin calls), and 3) the opportunity to profit from a bull market.

The bidding in an options market revolves around the right to buy or sell a commodity at a given price. Since farmers are primarily involved in selling a commodity, they are most concerned about the right to sell. In the new options market, the underlying commodity is a futures contract. The right to sell a futures contract at a stated price is known as a "put." The right to buy is a "call." As with futures, most farmers who buy options offset them before expiration rather than exercise them.

The prices around which the bidding takes place are called "strike" or "exercise" prices. The bidding to buy or sell at these strike prices is manifest in premiums, the prices of the options.

Options offer farmers an array of new forward pricing alternatives that force them to examine their attitudes toward risk.

Developing a Marketing Plan

The key to successful marketing is having a plan and following it. Farmers should go through a certain amount of introspection to determine the goals of the farm and of the family. Goals should be attainable. Farmers will need to determine how much risk they can afford and are comfortable in assuming. Executing the plan requires an understanding of the pricing tools available, records of past prices and "basis," and access to current market information and advice.

The plan may be a simple one. For example, it may call for forward pricing only when opportunities are quite favorable, using production costs or expected prices as a guide. For a "chartist"—who uses historical charts to determine if the market is going up or down—it might mean placing hedges when strong technical sell signs appear on the charts. Basis watchers may want to step up cash sales when basis is strong.

To illustrate the possible gains from a marketing plan, some simple rules for storing crops were developed and tested over a 12-year period from 1973 to 1984. (The cash market in this analysis was at Saginaw, MI.) The cash strategy was to sell corn, soybeans, and wheat regularly out of farm storage during the months when returns historically had been the greatest. The cash/hedge strategy was to: 1) sell at harvest if the basis was narrow and prices were above the Government loan rate; or 2) store hedged grain if the basis was wide and the price at harvest was above the loan rate; or 3) store unhedged grain if the price at harvest was below the loan rate and follow the sales pattern of the cash strategy.

The average returns were substantially higher on corn and soybeans from the cash/hedge strategy. On wheat, returns averaged higher on the cash strategy, but would have been much lower if 1973 (a year of an unprecedented price rise) were excluded. On all three crops, the standard deviation (dispersion of data from the mean) in net returns was noticeably less on the cash/hedge strategy. In essense, the cash/hedge strategy resulted in higher mean returns and less risk than taking chances strictly with the cash market.

Whatever strategy is chosen, it is important to build in flexibility while maintaining the basic structure of the plan. The process of developing and executing a plan can be educational and assist producers in improving their marketing skills.

Generic Advertising: A Marketing Strategy for Farmer Groups

Olan D. Forker, professor of agricultural economics, New York State College of Agriculture and Life Sciences, Cornell University, Ithaca, NY, and Ronald W. Ward, professor of agricultural economics, University of Florida, Gainesville, FL

When producers in a particular agricultural industry jointly advertise or promote their products through a commodity promotion program, we call it generic promotion or generic advertising. Today, almost every U.S. commodity group does it: More than 312 federally and state-legislated producer promotion programs cover over 80 farm commodities.

While the intensity of the advertising efforts varies across commodities, over 90 percent of all U.S. producers contribute to programs to support farm commodity promotion in some form. Interest in generic advertising of agricultural commodities has increased in the last decade, as producers have seen the potential benefits of cooperative efforts.

The potential value of generic advertising programs differs depending on the particular industry's economic environment. Such programs work best when

- The characteristics and attributes of the commodity are somewhat uniform across the group of producers
- The product does not have large extremes in brand differentiation, although brands can exist jointly with generic programs
- Producers have well-defined marketing objectives when designing and implementing generic advertising
- The industry is not monopolized by a few large players whose objectives are in conflict with those of the total industry
- There is an equitable mechanism for assessing everyone who benefits from the programs.

Nevertheless, there is no assurance that any commodity program will succeed. While success depends partly on the quality and intensity of the advertising effort, it also can be traced to a few conditions in each industry: 1) What is the current level of per capita consumption? Is consumption already near saturation? 2) How much information does the consumer already have about the commodity? 3) Can the industry maintain product quality to reinforce what is being advertised generically? 4) Is the product easily recognizable at the retail level or is it an ingredient with much of its identity lost when it reaches the consumer? 5) How important is the product to the final consumer, and what is its range of use?

Regional and national generic advertising programs can be complex to develop and implement, but they do offer producers a way to participate in the marketing process.

Generic Versus Brand Advertising

Generic advertising differs from brand advertising in several ways. Probably the most important difference is purpose. Brand advertising is usually sponsored by a single firm whose message conveys information about its brand. The primary purpose is to increase the sales volume and market share of the firm's branded product. For example, Coke advertises to increase the sales of Coke, partially at the expense of other colas. The aggregate sales volume of all colas might increase as a result of Coke's advertising, but that is generally not the overriding objective. Even so, studies of processed orange juice advertising show that both brand and generic advertising expand the total demand for orange juice, with generic and brand advertising having nearly equal effects on sales in the long run.

The primary purpose of generic advertising, on the other hand, is to increase the aggregate demand for a commodity, generally through longer term demand responses. Thus, generic advertising encompasses all products within the commodity group, including brands, without promoting specific brands.

Dairy farmers advertise to convince consumers to eat more cheese or drink more milk, yet these same farmers do not directly produce the manufactured milk products. They advertise to get consumers to pull more milk through the system or to pay a higher price for the milk produced.

There are a few examples of joint ventures between generic and brand programs. For example, the Florida Department of Citrus' Brand Advertising Rebate (BAR) Program uses generic funds to supplement brand advertising.

The National Dairy Promotion Board and the Ice Cream Manufacturers Association have worked together to develop a common advertising theme for ice cream. Yet the dairy farmers' promotion funds are used exclusively to promote ice cream as a commodity; the ice cream manufacturers use their own funds to advertise their branded products.

The second most important difference between brand and generic advertising is that brand advertisers may have more control over the product they produce and advertise. They can alter the quality or product characteristics and thus promote those characteristics. Generic advertising, however, is directed to a broader commodity group, and so it is often more general than brand advertising and is of a "softer sale" nature.

Funding Arrangements

Nationwide, producers contribute more than $530 million annually to promote their products through legislated checkoff (mandatory assessment) or marketing order programs. In addition, more than $30 million in producer-funded programs is generated through voluntary arrangements. Most of these funds are used for domestic advertising, promotion, and research activities. Substantial public funding supplements programs to promote foreign market development for U.S. farm commodities. In each year from FY 1986 through FY 1988, the Federal Government allocated $110 million to the Targeted Export Assistance Program (TEA), a matching fund program which generates foreign promotion activities. Generic efforts for foreign market development are generally funded through predetermined, shared contributions by the Federal Government, the commodity industry, and the foreign importers.

State and Federal Role

The Federal and State Governments provide the legal authority for farmers to assess (or tax) themselves to support generic advertising. Most commodity promotion programs started when small groups of farmers joined together and voluntarily

In 1935, Florida passed legislation requiring that all citrus producers be assessed to raise funds for citrus promotion activities. Studies of processed orange juice advertising show that both brand advertising and generic advertising of citrus products expand the total demand for orange juice. (Florida Department of Citrus)

pooled their funds. But to the extent that their generic programs were successful in generating an expanded demand for their commodity, all producers of the commodity benefited, even those who had not contributed. This "free rider" problem caused farmers to appeal to their governments for mandatory authority to assess all producers of the commodity.

State Governments responded positively to these farmer requests as early as the 1930's. Florida passed legislation in 1935 to assess all producers of citrus to raise funds for citrus promotion activities (see Robert M. Behr's article, *Florida Citrus Industry Sets High Standards*).

The 1937 Federal Agricultural Marketing Agreement Act allows the collection of promotion funds from several fruit, vegetable, and specialty crop marketing groups who market their commodities under Federal marketing orders. More recently, dairy, beef, pork, and other commodity groups have been influential in obtaining free-standing legislation (new legislation separate from Federal marketing order legislation) to authorize mandatory assessments. The early programs provided for refund provisions, so that someone strongly opposed to the program could petition for refunds even though the initial assessments were levied. Newer legislative programs have eliminated the refund provision.

The dairy industry gained authority in 1983 under the Dairy and Tobacco Adjustment Act for a nationwide assessment of 15 cents per hundredweight of milk produced. The law authorized the initial assessment to begin without a producer referendum but called for a referendum to be conducted after 18 months. This delayed referendum was intended to provide a time for advertising experimentation before producers voted on the program. While there is a real cost to such experimentation, it does provide producers with more definitive data from which they can make reasonable judgments. More than 80 percent of dairy farmers voting in 1985 approved continuing the mandatory assessment and dairy promotion research. Now the dairy program can continue indefinitely unless a large number of producers petition to have the checkoff withdrawn. This program generates a promotion and research fund of about $200 million annually.

Under free-standing legislation enacted in 1985, pork, beef, honey, and watermelon producer groups each have authority for mandatory assessments.

Examples of Domestic Generic Advertising[1]

The primary purpose of domestic generic advertising is to expand the demand for the commodity being promoted. Dairy farmers spend about $150 million annually on advertising and promotion for dairy products. In 1984-85, the National Dairy Board, the American Dairy Association, and more than 24 State

[1]For expanded description of generic advertising programs, see Part VI *Promoting Quality Products.*

or regional promotion organizations invested $71.7 million in advertising for the consumer fluid milk market. Campaign themes included "Milk, America's Health Kick" and "Milk, It Does a Body Good." An additional $49.3 million was invested in cheese advertising using themes such as "Cheese, Glorious Cheese" and "Say Cheese." About $20 million was invested in promoting dairy foods as a source of calcium, using the theme "Dairy Foods, Calcium the Way Nature Intended."

Beef producers spent about $30 million to advertise beef in 1987. The national beef advertising programs are developed and implemented by the Beef Industry Council on behalf of the Cattlemen's Beef Board, which was established in October 1986 with the enactment of the $1 per head checkoff program, and the 41-State beef councils. The advertising theme is "Beef, Real Food for Real People." A national referendum was held in May 1988 to determine if beef producers wished to continue the program.

Pork producers planned to invest about $9 million on generic advertising during 1988. The advertising programs developed by the National Pork Producer's Council for the National Pork Board promote primarily fresh pork products and feature the theme, "Pork. The Other White Meat."

International Promotion Programs

The Federal Government operates three programs: a Cooperator Program, an Export Incentive Program, and a Targeted Export Assistance Program. Each involves the Federal Government providing incentives in the form of matching funds and technical or information assistance to promote U.S. agricultural products overseas.

Under the **Cooperator Program** cooperator preference is given to nonprofit U.S. agricultural trade organizations that are industrywide or nationwide in membership and scope. Private firms may be eligible to participate if the Foreign Agricultural Service (FAS) determines that they meet certain conditions. Activities may include trade servicing, consumer promotion, market research, and technical assistance to actual or potential foreign purchasers.

Participants are selected for the **Export Incentive Program** if no cooperator program is feasible. Eligibility is limited to the registered brand of the participant or other brand that FAS approves in advance. Activities are usually limited to direct promotion such as consumer advertising, point of sale demonstrations, public relations and press servicing activities, and participation in trade fairs and exhibits.

The **Targeted Export Assistance Program** (TEA) was authorized in the Food Security Act of 1985 and was designed to stimulate exports of U.S. agricultural products through market development activities targeted at countering or offsetting unfair foreign trade practices. Two basic TEA programs are available. The first is conducted through commodity-specific

nonprofit agricultural trade associations, called "Participants."
The second, called the "TEA/Export Incentive Program
(TEA/EIP)," allocates TEA resources for the purpose of pro-
moting U.S. brand-identified products.

Research Findings

Research by commodity promotion organizations and their
advertising agencies typically involves surveying consumers
about their awareness of the group's advertising theme and
about their attitudes and beliefs toward the advertisements and
products. Information from these tracking studies or consumer
surveys helps the organizations and agencies design campaigns
and monitor consumer acceptance.

Little research has been conducted to determine the direct
or indirect connection between the advertising effort and
changes in consumer purchases. Many of these advertising
evaluation studies have relied on computer model building
where price, income, and demand are directly incorporated
into the analysis along with advertising. The few studies that
have been conducted do not provide all the answers that producers and legislators would like to have, but they do give
considerable insight into the performance of specific commodity programs.

Econometric studies on the advertising of fluid milk, cheese,
orange juice, grapefruit juice, and oranges indicate a positive
relationship between the amount of money invested in generic
advertising expenditures and sales of the advertised commodity. The research also indicates that the law of diminishing
returns applies. As advertising expenditures increase, sales will
increase, but at a decreasing rate. Also, most of the analysis
points to some type of advertising carryover effect; that is,
advertising today will influence future consumption decisions.
However, the response rate differs among products, advertising
campaigns, seasons of the year, and geographic markets.

Public Policy

While generic programs are designed to assist specific commodity groups, public concern continues over the total impact
of generic advertising on aggregate food consumption. Does
advertising one commodity simply lead to its substitution for
another? Is this an efficient way to assist the agricultural sector?
Does generic promotion play a useful role in nutrition education? Which commodities should and which should not qualify
for national checkoff authority?

The range and complexity of the public issues are far-
reaching, the questions difficult to answer. But increasing
numbers of commodity groups are likely to seek legislative
authority, so the public debate will continue. These issues are
not as critical when considering the international promotion
programs. Expansion of foreign markets generally is viewed as
a plus for all U.S. producers and for the U.S. economy.

Food Marketing Strategies for Firms

Emerson M. Babb, professor, Food & Resource Economics Department, University of Florida, Gainesville, FL

Marketing, in an agricultural context, has traditionally referred to activities that take place from the farm gate to the final consumer. Business firms think of marketing differently. To them, it relates to activities that influence sales of their products. Marketing strategies used by firms in the food industry use this concept of marketing. Marketing strategies position products so these firms can win the battle for the food dollar.

The marketing strategies used by food firms affect many people. They influence the price, volume, and mix of commodities sold by farmers as well as the return and risk on capital provided by investors. They influence the price, quality, and variety of products available to consumers. The strategies available to firms marketing food are different from those farmers can use, but not greatly different from those that firms marketing nonfood products use.

Firms have many goals, one of which is growth. Growth requires an adequate financial return in order to be pursued on a sustained basis, but it also influences financial return. Marketing strategies are developed to achieve the growth objective, which is a major concern of firms in the food industry.

Marketing Strategies

A firm must answer the question, "What business should I be in?" The business of a firm is defined by the scope of its products and markets and by the product and market segments it serves. Scope refers to the customers to be served and the functions to be performed. Segments are based on differences in customer needs and ways of satisfying those needs.

The following types of marketing strategies influence sales growth in products and markets selected by the firm. These strategies are highly interrelated, and consistency in their use is essential to achieve growth objectives.

Geographic Diversification

Expansion of the sales area increases consumer exposure to food products and leads to increased sales. With larger sales, economies of advertising, selling, and production also may be realized. However, a larger sales area can bring out regional differences in customer preferences, which must be accommodated.

Product Diversification

The desired product diversification can be achieved by developing new products or by reformulating and repackaging an existing product. Food marketing firms now introduce about 2,500 new food products each year, many of which are later withdrawn. Firms must develop new products or modify exisitng ones because most products have a life cycle: Sales increase after introduction, but reach a plateau and then decline. Total sales of the firm would thus decline if new products were not introduced.

A firm will market a mix of products that vary in design, packaging, ingredients, quality, or other product and service attributes. Each product or variation of a product is targeted to a specific group of customers. This mix of sales is supposed to achieve sales goals and protect the firm from loss of sales to rivals. Although product diversification strategies increase the variety of food products available to consumers, they can result in a proliferation of products with only minor differences in quality or other attributes. The firm may preserve or expand its market share by producing and marketing several variations of a product that might otherwise by introduced by a rival firm.

Branding

Food manufactures may label products with their brands, or with distributor brands (private label), or sell unbranded products (ingredients and generic). This decision is greatly influenced by the channels of trade that will be used and by product characteristics. (There is much less branding for highly standardized products such as milk, which are often subject to Government-imposed identity standards.) The firm must be able to differentiate its branded products from those of rivals and to communicate these differences to consumers.

As a result of these communications, consumers develop brand loyalty, which provides some bargaining power with buyers (wholesalers and retailers) and assures processors that their products will find their way to retail shelves. Development of strong brands requires paying attention to packaging and positioning the product with an eye to the competition.

Private label and unbranded products are often those which are difficult to differentiate and for which there may be few direct buyers. Efficiency and low cost are important to firms selling these types of products.

Advertising and Promotion

More than $9 billion—more than 2 percent of sales—is spent annually on advertising and promoting food products. Advertising expenditures as a percent of sales for food products are about double those for other consumer products, but they vary widely among food product groups.

Advertising expenditure is less intensive and its content more informative for food products that are less differentiable, such as milk, meat, lettuce. For products that are differentiable, more persuasive advertising content is used. Advertising informs consumers about product attributes and is often targeted to appeal to specific groups of consumers. Establishing a consumer franchise (loyalty to a product) through brands and introducing new products requires large expenditures for advertising and promotion.

Promotions may take many forms. Point of purchase displays, in-store demonstrations, and coupons are particularly effective in getting the consumer to try a new or modified product. Salespersons may be needed to provide technical information to wholesale and retail buyers, to arrange displays, and

Some supermarkets have coupon-producing machines at the cash register. As the shopper's order is processed, the coupon dispenser determines if there are related or competing items in the system and prints out corresponding coupons that can be redeemed on the next shopping trip. (Giant Food, Inc.)

to inform the buyers about the merits of a firm's products. Trade allowances and deals may be offered to buyers as incentives to stock the products. Some of the trade allowances and deals may require the buyer to advertise or offer coupons for the product locally. Some trade allowances and deals can be viewed as price concessions used to move products, especially where inventory imbalances occur.

Pricing

The prices that food manufacturers are able to obtain may yield thin profit margins for products that are difficult to differentiate, unbranded products, and private label products. Efficiency and low production and distribution costs are thus important for survival.

Pricing branded products is more flexible, but manufacturers are still subject to competitive forces by rival firms. The uncertainty about how rival firms will react to pricing strategy means that the firm must be prepared to make countermoves. Pricing is influenced by the design of the product and the segment of the market for which the product is targeted.

Foodstores and eating places likewise establish prices that are consistent with the mix of products and services they have targeted. Foodstores use the concept of blending margins (a margin is the difference between what the retailers pays for an item and what he or she sells it for) within departments and among departments to achieve an overall gross margin that will achieve the profit objective. This involves weighing changes in margins by product movement to determine the impact of margin changes on the total margin for the department or store.

Customer Focus

Food manufacturers can choose to place products in four basic channels of trade: 1) other processors (ingredients or industrial products, 2) foodservice, 3) private label, generic, and unbranded products sold through foodstores, and 4) manufacturer-branded products sold through foodstores.

The appropriate market strategies differ greatly among these channels. Market segments (groups of consumers that are somewhat homogeneous) within a channel may require different product design, pricing, and advertising. Product differentiation varies among trade channels—with low differentiation for ingredients, moderate differentiation for foodservice and distributor-branded products, and high differentiation for manufacturer-branded products.

Each firm determines its market niche by its choice of trade channels and market segments and by positioning its products relative to rivals. This selection relies on detailed information about customer needs, motivations, and preferences, as well as knowledge of the technological, marketing, and other attributes of the firm which give it an advantage in exploiting that

niche. Firms thus concentrate their efforts in one or two channels of trade. A firm would rarely sell products in all four
channels or have sales evenly spread among several, even
though this might reduce risk. The advantages of specialization
apparently outweigh risk reduction.

Strategies of Food Manufacturers in Various Channels

Annual sales of the 16,000 food manufacturers total $315 bil-
lion. For many industries, such as breakfast cereals and wet
corn milling, sales are concentrated in a few firms. The particular marketing strategies used by food manufacturers vary
among industries and channels of trade.

Channels of Trade for U.S. food manufacturing companies

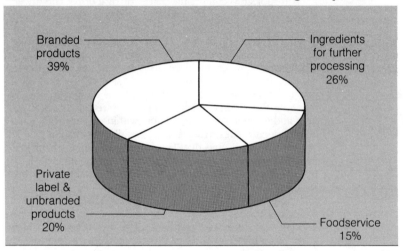

Branded products 39%

Ingredients for further processing 26%

Private label & unbranded products 20%

Foodservice 15%

Ingredient Channel
The products of some industries, such as sugar and soybean
milling, are used as ingredients by other manufacturers. The
ingredient channel accounts for about 26 percent of shipments
by food manufacturers. Direct buyers are few, and purchases
are made in very large quantities. The products may meet rigid
specifications but are undifferentiated and thus not advertised.
Prices usually result in narrow margins, which places a premium on efficiency.

Foodservice Channel
The 700,000 foodservice establishments vary from snack bars to
large plant cafeterias, and their product and service requirements are equally diverse. Brands are often not important to
foodservice firms, but rigid product specifications, including
portion control, may be required by institutional buyers and

fast food chains. Price competition for these large accounts is intense. Small processors, who may be unable to handle the volume required by some foodservice firms, concentrate on the many eating places where service is more important. About 15 percent of food manufacturer sales are in the foodservice channel.

Private Label and Unbranded Products Channel

Entry into the private label and unbranded products channel (for example, fresh produce and fresh meat) is relatively easy. There is moderate product differentiation and little or no required advertising. Shelf space does not have to be gained by overcoming the brand loyalty of competing products; it is allocated by the buyer. Buyers specify product quality and packaging requirements for many private label products.

Price competition in this channel is intense and resembles bidding for a contract. Firms do not have to pay the cost of establishing a consumer franchise and are thus willing to accept lower prices. They have low involvement with marketing decisions and little power in negotiations with buyers.

Some food retailers have integrated back into food manufacturing. They process their own brands, especially in dairy and bakery products. This happens where food retailers can achieve lower costs in processing or distribution than the food manufacturers who are willing to bid for their business.

Food manufacturer sales in the private label and unbranded products channel are about 20 percent of the total.

Manufacturer-Branded Product Channel

In contrast, the emphasis of firms in the branded products channel is on marketing strategies which establish their consumer franchise. The consumer franchise is the basis for favorable shelf space and location in retail stores.

Developing a consumer franchise is not a simple task. It is also very expensive. Extensive information must be obtained about consumers, the portfolio of products offered by rival firms, and their marketing strategies. Research is conducted on consumer motivations, needs, desires, and attitudes relating to categories of products to identify voids in existing product mixes that a new or modified product might fill. The research also identifies market segments and groups of consumers who will buy or might be persuaded to buy a product with the specified attributes. Firms need intelligence about the products that rivals market in various market segments, and the rivals' strategies must be understood.

Suppose a firm decides to develop a new product. It may be tested by panels of consumers during the development phase, and it is usually test marketed before a general introduction. The test marketing may cost more than the development of the product, but it provides an indication of the product's sales potential and the effectiveness of marketing strategies that have been planned for the product. On the basis of test-market results, the product may be abandoned, redesigned, or introduced for general distribution. If the test market results reveal major flaws in product design or marketing strategies, the product might be modified and go through the test market phase again to obtain more data.

All of the marketing strategies are employed when a product is introduced and a consumer franchise established. The penetration of the product in various market channels and segments is monitored through sales data of the firm and from movement and market share data supplied by research firms. Based on this information, the firm may reposition the product, adjust marketing strategies, continue current strategies, or withdraw the product. This monitoring continues over the life cycle of the product.

Branded products comprise 39 percent of food manufacturers' sales. About two-thirds of processed food products sold in food stores are manufacturers' brands, but the shares vary among product lines from less than half to almost 100 percent.

Strategies of Other Food Marketing Firms

Wholesalers, foodstores, and foodservice firms employ essentially the same marketing strategies as food manufacturers. They target a mix of products and services for specific market segments and groups of consumers and use the appropriate advertising and pricing strategies. For example, foodstores may be just as successful with high prices and extensive services as with low prices and minimum services. Different types of customers with different needs will be attracted by the two sets of strategies. Strategies of fast food chains are designed to attract different people than those of elegant restaurants. Many of the foodservice product lines have matured and are undergoing modification with new product or service introductions. Food product life cycles also apply to foodservice products.

Some foodservice firms specialize in products that have uniform characteristics (for example, hamburgers of the same shape and weight), just as products in the private label channel do. Some eating places such as hospitals, office cafeterias, airlines, vendors, and fast food chains may purchase partially or fully prepared meals that meet their specifications at negotiated prices. In such cases, the selling firm focuses on efficiency so it can compete on the basis of price and reliability, rather than on marketing strategies.

Marketing Environment

The firm develops marketing strategies to achieve its growth objectives, given its own resources, capabilities, and skills. The premier marketers consider more than just their own attributes and domestic markets in setting strategies. They anticipate changes that will permit the creation of new products and that influence the demand for products. Recognizing that domestic markets are not isolated, they position their products and activities in a global context. Marketing strategies are thus shaped by external forces such as the following:

Technology

Developments in technology are changing the characteristics of both raw and finished products. Membrane technology (a filtration technique used in food processing) permits concentration and purification. Irradiation and aseptic processing and packaging extend shelf life. Biotechnology can alter the characteristics of products. Computerized process control and robotics can improve quality and reduce cost. Technology can thus be used to create new products or modify existing ones so that they better satisfy the needs and preferences of consumers in different segments of the market.

Trends in Consumer Behavior

Consumer needs and preferences are continuously changing as a consequence of demographic and psychological factors, assimilation of new knowledge about foods, fads and fashions, concerns about health and nutrition, and many other forces. Demographic factors can be accurately projected so their effects on consumer behavior can be anticipated. Marketing strategies will call for the development of new or modified products that are positioned in channels and market segments where growth will be most rapid and where the firm will benefit most from changes in consumer buying patterns. For example, softer, more easily digested products might be developed for an aging population; package size might be reduced to accommodate the needs of single-occupant households.

International Competition

U.S. markets for raw and finished products have become more open to foreign competition, so that marketing strategies must consider the international perspective. U.S. food marketing firms must weigh the advantages and disadvantages of procuring and processing raw products here rather than elsewhere. To enter foreign markets, they can acquire firms in other countries, export finished products, or license the production of their products in foreign countries. Foreign firms have been active in the acquisition of U.S. food marketing firms and in licensing the production they control.

The competitive position of U.S. products is constantly changing. There are many instances of the use of a raw product shifting from one finished product to another because of changes in competitive position. Marketing strategies position the products of the firm so that they have a competitive advantage in a global market.

Impact of Global Market Changes on U.S. Agricultural Producers

Jerry Siebert, economist, Division of Agriculture and Natural Resources, University of California, Davis, CA

World markets for agricultural products have changed greatly during the past 15 years, the result of many factors largely beyond the control of U.S. farmers. Furthermore, other countries have greatly expanded their capacities to produce and market commodities competitively against us—and in many cases at a cost advantage. Markets for agricultural products have become international in scope, so changes that take place in world markets affect U.S. farmers and domestic markets.

Operating Environment

The operating environment in which a producer makes decisions has become more complex. Factors influencing this environment include macroeconomics, productivity, and Government policies and programs. These factors are largely beyond the control of the producer.

Macroeconomic factors include interest rates, Government fiscal policies, economic growth, and trade arrangements that significantly affect the financial considerations of a producer. An example is the influence of high interest rates on costs of production coupled with a shift in exchange rates which, for a while, made U.S. products less competitive.

Productivity factors include such variables as weather, technology, input prices, and Government restrictions (e.g., standards and regulations on health, pollution, and the environment).

Weather extremes in any part of the world can infuence domestic markets by affecting supplies in relation to demand.

Where once the United States dominated world production because of its technological competitive advantage, the transfer of technology is now international, and other countries quickly adopt the same practices as U.S. producers.

Changes in transportation technology and structure have provided foreign suppliers easier access to the United States, and U.S. Government restrictions increasingly hamper productivity growth in agriculture.

Government policies and programs affect farmers' ability to produce efficiently and sell in a world market. Increasingly, producers are dependent on Government programs and often subsidies to survive. On the supply side, Government programs have led to overproduction, depressing prices in world markets. On the demand side, the Government is increasingly a partner in assuring appropriate agreements in the sales of products into world markets. However, there are danger signals: Many countries, including the United States, are becoming increasingly apprehensive about continuing massive subsidies to agriculture.

Markets reflect all the economic and political forces that affect sales of agricultural and natural resource products. Markets are dynamic and variable, reflecting the combination of forces that have come together to match available supplies and demand. Agricultural producers must appreciate the changes taking place in the marketplace so they can make appropriate long- and short-term decisions.

A Framework for Decisionmaking

It is not enough to be an efficient producer. Production decisions must be more closely coordinated with marketing decisions and changes. In addition to the usual animal and crop management decisions, the producer must consider financial structuring, debt/financial management, Government programs and regulations, market/contractual arrangements, risk management, and changing market requirements. The goal is to remain as efficient as possible—not only in production but also in marketing—and to remain competitive.

In the future, the producer will need to work more closely with others to influence as much as possible those external factors affecting operational decisions. Not only will the producer increasingly need to broaden understanding of external market forces, but so will those who provide support—such as bankers, suppliers, and processors. It is also likely that, in order to obtain necessary financing, producers will have to provide not only a production plan, but a marketing plan, as well. Where many financial organizations once provided this service, the shakeout of the early 1980's has led to retrenchment and a shifting of the burden of proof regarding marketing strategies.

The complexity of market considerations as shaped by Government, productivity, and macroeconomic factors needs to be incorporated into a systems management approach to decisionmaking by the producer. This approach requires the ability to analyze various factors, place them in perspective, and make appropriate decisions.

The systems approach is not new. Systems are being developed in integrated pest management, irrigation management, and animal reproduction, for example, which involve the integration of several factors into a decisionmaking model. Concurrent with the development of these models are new information and data bases to make them work. The innovative producer is using the computer to assimilate and analyze data and information into a framework for faster and more accurate evaluation of production factors. The end result of this development is a continuing increase in productivity. What is now required is an expansion of the models underlying this management approach that incorporates marketing considerations.

Innovative producers are using computers to assimilate and analyze data for faster and more accurate evaluation of production factors. This development has resulted in a continuing increase in productivity. (William E. Carnahan)

Marketing Considerations

In developing a marketing strategy, the producer must consider a number of factors to assure that production decisions take market forces and changes into account:

Alternatives
Farmers can evaluate the options of transferring out of agricultural production, restructuring the production enterprise, or considering new crops or commodities or new uses of existing ones.

The decision to transfer out of production is the most difficult and traumatic, but it may be the only way to preserve assets. When a particular enterprise becomes unprofitable, and the prognosis is that this situation will continue for a long time, the producer must assess the long-term viability of the operation. It may be wiser to quit rather than continue to lose financial equity. In this vein, perhaps the marketing strategy can be designed to preserve as much equity as possible. For example, some producers in California have sought to market water allotments (legal rights to water), which would provide more income than producing the crops for which the water was intended.

A second option is the restructuring of the farm enterprise. While some of the restructuring may deal with managerial methods, marketing and financial considerations come into play as well.

Farmers must consider new crops and commodities that might replace unprofitable ones. Currently profitable crops may become rapidly unprofitable as new entries appear in the marketplace and supplies expand. Producers need to assess the long-term viability and competitiveness of new crops, taking into account the comparative advantages in production and marketing of different regions.

One exciting direction is the development of new— particularly industrial—uses for existing crops. This is an important research area for both the private and public sectors.

Government Programs and Policies

Government programs and policies greatly influence producers' welfare. This influence comes not only from such well-known mechanisms as subsidies and price supports, but also from health and environmental regulations, tariffs, quotas, trade barriers, and monetary and fiscal policies. Not only is it important for producers to know about current policies and those that will affect the next crop year, but they must also anticipate fundamental shifts that could require changes in the nature of the agricultural operation. For example, the shift in policy in the 1985 Food Security Act greatly enhanced the ability of U.S. farmers to compete in world markets by revising U.S. pricing structures and introducing the Targeted Export Assistance Program, which enhances exports by providing matching funds for export promotion.

Many producers and their representatives have maintained that in the international arena, all that is desired is a "level playing field." Yet it is doubtful that many understand the consequences of the elimination of trade barriers and subsidies not only by foreign competitors, but also by the United States. If such a change were to take place, some producers would gain but others would lose.

Consumer Trends

At the heart of any market-oriented program is an identification of consumer needs, wants, and trends. Consumers are becoming more knowledgeable about food and fiber issues. Emerging trends in consumption patterns need to be translated into production and marketing decisions. Currently, this translation is being done slowly or not at all. In many cases, basic shifts in consumer preferences are accommodated grudgingly. A classic case is the decline in consumption of red meats owing to concern about high cholesterol. Red meats are belatedly mounting a comeback through aggressive promotion. But more important, farmers are producing and marketing leaner animals. Increasingly, consumer preferences need to be translated into marketing and production decisions.

Market Promotion
Marketing orders have traditionally been instrumental in promotion efforts. Trade associations also have helped. In addition, the Federal Government has lately introduced the Targeted Export Assistance Program. Producers need to support such programs.

Reducing Costs
In the past, producers paid little attention to forces beyond the farm gate. Reduction of production costs is important. but so is reduction of marketing costs. Production and marketing efficiencies and cost reduction need to be coordinated to maximize the competitiveness of a product in the marketplace.

Quality Considerations
Quality helps differentiate a product for price advantage. Current grades and standards for U.S. products provide a guide to quality assurance. However, because they may not be in concert with current consumer tastes and needs, they should be reassessed. In addition, grades and standards for use in the United States may not reflect foreign tastes, cultures, and needs. Ideally, the production and marketing of agriculture and natural resource products should be tailored to the consumers' needs, tastes, and preferences wherever they live. In addition, grades and standards should contribute to efficiency and cost reductions in processing and marketing.

Toxics
Increasingly, alarms are sounded over the safety of the food supply, not only from domestic sources but from foreign suppliers as well. While pesticides have contributed to the production of plentiful and nutritious food supplies, their toxicity is of public concern. Producers should work with consumer groups to maintain reasonable standards for food safety. For example, the recent scare from finding aldicarb in watermelons not only eliminated profits for a whole season, but necessitated further investment in following seasons to reassure consumers. Reducing or not using pesticides may increase production costs, but it proves profitable because markets are gained. There are many success stories of marketing pesticide-free products.

Risk
Futures, options, forward contracting, long-term contracts, and other arrangements reduce risk but farmers still need improved methods of avoiding it. Reliable sources of information and improved analysis help reduce risk and market variability.

Information Needs

With the changes in agricultural markets and the increasing complexity of management systems, new data bases and information networks will need to be developed. Integrated production systems are much more advanced than models for marketing. For example, in developing integrated pest manangement models and methodologies, new data bases have been created for weather information, pest populations, and registered chemicals. Improved data bases and information systems need to be developed for marketing information and analysis as traditional data and information become outmoded. Sources of information need to be developed that reflect new and developing market situations, and how these changes affect decisions.

Forecasting, a key factor in marketing programs, is risky but essential. It involves an evaluation of current situations, trends, and economic and political factors. New forecasting tools need to be developed, and more attention given to information and analysis of changing market trends, and ways to use the information in decisionmaking.

Impact on Supporting Organizations

The changes now being reflected in markets throughout the world pose unique challenges—not only for producers, but also for the organizations, both private and public, that support them. Usually, when market changes occur, it is too late for many producers and marketing firms to adopt strategies to cope with the dislocations. Hence, supporting organizations and institutions (for example, cooperatives, banks, and farm bureaus) need to restructure their programs to build a capacity to identify the forces causing change in markets and to assist producers and marketing organizations in making appropriate decisions.

Remaining Competitive

Changes in research and advisory programs will be particularly important. Farm organizations and cooperatives need to consider developing an analytical capability and programs that will better inform and assist producers. Government programs need to be reexamined to assure that their objectives correspond with market realities. By assessing the changes taking place and developing new focuses involving the dynamic forces reflected in markets, organizations and institutions will assure that U.S. producers remain competitive.

International Marketing Strategies

Leo V. Mayer, deputy assistant secretary for economics, U.S. Department of Agriculture

Starting in 1933, nearly all U.S. farm legislation has included an international marketing strategy. Now more than ever, the scope and effectiveness of that strategy bear heavily on the health of U.S. agriculture. Four out of ten acres of U.S. crop production are exported, and overseas sales of livestock products now help livestock farmers have profitable operations. Three efforts—promotion, negotiation, and competitiveness—have been important parts of the U.S. strategy for marketing our farm products in international markets. A substantial part of the U.S. export strategy is accomplished through private sector groups that work in various countries to promote U.S. farm products abroad. Another phase is represented by Federal Government efforts to reduce barriers to agricultural trade through trade negotiations. The Uruguay Round of Multilateral Trade Negotiations—the 8th such round since the General Agreement on Tariffs and Trade was signed in 1947—should strengthen the U.S. position in world markets. Equally important, U.S. farm legislation—designed to make U.S. commodities more competitive on the world market—has laid the foundation for expanding farm exports.

Programs of the Food Security Act of 1985

The most recent description of the U.S. export strategy was included in the Food Security Act of 1985. That legislation helped reverse the trend in the early part of the decade toward declining U.S. farm exports. Through a combination of subsidy programs, intensified efforts of private organizations (mostly commodity-producer associations) and revised market price levels, sales and overseas consumption of U.S. farm commodities have increased.

GSM-103

The Food Security Act of 1985 established the GSM-103 intermediate export credit guarantee program (for a loan term of 3-10 years) to supplement existing Commodity Credit Corporation (CCC) credit guarantee programs. (GSM refers to the General Sales Manager, a USDA official responsible for administering Public Law 480 and specific CCC promotion programs.) The CCC's guarantee of repayment facilitated the extension of private commercial credit to importers in Iraq, Bangladesh, Morocco, and other countries in fiscal year 1987.

GSM-102

The act continued the GSM-102 export credit guarantee program for short-term (up to 3 years) credit. During fiscal year 1987, Iraq, Mexico, and the Republic of Korea made substantial purchases using this program.

Public Law 480

The 1985 act amended title I of Public Law 480. Over the years, through title I, the United States has provided long-term credit at low interest rates with terms of up to 40 years for the purchase of specific commodities. The recipient government sells these commodities on its domestic market. The concessional credit used to finance a Food for Development Program can be forgiven if the recipient government achieves certain agreed-upon development activities. At least 10 percent of the title I funds must be allocated to this program. The act authorized cash sales payable in the local currency of the recipient and also authorized a Food for Progress Program to help countries achieve specific agricultural policy reforms.

Agricultural Export Credit Sales Programs

| | | Term Structure | | |
Program	Lender	Maturity	Interest	Period of operation
GSM-5[1]	U.S. Government	1-3 years	Market rate	1956-81; 1983-85
GSM-101	Commercial banks with U.S. Government guarantee	1-3 years	Market rate	1979-81
GSM-102	Commercial banks with U.S. Government guarantee	1-3 years	Market rate	1981-present
GSM-103	Commercial banks with U.S. Government guarantee	3-10 years	Market rate	1986-present
Blended credit package[2]	U.S. Government and commercial banks	1-3 years	Average below market rate	1983-85
GSM-201	U.S. Government	3-10 years	Market rate	1980
GSM-301	U.S. Government	3-10 years	Market rate	1981-82
P.L. 480 dollar credit	U.S. Government	Up to 20 years	Below market rate	1959-present
P.L. 480 convertible currency credit	U.S. Government	Up to 40 years	Below market rate	1966-present

[1]The authorization for direct credit in 1983-85 included interest-free loans as part of a "blended" credit package.
[2]Blend of GSM-5 and GSM-102.

Export Enhancement Program

The 1985 act authorized $1.5 billion to fund an Export Enhancement Program (EEP) through fiscal year 1988 to help make U.S. commodity prices competitive. Under the EEP, the CCC awards exporters certificates redeemable for CCC-owned commodities to make up the difference between the domestic market price and the international price. Thus, the exporters can sell specified commodities to specified countries at prices below those of the U.S. market.

Both houses of Congress have passed trade bills expanding the EEP to a maximum of $2.5 billion through fiscal year 1990. Most EEP sales have covered food and feed grains. The largest sales have been wheat to the Soviet Union and barley to Saudi Arabia. Importers in Egypt, Algeria, Morocco, and China also have bought significant amounts of wheat.

Targeted Export Assistance Program (TEA)

This program, also established by the 1985 Act, authorizes the Secretary of Agriculture to use CCC funds or generic commodity certificates to reimburse export promotion costs of U.S.

Program Allocations by Commodity for Specified Destinations, fiscal year 1988[1]

Program	Wheat[2]	Feed grains	Rice	Oilseeds	Vegetable oils
GSM-102	Algeria Brazil Egypt Iraq S. Korea	Algeria Iraq S. Korea Mexico Turkey	Algeria Brazil Iraq Jordan Turkey	Colombia S. Korea Mexico Morocco Turkey	Algeria Iraq Mexico Pakistan Tunisia
GSM-103	Bangladesh Jordan Mexico Morocco Yemen	Morocco Tunisia			
Export Enhancement Program	Algeria China Egypt Morocco Soviet Union	Algeria Israel Poland Saudi Arabia Switzerland	Jordan Turkey		Algeria India Morocco Tunisia
P.L. 480, titles I and III	Bangladesh Bolivia Egypt Sri Lanka Sudan	El Salvador Ghana Guatemala Jamaica	Bangladesh Ghana Jamaica	Jamaica	Dominican Republic Egypt El Salvador Morocco Pakistan

[1]Top five destinations, except where there are fewer than five, are listed for each commodity.
[2]Includes wheat flour.

producer groups representing commodities that have been disadvantaged by unfair foreign trade policies. USDA allocated $110 million for the TEA Program in each of fiscal years 1986 through 1988.

Developing Future Markets

Food aid to developing countries serves to meet immediate needs in poor countries and to lay the foundation for future markets. U.S. food aid programs involve sales on concessional credit, sales for local currencies, and donations.

Food aid allows recipient governments to conserve foreign exchange and build their economies. As economic activity grows and per capita income rises, these countries increase their purchases of various products, including food.

Food aid also provides nutritional assistance to people in countries that face droughts or other natural disasters and in countries that would not otherwise be able to afford food imports. Because U.S. law requires that food aid neither interfere with commercial trade nor compete with agricultural production in the recipient country, food that is donated or sold on concessional terms represents increased U.S. exports in the year in which it is shipped. U.S. donations are distributed under Public Law 480, title II, and section 416 of the Agricultural Act of 1949, as amended.

Title II authorizes commodity donations through government-to-government agreements, private voluntary organizations, and the World Food Program. The 1985 Act requires the United States to donate a minimum of 1.9 million tons through fiscal year 1990, of which 1.425 million tons for nonemergency programs must be distributed through private voluntary organizations, cooperatives, and the World Food Program.

Donations under section 416 were previously limited to CCC-owned dairy products, wheat, and rice. The 1985 Act expands that list to include all CCC-owned edible commodities. That act also sets an annual minimum of 500,000 tons or 10 percent of CCC's uncommitted stocks of grains and oil-seeds, whichever is less, and 10 percent of CCC's uncommitted dairy stocks, to the extent that dairy stocks are available.

In addition to the multitude of legislative authorities designed to specifically expand farm exports, legislation also supports the promotional efforts of private sector producer groups that work overseas to build the demand for farm commodities. Some 58 commodity-producer organizations and commercial agribusiness firms have joined with USDA in promoting U.S. farm exports. These "cooperator" organizations promote sales of their commodities to import officials of foreign governments, commercial importer firms, retail stores and restaurants, and individual consumers. Their clientele includes the affluent developed countries as well as developing countries.

Government Efforts through Trade Policy

The Uruguay Round of negotiations under the General Agreement on Tariffs and Trade (GATT) has underscored the U.S. interest in making world markets more open. The United States wants other countries to reduce or end export subsidies for agricultural products, improve market access, and develop standardized guidelines for imposing health and sanitary regulations. The European Community and the Cairns group of exporting countries (Argentina, Australia, Brazil, Canada, Chile, Colombia, Hungary, Indonesia, Malaysia, New Zealand, the Philippines, Thailand, and Uruguay) also have called for reduced subsidies and a move to market-oriented agricultural trading.

Bilateral agreements, such as the recent U.S.-Canada trade accord, may prove important in expanding trade among developed countries. That agreement, signed January 2, 1988, by President Reagan and the Canadian Prime Minister, has several provisions that will affect agriculture:

· Both countries will eliminate all agricultural tariffs within 10 years.
· Current tariff rates may be reimposed on fresh fruits and vegetables under certain conditions for up to 20 years.
· The United States will not impose restrictive quotas on Canadian products containing 10 percent sugar or less.
· Canada will eliminate import licenses for U.S. wheat, barley, oats, and products of those grains when each country's support prices for those grains are equal.
· Canada will remove transportation subsidies for products moving through western ports destined for U.S. markets.
· Canada will increase global import quotas for poultry, poultry products, and eggs to the annual average of actual shipments during the past 5 years.
· The United States and Canada will exempt each other from meat import laws.

These and some other provisions of the U.S.-Canada accord may set an example for other bilateral agreements and may influence multilateral negotiations.

Marketing Abroad Essential

The 1980's have been turbulent years in many sectors of the world's economy. The United States has taken a new approach to revitalizing our farm sector by emphasizing the importance of export trade. The programs of the Food Security Act of 1985, the work of the private sector cooperator organizations, the multilateral interest in freeing world trade, and generally better economic conditions should all contribute to a brighter future for U.S. agriculture.

Part III
Discovering What Buyers Want

What Do American Women Eat?

Laura S. Sims, administrator, and Alanna J. Moshfegh, assistant
to the administrator, Human Nutrition Information Service,
Hyattsville, MD

The food supply in the United States is one of the most abundant in the world. Our food choices are endless. American consumers have an estimated 20,000 food items to select from supermarket shelves. From this vast array, what do we eat? Does the type of eating occasion affect our food selection? Are our food choices changing? Answers to these types of questions are sought by food producers and manufacturers to assist in marketing and promoting their products to consumers. And these answers can be found in the U.S. Department of Agriculture's Nationwide Food Consumption Surveys.

Capturing nationally representative information on what people eat is a complex process. USDA has been conducting the Nationwide Food Consumption Survey (NFCS) at approximately 10-year intervals since the mid-1930's. Nationwide surveys on food intake ask individuals for a detailed description of all foods and beverages consumed, the quantities eaten, the form of the food eaten, the sources of the food, and the kind of eating occasion.

In 1985, USDA started the first nationwide dietary intake survey to be conducted year by year in this country—the Continuing Survey of Food Intakes by Individuals (CSFII). The Continuing Survey complements the larger NFCS with yearly data collection that provides up-to-date information on diets of selected population groups and gives early indications of dietary changes. These are important considerations for food producers and manufacturers who must constantly be aware of consumer preferences and behavior.

To answer questions about what we are eating and when are we eating it, diets of women 19-50 years of age were assessed using the 1985 CSFII. In the survey, about 1,100 women from across the country recalled what and how much they ate and drank at home and away from home for 4 days spread over 1985. Other information related to food consumption was also collected, such as the name of the eating occasion (breakfast, lunch, dinner/supper, or snack), age and income of the respondent, and general self-reported information about diet and health. To answer the question of how our food choices have changed, the data were compared with similar data collected in 1977.

Average Daily Food Intake

On the average, the women said they ate, per day—

- 11 ounces—or about 3 servings—of vegetables, fruits, and juices.
- 3-1/2 to 4 slices or an equivalent weight of bread and other baked goods.
- 1/3 ounce of ready-to-eat cereal, or about 2 servings per week.
- 1/2 to 3/4 cup of cooked cereals, pasta, and grain mixtures.
- More than 1 cup of milk as a beverage or in dairy products. About 2/3 cup of this was consumed as fluid milk.

What Women Ate in 1977 and 1985[1]

Food group	Individuals using 1977	Individuals using 1985	Average intake 1985	Average intake Change from 1977
	Percent		Grams	Percent
Total meat, poultry, fish	92	88	181	-3
Meat mixtures	33	37	88	+35
Beef[2]	35	23	27	-45
Poultry[2]	18	19	19	-8
Pork[2]	24	20	14	-22
Fish and shellfish[2]	10	12	13	+18
Milk, milk products	74	77	259	-5
Skim, low-fat	16	26	77	+60
Whole milk	39	26	64	-35
Cheese	28	34	18	+6
Eggs	29	24	18	-28
Legumes, nuts, seeds	17	22	22	+5
Vegetables	84	83	173	-8
Fruits	50	47	119	-7
Grain Products	92	94	209	+29
Grain mixtures	19	26	74	+72
Other baked goods	49	53	48	+14
Breads and rolls	71	70	47	+7
Cereals, pastas	30	32	40	+25
Carbonated soft drinks	42	54	287	+53
Regular	33	36	179	+28
Low-calorie	10	20	105	+123

[1]CSFII compared the first day of intake data for women with a day's data for about 2,200 women of the same age range interviewed for the 1977 NFCS.
[2]Reported separately.

Source: Continuing Survey of Food Intakes by Individuals (CSFII), 1985, and Nationwide Food Consumption Survey (NFCS), 1977.

- 3-1/4 ounces of cooked meat, poultry, and fish reported separately, excluding the weight of bone and fat not eaten.
- 3 ounces of mixtures with meat, poultry, and fish as the main ingredient.
- 32 ounces of beverages, excluding water, juice, and milk. About one-third of these beverages were soft drinks.

Smaller amounts of other foods also were eaten.

Food Selections: Similarities and Differences

Compared to about a decade ago, women have made changes in their food selections. The changes between 1977 and 1985 vary depending on the food group. In both years, most women had at least one meat, poultry, or fish item, one grain product, and one vegetable, and about three-fourths had milk or a milk product on the day surveyed. Average intakes for these groups changed no more than 8 percent from 1977 except for grain products, which increased by about 30 percent.

Although average intake of total meat, poultry, and fish by women changed very little, certain subgroups changed markedly. More women ate more food as mixtures of two or more ingredients. Average intake of meat mixtures, including items such as stews and sandwiches, increased by more than a third. Consumption of fish and shellfish both increased, while beef and pork decreased.

More women reported using skim and low-fat milk in 1985 than 1977, and in all drank about 60 percent more of these products. This trend was offset by a drop in whole milk consumption. Fewer women used whole milk and consumed less of it in 1985 than in 1977.

Overall, consumption of grain products increased by nearly 30 percent. Although consumption of all subgroups of grain products increased, the largest increase was in grain mixtures which included foods such as pizza and spaghetti.

Percentages of selected foods consumed by women at meals and snacks

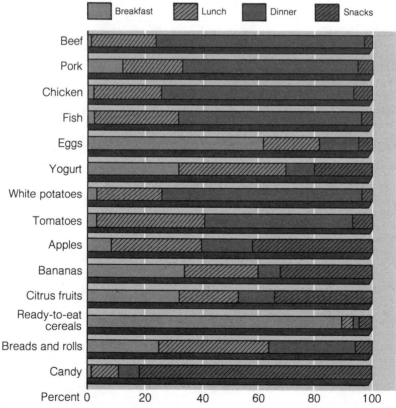

Source: Human Nutrition Information Service
1985 Continuing Survey of Food Intakes by Individuals (CSFII)

Average intake of grain mixtures also increased by more than two-thirds from 1977 to 1985. Consumption of eggs and egg dishes declined from 1977 to 1985, but consumption of cheese increased. Average intake of vegetables and fruits by women did not change greatly. In both years, about one-third more women reported using vegetables as compared to fruits, with average intake of vegetables about one-third more than fruits.

Consumption of carbonated soft drinks increased from 6 ounces a day in 1977 to 10 ounces in 1985. The largest gain was in low-calorie types.

Food Intake At Meals and Snacks

Over the past decade, various changes have affected our lifestyles. More women are working outside the home, there is increased public attention to health and fitness, and there is concern with the influence of diet on health. These changes, and countless others, can influence eating patterns and food choices. What meals people are eating, what is eaten at various meals, and where it is eaten are all important pieces of information that shape the demand and market for food products.

Not only have food choices changed for women, but also eating patterns have changed. The average number of meals reported per day by women increased from 3 in 1977 to 4 in 1985. The proportion of women who reported snacking increased from 60 percent in 1977 to about 75 percent in 1985. Although almost all women reported snacking and eating breakfast at least once over the 4 days in 1985, this was not a daily pattern for everyone. Only 53 percent had breakfast and 42 percent had a snack on each of the 4 days surveyed.

What women drank at meals and snacks

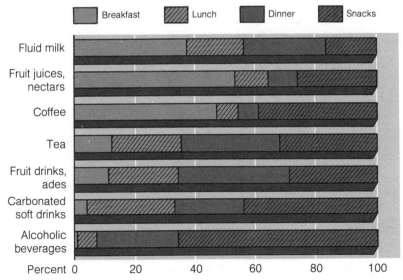

Source: Human Nutrition Information Service
1985 Continuing Survey of Food Intakes by Individuals (CSFII)

Food eaten away from home by women

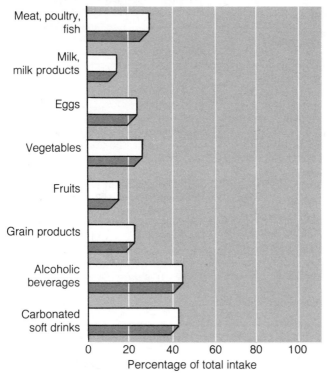

Percentage of total intake

Source: Human Nutrition Information Services
1985 Continuing Survey of Food Intakes by Individuals (CSFII)

In 1985, what women ate of the major food groups was not divided equally among various eating occasions, with the exception of milk and milk products. Women's average food intake over 4 days was grouped by reported eating occasion: breakfast, lunch (including brunch), dinner (including supper), and snacks. Women ate almost one-half of milk and milk products, almost three-fourth of grain products, and almost all of their meat, poultry, fish, and vegetables at lunch and dinner. Women ate the largest proportion—more than one-third—of fruits at breakfast. Information about consumption of discrete types of foods can assist food producers and manufacturers in promoting their product to a specific market segment or for a specific use.

Beverage Intake at Meals and Snacks

The proportion of total intake of beverages that women drank differed among meals and snacks. Breakfast was the most important eating occasion for fluid milk, fruit juices and nectars, and coffee. More of the alcoholic beverages and carbonated soft drinks were consumed at snacks than at any other eating occasion.

Food Intake Away From Home

Eating away from home is becoming more a part of our everyday life. Of the women surveyed in 1977, 45 percent ate out compared to 57 percent in 1985. Over the 4 days surveyed in 1985, 88 percent of the women ate out on at least one of the days.

The marketplace has responded to this trend. When we eat away from home in the 1980's, we have a variety of choices of restaurants and eating establishments that cater to our preferences, our budgets, and our time or lack of it. Restaurants/cafeterias and fast food establishments accounted for at least half of all food eaten away from home with the exception of fruits and alcoholic beverages.

Eating away from home by women was not only at established foodservice institutions. Food consumed as a guest in someone else's home accounted for about 15 to 20 percent of the food eaten away from home by women with the exception of alcoholic beverages, which accounted for about one-fourth and carbonated soft drinks, which accounted for 9 percent. Also, food was purchased at a deli or supermarket and eaten in the car, at the desk in the office, or at a picnic in the park, for example. One-half of the fruits, about one-third of the alcoholic beverages, and about one-fourth of the milk and milk products, eggs, and carbonated soft drinks were eaten at these other locations.

More Marketing Information Available

The Nationwide Food Consumption Surveys provide marketing information about the types of food or food products. Answers can be found to such questions as Who is eating the product? When is the product being eaten? Is it eaten alone or with other foods, and what other foods? and Does consumption of the product vary by region of the country or income? Given the dynamics and abundance of the food marketplace today, information of this type will continue to be important to food producers and manufacturers.

Challenges Ahead for Supermarkets

*William T. Boehm, vice president, Corporate Planning &
Research, The Kroger Company, Cincinnati, OH*

The story of food distribution in the
United States is a remarkable one. As
a nation, we are blessed with abundant agricultural resources. We have a
national agricultural policy that has
emphasized efficiency (output per
unit of input). And, perhaps most of
all, we tend to believe that markets
serve consumers best.

This belief has helped produce an
industry characterized by change.
Over the past several years, many
changes have taken place in both
industry structure and in the products
for sale. The result is that U.S. consumers spend proportionally less and
eat better than people anywhere else
in the world.

Numerous challenges lie ahead for
supermarkets. Most will be evolution-
ary. Supermarket firms that anticipate
and respond best to the need for
change will survive and grow. Consumers will continue to be well
served.

Marketplace Demographics and Lifestyle Changes

Purchasing patterns reflect consumer
lifestyles. To be successful, supermarket companies must understand
changing lifestyle needs. But understanding them is not enough. There
must also be a willingness to respond
and an effective and efficient follow-
through. In execution, the outstanding supermarket firms are separated
from the rest.

Before dealing with the challenges,
let's first identify the major lifestyle
trends creating the need for change.

Working Women

The substantial increase in the
number and proportion of women
who work outside the home is perhaps the most significant lifestyle
change of the 1980's. Women who
work outside the home tend to have
less discretionary time, but more discretionary income that the stereotyp-
ical housewife of the 1960's. More
important, they think differently
about themselves and their "homemaker" responsibilities.

Generally speaking, women (who,
by the way, still account for the lion's
share of all dollars spent in food
stores) approach the marketplace
with a changed view of the traditional
time vs. money tradeoff. In short, they
place a higher value on their time
than they did 10 years ago. This does
not mean, however, that they will-
ingly pay higher prices. They expect
the marketplace to help simplify their
personal high-wire balancing act.
They want their shopping time to be
efficient.

Aging Population

The "baby boomers" are growing up.
In 1985, persons aged 20-39 num-
bered 80 million and represented
33.6 percent of the U.S. population.
By the year 2000, persons in this age
group will number just 74 million
and account for 27.4 percent of the
population. The number of persons
aged 20-29 will fall 17.6 percent by
2000 even though total population is
increasing. By the year 2000, the
median age of the U.S. population
will be 36.3 years vs. 30 years in 1980.

Our aging population affects the food and merchandise distribution system in many ways. Today's "seniors" are very robust physically and mentally and have been able to accumulate more wealth during their working years than in prior generations. (The Kroger Company)

The aging of our population will affect the food distribution system in a number of ways. The product mix and merchandising approach will need to reflect the fact that households at different ages have different basic product needs. Today's seniors are a great deal more robust physically and mentally. They have accumulated more wealth during their working years than in prior generations. As a result, their product purchases will be different from the stereotypes of earlier times.

More Diverse Household Units
The married couple family is fast becoming a less important component of the food market. In 1983, "nontraditional" households (those other than married couples with children) represented about 40 percent of all households. By 1990, such households will represent 46 percent of all households units. Forty percent of the money spent in supermarkets today is accounted for by one- or two-person households compared to less

than one-third of the expenditures 10 years ago.

These new households challenge the supermarket distribution system to produce, package, and sell differently. The "family dinner" is fast becoming a thing of the past. More meals are being prepared for one person—and by the person who will be eating them. Shopping responsibilities are being shared more generally by men and even teenage children. Each case presents new challenges for full, efficient service.

Growing Sense of Ethnic Background
In the 1970's, symbols and values from past decades were rejected out-of-hand by the "baby boomers." Today, as they begin to take a more active role in the marketplace, they are projecting their sense of individual freedom in more traditional ways.

There is a renewed sense of patriotism; people want to express their love of country and city. Ethnic roots are more important, and people want to make their heritage more visible. And, there is a broader participation in, and patience with, the ethnic background of others.

Each of these has implications for food purchasing and preparation. Products that lend support to these heightened feelings of patriotism and heritage are in increased demand. There is more of an opportunity for specialty and "gourmet" product marketing. *Target marketing*—the concept that the products offered by each store should meet the needs of those who shop there—has become almost a necessity. These are big changes for a food retailing industry that used mass marketing in the past.

Supermarket Responses

These lifestyle changes give rise to the marketing challenges facing food retailers today—the need for more variety in both product and package, more freshness, and better service both in the departments and at checkout.

Larger Stores and Prepared Foods.

The challenge to offer variety is often discussed in terms of store size and new product introductions. But that is only the beginning. Modern supermarkets, which average more than 40,000 square feet, typically cost $5 million to build. It is not unusual for these stores to employ 200 or more people. To deal with the management challenges in such stores, supermarket companies are developing and testing new organizational structures, employee training programs, and computer-based financial analysis tools for use in the store. Store employees are being given more responsibility for decisions affecting product offering and in-store merchandising.

The variety challenge extends throughout the entire supermarket. Take, for example, the supermarket delicatessen. Modern consumers wish to spend less time cooking, yet increasingly they prefer to eat at home. Reflecting this trend, the variety of products offered in the supermarket deli has expanded dramatically.

In-store bakeries are also responding to this trend with a personal touch. Today's shopper can select customized birthday cakes, fancy desserts, and even gourmet cakes—all designed to meet each customer's personal requirements.

The key, however, is that these selections are available amid the convenience of the full-service combination food and drug store, where shoppers can visit the floral shop, have a prescription filled, or complete other daily shopping errands—and pick up an already prepared evening meal—all in the same trip. For today's no-time-to-waste lifestyles, that kind of convenience gives a new dimension to meal planning.

Target Marketing

Target marketing is the title frequently given to today's specialized marketing focus. It takes supermarkets far afield from the days when chain stores were built and stocked according to cookie cutter standards. Through demographic and lifestyle research, it is possible to target product offerings to those areas where purchases are likely to be highest. Wine, fresh seafood, fresh salads, and juices are examples of products with important demographic purchase tendencies.

Actually, the targeted marketing of grocery stores is nothing new. Good retailers have always had a good understanding of who their customers were and what they wanted. Today's huge demographic data systems and elaborate computer models are useless unless local managers make them a part of their decision framework. Checkout scanner systems produce tons of data. The challenge is to convert it into useful information.

Food Safety

According to the Food Marketing Institute, the buzzwords in supermarketing today are "fast, fit and fresh," "fast" to meet the needs of the time conscious, "fit and fresh" to be compatible with today's concern for health and nutrition. Within this "freshness" context is another emerging challenge for supermarkets: food safety.

Already, public interest in food safety is mounting. A March 13, 1988, headline of the *Wall Street Journal* read, "As 'Fresh Refrigerated' Foods Gain Favor, Concerns About Safety Rise." The trend can be tracked to many areas of recent attention including California Proposition 65, the use of Alar and other pesticides, and the sobering 1987 "60 Minutes" report on poultry processing and salmonella.

An estimated 2 million cases of food poisoning a year occur because of improper food handling at home. What's more, the problem is changing from macro (observable contamination) to micro (bacteria, mold, viruses, yeast, and parasites). As the selection of in-store prepared foods expands, supermarket operators must increasingly contend with the invisible enemy of microbiological contamination.

Many supermarket companies have already implemented scientific testing and employee training programs to address these concerns. Such companies are fully aware that any incidents involving the safety of food prepared in-store will surely harm the consumer confidence that is so vital to the continued growth of these categories.

Better Service

Service is the last in this list of supermarket challenges due to the emerging lifestyle changes. There was a time when service was an "either-or" challenge—supermarkets were either "full service" or "self-service." Today, it is more a question of quality service than one of quantity. Increasingly, consumers expect knowledgeable help. A friendly face at the checkout counter is taken for granted.

This need for knowledgeable service is evidenced in an increasing demand for consumer education. Simply stated, today's consumers know less about the food system and about food preparation. Prepared foods in the service meat department may help make cooking less of a mystery, but supermarket employees are increasingly being looked to for help in providing information.

The demographic trends discussed earlier are making it more difficult to respond to this desire for better service. The traditional pool of service workers, ages 17-29, is shrinking. Supermarkets, like other service industries, are challenged to look outside this labor pool for help. Senior citizens, the middle-aged, and even the handicapped account for a growing proportion of the supermarket work force. That trend will continue.

The Future

These challenges make food retailing one of the most exciting segments in the entire industry. Change will continue to be the norm with new store formats, new departments, new product offerings, and new opportunities for customer service. "Neighborhood" supermarkets will continue to evolve—as unique and as individual as the shoppers who walk through their doors.

On your next trip to the supermarket, take the time to look closely. You may be surprised at what you see.

Do Your Own Market Research

Judy Green, coordinator, and Nancy Grudens Schuck,
education director, Farming Alternatives Project, Department
of Agricultural Economics, Cornell University, Ithaca, NY

Innovation, experimentation, and change are not new to farmers. Over the years, most farms have been through many changes in production, marketing, and management strategy. Interest in developing new markets and nontraditional agricultural enterprises, however, has risen dramatically in recent years as farmers look for new ways to generate income from their farm resources.

Typical Challenges

As examples of farmers facing marketing decisions, we offer several families—fictional, but based on composites of real farmers.

The Evans family has been in the dairy business for 48 years. "When my dad started in dairy," says son Paul, "he was milking 40 cows. Now we milk 85, and we do a good job. But with folks moving out here from the city and property taxes are going up all the time, we've been thinking about ways to diversify to keep the farm in business. We're thinking about putting in a roadside vegetable stand to take advantage of all that traffic that goes by. But we've got a lot of competition already—we don't know whether the area can support one more roadside stand or not."

Bill and Colleen Ryan have been raising free-range chickens on a small scale for the past few years. This year, they have been selling broilers along with their market vegetables at the Farmers' Market every Saturday. "It seems we just can't begin to meet the demand for fresh, locally raised chicken," says Colleen. "We're considering building a small-scale slaughter facility next year and tripling our production of broilers. We're just not sure if we'll be able to sell that many birds at Farmers' Market alone."

Don Delevan raises beef cattle on his 400-acre ranch, and sells them at the auction house 50 miles away. He's interested in developing his own label and marketing his beef as high quality, lean, and free of chemicals, to customers who will pay a premium price. "I need to find out where my customers are and how I can get my product to them. I know they're out there somewhere."

Evaluating New Ideas

You also may be faced with evaluating a new idea—one you think may generate higher profits for your farm business. But before launching any new enterprise, look carefully at all the factors in starting up and developing the idea. Five key questions should be answered before committing dollars and time to a new venture:

1. Is there a market for this new enterprise? Will you be able to sell enough of your new product or service at a price above your cost of production? In each of our examples, critical questions about the market need to be answered before we can judge the feasibility of the idea.

2. Is the new enterprise consistent with your family's goals and your

farm business goals? If you don't know what your goals are, or if family members disagree about goals, you will need to sort this out before proceeding with the idea.

3. Do you have the resources needed to be successful in this enterprise? A complete inventory of your resources should include:
- Land (soil and water)
- Buildings and equipment
- Labor and management skills
- Time
- Sources of information and assistance
- Credit
- Suppliers, processors, and distributors.

Try to take advantage of underutilized resources, and be wary of enterprises whose peak labor requirements coincide with existing labor needs.

4. Will it be profitable? You will need to carefully project income and expenses for an "average future year" to determine whether revenues will be higher than projected costs of production.

5. Can you afford to get into this business? Initial investment and cash flow may be problematic even if the enterprise is a profitable one. A new enterprise may take some time—up to several years—to become profitable.

It is surprising how often people jump into a new venture without taking a good, hard look at feasibility. Unfortunately, many end up wasting precious resources that could have been put to good use with proper planning. Answering each of the questions listed does require quite a bit of homework. But remember, the time spent in planning is one of the best investments you can make in your farm business.

Why Do Market Research?

Perhaps the most challenging problem in developing new enterprises is assessing the market. Marketing may be new and somewhat intimidating for many farmers who may not have had an active role in marketing their products in the past.

The first step is to understand that there is no magic to market research. It is not a crystal ball that predicts future markets with certainty. It can provide information, however, that will make projections about the future far more accurate, and it can help immeasurably in developing a successful marketing strategy.

Market research has two goals:
- To project the volume of sales and the price you might reasonably expect to achieve with a new enterprise, which is information you will need to analyze profitability and cash flow potential, and
- To gather information about potential buyers and competitors that will help in developing a marketing strategy.

Also, you don't need any esoteric knowledge or advanced technical training to do useful market research. Like any other information-gathering process, it is a matter of asking the right questions and looking in the right places for the answers. Here are some important questions to ask:

What is the *total market size* presently for this product (or service) within a given area?

How many *competitors* are there for this market? What are their strengths and weaknesses? What type of buyer are they targeting?

What *prices* can you expect to receive for a given level of quality?

What *trends* do you see in consumption, competition, and pricing?

What are the *characteristics of buyers* of this product or service? Age? Income level? Lifestyle? What are they looking for? Where are they looking for it? And how can you do a better job than your competitors in meeting their needs?

What proportion or *share* of the total market might you expect to capture?

Market Research Techniques

There are two general types of market research: primary and secondary. Primary research involves going out into the real world and gathering information for yourself—by observing people, counting cars or pedestrians, doing surveys, conducting interviews, or other direct means. Secondary research involves studying data that has already been collected and published by somebody else. Chances are you will need to use both types of research to understand the market for your particular enterprise.

Secondary Research: Using Existing Data

Despite the name "secondary," this type of research is described first because it is often the easiest and cheapest way to obtain the following information.

1. Population and demographic data about the number of people within a given geographic area and their characteristics, such as income level, age distribution, level of education, and household size. This information is important in estimating the total size of the market, and in knowing how many of what type of customers you have access to. Demographic trends within your area can also be analyzed.

2. Information about your local and regional economy, which can tell you about the numbers of various types of

Primary research means gathering the information you need by asking questions yourself. Surveys, like the one being taken here at a roadside farm market, can be used to solicit information from potential buyers about their buying patterns and preferences. (William E. Carnahan)

business establishments, availability of support services, credit sources, zoning, and other regulations that may affect your marketing strategy.

3. Production data that will show the existing level of production of the product or service you are considering, as well as production trends. If your idea is new or simply not a major commodity for your region, however, little information may be available.

4. Consumption data showing the per capita level of purchases by consumers for a given product or service. Again, this information may not be available for your particular enterprise.

Sources of secondary data are numerous, and include public libraries, Census Bureau, Chambers of Commerce, universities, local transportation departments, planning boards, economic development agencies, and State Departments of Agriculture. Extremely useful information can often be found in the most unlikely places. In fact, the most difficult aspect of secondary research is figuring out where to find the information you need.

Primary Research: Do It Yourself
Because you are unlikely to find all the answers to your marketing questions using secondary data, plan on rolling up your sleeves for some real do-it-yourself market research. Primary research is especially important when you are considering an innovative enterprise, a new market, or a local market for which there is not much published data. This research can be extremely elaborate, sophisticated, and expensive, but it also can be very simple and inexpensive. Having a small budget is no excuse for not doing your marketing homework. It just means you will need to be creative in developing the most cost-effective method for collecting the

information you need. Some common methods for conducting primary research include the following:

Observation (counting the number of things or events that may be relevant to your marketing situation). For example, the Evans family in our example might want to observe and count the number and location of roadside stands within a 30-mile radius of their farm, product lines, number of customers per hour, rate of traffic flow past the stands, and the rate of traffic flow past their own farm at various times of the week.

Written Surveys. You can use surveys to solicit information from potential buyers about individual buying patterns, preferences, and unfulfilled needs and wants, and to ask other questions that may affect your marketing success. For example, Bill and Colleen Ryan would do well to survey their present Farmers' Market customers to find out how often and in what quantity they would like to purchase fresh broilers next year. They might also use the survey to find ways to improve their service to customers.

A survey must be carefully designed to yield useful information, and its distribution must be well planned to avoid biasing your results. Some tips for good survey design are:

- Keep it short. A single sheet of paper printed on both sides is usually plenty.
- Phrase your questions so that you receive clear and meaningful answers. For example, instead of asking "Would you buy more broilers from us next year if they were available?" the Ryans might ask "How many 3-lb broilers would you expect to purchase from us each month between June and October?"
- Use multiple choice questions rather than open-ended questions wherever possible to make it easier to

fill out the survey and to analyze the results.

- Don't be afraid to request personal demographic information. For example, information about your respondents' ages, income levels, and areas of residence can be valuable. You may even want to ask for an address for your mailing list. However, most people are sensitive to the way in which this information is solicited. Be sure to *ask* for, not *demand,* the information, and explain how it will be used (perhaps "to serve you better"). Provide multiple-choice categories of ages and income rather than making people reveal their exact age and salary.

The procedure used to distribute the survey is critical in determining how to interpret the results. For example, if Don Delevan wants to find out about consumer interest in purchasing lean, chemical-free beef, he is likely to get different responses depending on whether he surveys shoppers at the local health food store or at the supermarket. Either approach would be valid—Don simply needs to be careful about interpreting his results and making projections based on his particular sample.

Test your survey on a small number of "guinea pigs" first. You will be surprised at how often your questions are misunderstood. A simple test usually results in great improvements in the survey's usefulness.

Telephone Surveys are increasing in popularity. They can yield much information quickly and can be relatively inexpensive. Don Delevan might use a telephone survey, for example, to reach 50 supermarket meat buyers within a 200-mile radius and inquire about their interest in lean, chemical-free beef, their delivery schedules, packaging requirements, and so on.

In designing a telephone survey, follow the same principles described for writtens surveys, but include only the most critical questions and keep them short. Work from a written script so that you are sure to ask questions consistently. Before calling, prepare a form for recording responses efficiently and, as always, test your survey and make any needed adjustments.

Personal Interviews can be extremely informative and are the method of choice when dealing with a limited number of potential buyers. A market research interview will often be your first step in establishing working relationships with wholesale buyers. It will not only provide you with detailed information on the buyer's policies and preferences, but also will provide the buyer with that all-important first impression of your professionalism and commitment. Be prepared with a list of specific questions and with information about the product or service you are proposing to provide. Be sure to leave a calling card. But above all, don't make commitments you cannot live up to. There is nothing that will ruin a good marketing relationship faster than a broken promise.

Personal interviews can also be used to sample potential consumers in a variety of situations. For example, the Ryans could conduct personal interviews with their Farmers' Market customers rather than having them fill out a written survey. Again, the method of selecting people to interview will affect the results.

Test Marketing involves offering your product or service on a limited basis in order to evaluate potential sales; it is especially important when your product is new and unfamiliar to most of your customers. Don Delevan might conduct a market test as simple as offering tastes of his lean beef to customers at the fair, or as elaborate as a 3-month sales campaign in cooperation with a regional supermarket chain.

Test marketing will obviously be impossible until you are producing a product or service in some quantity. The best use of test marketing is as a followup to some of the previously discussed market research techniques, to fine tune your marketing strategy, or to provide better information on costs and returns. It is also a useful strategy when evaluating minor changes in your enterprise, or when attempting to tap into a new market with a product or service you are already providing.

Evaluating the Competition

Studying your competition will help to determine the volume of similar products and services already in the marketplace, the strengths and weaknesses of your competitors, and the various "segments" of the market— that is, the specific types of buyers— that are being served by each competitor. This information may help you identify a "niche" in the marketplace where you can gain a foothold by outdoing your competition in serving a particular market demand.

You can learn about your competition in a number of ways. Visit your competitors' businesses, use their products or services, survey their customers, or interview them directly if possible. Some competitors may refuse to share any information with you, but you may be surprised to find some that are quite helpful. They may have suggestions that can decrease direct competition, or that can even be of mutual benefit.

Plan your Market Research Strategy

Market research can be simple or complex, cheap or fantastically expensive, depending on your needs and your budget. Make sure your research is targeted and cost-effective by following these guidelines:

First, allocate a reasonable amount of your time and money to this effort, and plan to work within that allocation. What is "reasonable" depends, of course, on your judgment of the risks and rewards. Second, develop a list of specific questions about your market that you feel you *must* answer before proceeding to develop the new enterprise. Third, define the specific type of data that you need to collect in order to answer those questions. Fourth, determine what data is already available from secondary sources. Fifth, determine what primary research techniques you will use to collect the data not already available.

If your plan appears to fit within your research budget, you are ready to implement it except for one important step: **Seek assistance!** You can save a tremendous amount of time and energy by enlisting the aid of competent professionals, and you need not spend a dime to do so. Find a small business development program in your area, whose staff can review your market research plans, suggest tactics, and even help in developing and analyzing surveys. Find a librarian who can help track down the secondary data you need. Your local Chamber of Commerce or Cooperative Extension office can identify local resources to help you in designing and carrying out your market research.

Unless you can hire a consultant, you will have to do most of your own marketing homework yourself. But with some planning, assistance, and hard work, do-it-yourself market research will pay off in improving the odds for your new enterprise. And it is a skill that you will use over and over as your farm business grows into the future.

U.S. Foodservice Industry: Responsive and Growing

Steven D. Mayer, director of marketing, Restaurants & Institutions Magazine, Des Plaines, IL

In 1954, before the Federal interstate highway system paved the way to suburbia, and before Ray Kroc opened his first McDonald's, the U.S. foodservice industry was a $15-billion-a-year business. Except for the rich, Americans generally ate out only when they were truly away from home, on business trips or on vacation, or for a very special occasion. Only 195,000 restaurants were in the country at that time, and foodservice accounted for only 25 percent of total consumer spending for food.

Today, eating out is part and parcel of our lives, more a necessity than a luxury, and foodservice accounts for more than 44 percent of total food expenditures. At its present rate of growth, it should reach 50 percent within 10 years.

The foodservice industry has increased its share of market relative to its traditional rival, the supermarket or retail grocery. It has expanded to become a $207-billion industry, with 583,000 outlets all across America. It employs more than 8 million people and, by the year 2000, is expected to employ 2½ million more, generating more new jobs than any other industry.

Every day, about 100 million Americans, including 42 percent of the total U.S. adult population, eat out at least once. Over the course of a year, more than 78 billion meals and snacks are served in the foodservice industry. This industry uses more than 40 percent of all the meat, 55 percent of all the lettuce, 60 percent of all the butter, 65 percent of all the potatoes, and 70 percent of all the fish produced in the United States.

Without question, this tremendous growth could not have taken place without dramatic changes in consumer demographics and consumer lifestyles. Increased mobility, rising disposable incomes, the emergence of the baby boom generation, working women, and the demand for convenience and variety in our lives, have all contributed to the growth of foodservice. Equally important, however, the foodservice industry has responded to these changes by satisfying consumer demands.

Scope of the Industry

The foodservice industry is not only very large but also extremely diverse. It includes restaurants ranging from fine dining to fast food, cafeterias and coffee shops, hotel banquets and room service, school lunch and breakfast programs, employee cafeterias and executive dining rooms, patient and staff feeding in hospitals and nursing homes, meal service on planes and trains, and more.

Efforts to segment the industry usually start with commercial restaurants on the one hand—establishments that are in business to serve food to customers—and noncommercial institutions on the other—establishments that offer foodservice but are not primarily in the foodservice business. This institutional group includes plants and offices, schools and colleges, hospitals, nursing homes, the military, and others, which either operate their own foodservice or contract it out to a

Foodservice share of total food dollars

% Share

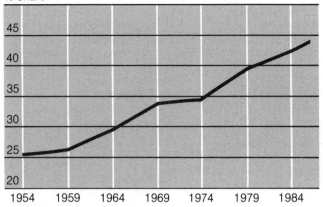

| 1954 | 1959 | 1964 | 1969 | 1974 | 1979 | 1984 |

Source: U.S. Dept. of Agriculture

foodservice management firm.

It is becoming increasingly difficult to distinguish, however, between commercial and noncommercial establishments, as cost and competitive pressures force institutions to think of their foodservice operations as businesses, and their clientele as consumers. Colleges and employee feeders today are much more merchandising-oriented and realize that they must compete with local restaurants to be successful. Nursing homes are evolving more and more into lifecare centers and are marketing their services, including first-rate foodservice, to a fast growing, more sophisticated mature market.

Similarly, hospitals and schools, hard hit in recent years by budget cutbacks and regulatory constraints, are today reaching out into their communities, offering catering and banquet services, "meals on wheels," etc. It is not uncommon today to find white tablecloth service offered in the maternity ward of a hospital, or pizza, tacos, and salad bars in the school cafeteria.

In commercial restaurants, too, menus, service styles, design,and decor are all changing, to the point where it is no longer so simple a matter to distinguish between a full service and fast food restaurant. Fast food, once synonomous with limited menus, today offers some greatly expanded menu options.

McDonald's, for example, introduced the industry's first breakfast sandwich, the Egg McMuffin, in the early 1970's, and succeeded in transforming a whole generation of breakfast skippers into breakfast eaters. It has since introduced Chicken McNuggets and become the Nation's second largest purveyor of chicken (behind Kentucky Fried Chicken). These two products alone account for $3-4 billion a year in sales for this "hamburger chain."

In appearance and setting, too, today's fast food units are often quite different from the fast food "joints" of the past. Several McDonald's units, as well as those of Burger King and other fast food chains, have recently won national awards for architectural distinction. Located in city centers and other less traditional locations, they exhibit a more individual look and design, suited to their surroundings.

Many full service restaurants, on the other hand, are developing downscaled versions of their restaurants as cafes or bistros, or are introducing takeout and home delivery services to expand their customer base. Quick service, once a fast food trademark, is now a buzzword everywhere. Dinnerhouse and theme restaurants, borrowing from the successful experience of fast food chains, are also becoming chains.

Despite the blurring of traditional definitions, it is possible to delineate segments of the foodservice industry.

The largest segments of the industry, whether considered commercial or noncommercial, in rank order, are full service restaurants, fast food restaurants, employee feeding, schools, and hospitals. Next come hotels and motels, colleges and universities, and the military.

In aggregate, the commercial segments represent approximately 61 percent of the foodservice industry's total food purchases; noncommercial or institutional segments represent approximately 39 percent.

The commercial segment is often further subdivided into chain-owned or franchised operations, and those that are independently owned and operated. The major chains represent a significant concentration of buying power for food and other items, and have been one of the fastest growing segments of the industry for many years. Out of $113 billion total sales by commercial restaurants, about $52 billion or 46 percent is now controlled by the top 100 chain restaurant companies.

In 1987, however, growth of the major chains has slowed. As they have expanded their menus and lost some of their distinctiveness, competition has increased and the chains have found themselves engaged in a fierce battle for market share. Many have also overbuilt, with the result that supply has outstripped demand, and average unit volumes have slumped.

With some exceptions, of course, the focus seems to have shifted back to independents and to smaller, second-tier chains, as sources of new ideas and growth. Institutions that have made the transition to more commercial modes of operation also are looking forward to a bright future.

Taste Trends and New Operating Styles

It is hard to say whether the foodservice industry really adapts to meet existing consumer needs, or if it often anticipates the needs and wants of the consumer and creates new markets where none existed before.

Salad bars, the away-from-home breakfast market, the frozen pizza market, popular Mexican foods, and, more recently, gourmet cookies, Cajun cooking, and pasta—in all these cases, was the industry truly responding to consumer demand, or was it, by its own marketing savvy and skill, devising new ways to expand the market and make eating away from home ever more inviting and enjoyable to consumers? Often, the innovations of a single individual have made for change.

The success of Debbie Fields' cookies, for example, has spawned muffin shops and chains of fresh-baked cinnamon rolls all across America. Despite our nutritional concerns, our collective sweet tooth and the appeal and aroma of fresh baked goods seem to reign supreme. They are, truly, the ultimate impulse purchase.

Similarly, Paul Prudhomme's blackened redfish has given rise not only to the blackening of almost anything on almost any menu, but also—beyond Cajun—has fueled a positive rediscovery by many leading American chefs of our home-grown ingredients and culinary heritage. (See Larry Michaud's article, *Louisiana, We're Really Cookin' Cajun.*)

Eating out today is part and parcel of our lives. Foodservice accounts for more than 44 percent of total food expenditures. It is expected to reach 50 percent before the year 2000. (Restaurants & Institutions Magazine)

Local pedigrees on foods, like designer labels on clothes, are definitely "in" today. Chefs are exploring not only the roots of American regional cuisine but also more authentic ethnic cuisines, and they are unabashedly fusing the cuisines, flavors, and cooking styles of many lands, creating new hybrids such as Chinese-French and Italian-Southwest.

And talk about consumer lifestyles and new restaurant concepts, which came first, couch potatoes or Domino's Pizza? Tom Monaghan's unique pizza delivery chain has revolutionized the way all foodservice operators think about service. Much of the total growth of the industry since 1983 can be attributed to the increase in off-premise traffic—takeout, drive-thru, and home delivery.

Since 1983, the number of consumers who have ordered food for takeout has increased 47 percent; drive-thru has increased 45 percent; and home delivery a phenomenal 280 percent. The implications and import of this trend have not been lost upon supermarkets and convenience stores, which have raced to expand their deli operations, install salad bars, and develop their own fast food programs. Whether or not these programs will prove successful, and whether they will compete with existing foodservice operations or expand the total market, remain questions to be answered.

In any case, these questions highlight what has become a gray area between traditional foodservice and retail. Some have suggested that the definition of foodservice be enlarged from food consumed away from home to food prepared away from home, whether in a restaurant or supermarket.

One final challenge to the industry is the maturing of the U.S. population. This represents both a problem and an opportunity. There is right now a serious shortage of teenage workers in the industry. "Help wanted" signs are almost as prevalent as new products or price promotions. The baby boomers who fueled the growth of industry for so many years also staffed the counters and grills, and they are no longer available.

As they have aged, however, they have gotten better paying jobs, are now having families, and are completely accustomed to eating out. They are more experienced diners,

Recent growth trend of the foodservice industry

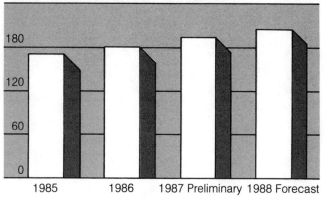

billion $

180			
120			
60			
0			

1985   1986   1987 Preliminary 1988 Forecast

Source: Bureau of Foodservice Research.

and the industry must cater to them. The family market is reemerging, along with a new breed of upscale family restaurants. And school foodservice, long in decline, is responding now to enrollments that are increasing for the first time in over 10 years.

Forecast for Industry Growth

The foodservice industry has grown with a real (inflation-adjusted) growth rate of between 2 and 4 percent every year since 1980. While that is not equal to the growth rates achieved earlier, it is good, consistent growth and shows no signs now of coming to an end. The forecast for 1988 again calls for approximately 2 percent real growth in the industry.

Many things changed with the stock market crash of October 1987, but consumer confidence and consumer spending have yet to show any serious decline. Consumers are more likely to trim or delay purchases of major durable goods like cars and appliances than they are the "little luxury" of eating out.

The real impact of the crash appears to be on the chains, which definitely will feel constrained in their ability to finance new unit

expansion, and probably will be more cautious in terms of new product introductions or other menu or marketing innovations.

In the past, with the hint of increased inflation or recession, many have looked to the price differential between restaurants and supermarkets, believing that consumers would return to their kitchens instead of eating out. At this time, however, consumer perceptions of the value of meals eaten away from home have never been stronger. Foodservice operators who pay attention to the price/value relationship should be able to avoid even any "trading down" or "trading off."

Foodservice is an industry which, like the food industry overall, is relatively recession-proof. It is driven more by employment, consumer confidence, and disposable income than by deficits, interest rates, and gross national product.

Despite all the economic uncertainties, the foodservice industry should be able to adapt and respond to this changing environment. Staying in tune with consumers always has been and will continue to be the strength of this industry.

Tailoring U.S. Pork to Japanese Style

C. Lynn Knipe, meat scientist, Meat Export Research Center, Iowa State University, Ames, IA

If the United States is to become competitive in the Japanese pork market, packers and processors need to tailor their products to meet Japanese requirements and tastes.

A number of potential barriers to exporting pork to Japan exist, but importers there indicate that if U.S. processors were more export minded, these problems could be overcome. Often, Japanese importers are testing the U.S. businessperson's interest and flexibility and would welcome a response even if it meant a compromise. Where U.S. efforts may have failed in the past is in trying to sell the Japanese consumer the exact same product consumed in the United States, and in distributing this product to Japan in a frozen state.

Tips for Exporters

U.S. exporters must understand the way the Japanese market works, and they must supply a product acceptable to Japanese consumers' highly discerning tastes.

The first consideration in trying to sell pork in Japan is to identify the right trading company. Trading companies have historically served as intermediaries between Japanese buyers and foreign exporters. A number of Japanese trading companies have offices in the United States in cities such as Chicago and Los Angeles.

Making personal contacts with the trading company's home office in Japan also helps exporters establish rapport with the trading company and learn Japanese ways of doing business. Personal relationships between business partners are much more important in Japan than in the United States. The Japanese want to deal with a company that has a long history of reliability, and where they can establish a personal relationship with the owner or top management. If Japanese buyers like your company, you'll have a loyal customer for years.

The Japanese trading company will want to look at samples of your product and will likely want to visit your plant.

In addition to contacting Japanese trading companies, U.S. packers can work through U.S. supermarkets that have already embarked on joint ventures in Japan. Packers can also opt to produce a private-label product for Japanese ham and sausage manufacturers, or sell a product in bulk to Japanese companies that then package for retail sale with their own locally recognized label.

Japanese Distribution System

An understanding of the Japanese distribution system and the variable levy system also is needed. Only about 1 percent of the pork is moved on direct-access basis to Japanese supermarkets. Imported fresh pork generally moves from a foreign packer to a trading company and then to the ultimate distribution point.

Direct access distribution has many advantages, particularly when a company is trying to establish brand identity for products.

The variable levy is applied to fresh and fresh-frozen pork at 5 percent of the "cost of goods, insurance, and freight" (c.i.f.) price, and to ham and bacon at 10 percent. It prevents lower priced imported pork from undercutting the price of Japanese meat. Therefore, competitively priced pork is penalized the most by this system. Sausage and canned hams or canned luncheon meats are assessed a flat 25-percent duty.

The variable levy system has encouraged exporters to sell mixed loads to meet the established "gate price"[1] (the price the farmer receives).

Inspection Certificates a Must

Japan requires inspection certificates for fresh-frozen pork. These are available through USDA inspectors and indicate the name and address of the slaughtering and breaking companies, and the dates of slaughter and inspection.

Some typical complaints Japanese importers have made in the past about U.S. products include a higher percentage of pale-colored, soft pork, knife cuts or gouges, and inconsistent piece sizes.

U.S. exporters should follow the lead set by competitors, which includes tailoring products to meet Japanese demands. For instance, Danish cutting methods produce cuts preferred in Japan, such as a collar butt, not common in the United States.

Health Standards for Processed Pork

Recently U.S. exporters have recognized the potential market for processed pork—products such as ham,

bacon, sausage. This is currently a $2.3 billion market, with less than half of 1 percent of processed pork imported.

Japan's Ministry of Health and Welfare (M.H. & W.) requires that all imported processed meats must be "coliform negative" (free of a family of intestinal bacteria). The standard "brilliant green lactose bile broth" method is used to determine this.

The M.H. & W. randomly checks imported products, particularly ones new to the market, but also expects processing companies to monitor their own products for coliforms. While this requirement seems overly restrictive, the M.H. & W. is currently updating regulations relating to bacterial standards.

Cured products must not contain more than 70 parts per million (ppm) residual sodium nitrite. Most U.S. processed meat products contain less than 70 ppm after cooking or smoking.

For a product to be labeled "heated" (cooked), the product must be heated for a minimum of 30 minutes at an internal temperature of 145°F.

Other requirements include specified water activity levels of different products and restrictions on ingredients such an antioxidants.[2]

Other than safety requirements, there are no mandatory regulations for meat products. However, voluntary regulations for products bearing the Japanese Agricultural Standard (JAS) logo are numerous. The JAS logo guarantees a minimum standard of quality and is roughly equivalent to the Good Housekeeping seal of approval. The JAS logo is used on

---

[1]Seng, P.M., *The Japanese Pork Market - A Study of Opportunities for MEF Member Firms.* U.S. Meat Export Federation, Tokyo, 1985

---

[2]The Japan External Trade Organization (JETRO), 401 North Michigan Ave., Suite 660, Chicago, IL 60611 can provide more complete information on Japanese food regulations.

Eye appeal is important to Japanese buyers of packaged pork products. This display case in a large, modern Japanese supermarket includes sausages, luncheon meats, and gift boxes of hams. (C. Lynn Knipe)

processed meat products but not on fresh pork or beef.

A "Handmade" logo also is used to indicate very high quality products. The standards for its use are also voluntary. Currently some consumers want to do away with this logo.

Making Products More Appealing

Although U.S. processed meats are considered to be of high quality in Japan, some changes, such as the following, could make them even more appealing to Japanese consumers:

1. More attractive external appearance
Eye appeal is important to Japanese consumers. Shopping is often emotionally motivated and considered a pastime. A good smoke color is necessary for all products, as is internal-cured color. Natural and, to a lesser extent, collagen casings are preferred for small-diameter sausages.

Pay attention also to label designs. An English label on a package might be appropriate in an exclusive department store to confirm that the product is acually imported.

2. Smaller retail package sizes
Japanese people eat smaller portions of meat at each meal than Americans do, and also prefer a variety of foods. Japanese people also are interested in buying only the freshest of meat products. Because of their interest in freshness and variety, Japanese consumers shop more frequently than their U.S. counterparts and will often buy just enough of each item for one meal. A U.S. exporter, therefore, should consider using smaller retail packages for all processed meat products destined for Japan.

Japanese buyers do not want just another Japanese ham or sausage, but they want unique, and genuine "American" products with Japanese tastes in mind. It is said in Japan, for example, that if a Japanese woman wants a French dress, she won't expect it to look like a kimono.[3] However, the French dress is expected to fit.

[3]LeComte, A. *Keys to Success: Japan's "Food Lifestyle."* Japan External Trade Organization, 1983

3. Use of less salt

The major criticism Japanese consumers have about U.S. products is that they are too salty. Japanese consumers prefer processed meat products that are only mildly seasoned, yet rather sweet by U.S. standards. Tests by Iowa State University's Meat Export Research Center have shown that to duplicate the flavor of Japanese sausage, a salt content of 1.75 percent and a sugar content of 1.25 percent is needed.

Ham products in Japan contain close to 2.5 percent salt, which is almost totally masked with sugar. Regional differences in flavor preference also exist. A single product formulation will likely not work in all regions. For example, people in Kanto (Tokyo) prefer saltier foods than people in Kansai (Osaka). With lower salt formulations, the proper seasoning of sausage is more important.

4. Japanese Labeling

All packages need a Japanese label that includes an ingredient listing, handling instructions, and production date. Nonmeat ingredient listings on Japanese lables are rather vague by USDA standards and might contain words such as "chemical seasoning," "emulsifier binder," "color enhancer." Labels are verified by the Japan Meat Processors Association, but labeling would most likely be taken care of by the importing company. USDA's Foreign Agricultural Service has an Export Product Review Program which can assist exporters with labeling requirements.

As with fresh-frozen meats, Japanese consumers are concerned with processed meat freshness. Consumers are demanding, and supermarkets provide short expiration dates on packages. Most Japanese products are pulled from display cases at a maximum of 25 days. Some are pulled as soon as 10 days after production. Obviously, products sent by ship from the United States to Japan will be at least 25 days old before they can be placed in Japanese grocery stores. Imported items will be evaluated individually by importers to determine their length of shelf-life. Although special allowances will likely be made for imported products, the concern for freshness may be a major barrier to exporting processed meats to Japan.

Florida Citrus Industry Sets High Standards

*Robert M. Behr, economic and market research director,
Florida Department of Citrus, Gainesville, FL*

For more than 50 years, the Florida Department of Citrus (FDOC) has used market research, advertising, new product development, evaluation of consumer preferences, merchandising, foreign market development, and many other techniques to help sell Florida citrus products.

Producers of cotton, apples, nuts, berries, dairy and even beef products have all come to the FDOC to learn about its unique marketing techniques, because they illustrate how producers have organized to provide many of the marketing functions normally associated only with large food-processing and marketing firms.

Florida Citrus Commission

FDOC carries out the policies of the Florida Citrus Commission. The Commission—a 12-member "board of directors" composed of seven citrus growers and five grower/handler representatives—was established by law in 1935. It regulates the quality of citrus products being shipped from Florida as well as the firms doing business in the Florida citrus industry. It also promotes Florida citrus products and conducts research in the area of product quality, marketing, and economics.

Funding comes from an industry-wide excise tax on each box of fruit moving into commercial trade channels. Most of that revenue is used for advertising and promotional efforts to expand market demand for Florida citrus products. For example, in 1986-87, 85 percent of the $52 million budget was used for promotion and marketing, with the remaining 15 percent used for regulatory, research, and administrative activities.

Marketing Process

In developing a marketing program, FDOC follows a systematic approach:
1. Analysis of the market situation
2. Formulation of a market strategy
3. Development of a specific program to implement the strategy
4. Development of specific action plans
5. Evaluation of program performance

Analysis of Market Situation

The first phase of program development is typically research. Since consumer demand is the end result of many sociological, psychological, economic and institutional stimuli, review of sales and revenue trends is not enough to understand how to position products properly in the market. Changing consumer lifestyles, tastes, and preferences also must be considered.

The economic and market research that has supported the development of programs for the domestic orange juice market serves as an example of the effort that takes place in the early stages of program development. During the last two decades, significant consumption and demographic trends have occurred which have altered the manner in which orange

Per capita consumption of Florida citrus in 1986 was 117 pounds, an increase of more than 20 percent over 1971 when per capita consumption was 97 pounds. (Florida Department of Citrus)

juice has been marketed. For example, in 1971 per capita consumption of citrus in the United States was 97 pounds according to USDA. By 1986, per capita consumption had increased more than 20 percent to 117 pounds.

A significant economic trend in recent decades is the declining share of consumer expenditures on food purchased for consumption at home. The share of consumer expenditures on meals purchased at restaurants, cafeterias, and fast food chains has remained constant at 4 percent of personal income. Consequently, the consumption of meals purchased away from home has become more important relative to food consumed at home. According to national consumer studies, close to one-third of the consumers surveyed reported away-from-home orange-juice con-

sumption in September 1987, compared with one-fourth in September 1986.

Other statistics reveal changing lifestyles that have had an impact on the form of the product. For example, demand studies suggest that, with more women in the work force, retail food purchases show a demand for convenience. Convenience, according to consumer studies, is one of the major factors contributing to the growth in demand for chilled orange juice and the decline in sales of frozen concentrated orange juice.

Assessment of the market situation goes beyond review of basic consumption and demographic trends. Formulation of a market strategy requires matching product characteristics with consumer needs. A major research effort includes interviews with a broad range of consumers and focuses on the assessment of attitudes regarding Florida citrus and how these products fit into current lifestyles. These studies are updated as needed, based on changes in the industry and marketplace.

This planning approach is also evident in FDOC export programs, espcially for fresh fruit. In the 1986-87 season, Florida exported nearly 25 percent of its fresh fruit, mostly to Europe and Japan, an increase of 40 percent from the previous season. Recent expansion in promotional activities and a decline in the value of the dollar have contributed to that export growth. Until the 1985-86 season, FDOC support for fresh grapefruit in Europe consisted primarily of a three-party program in which the Foreign Agricultural Service (FAS), FDOC, and European importers shared funding of activities that were primarily promotional. A promotion-oriented program, supplemented by television advertising in selected markets, provided past support for Florida grapefruit. In 1985, FAS introduced the Targeted Export Assistance (TEA) Program to develop export markets for U.S. agricultural products.

To support FDOC advertising and promotional programs, consumer research and awareness studies were conducted in Japan and Europe. Since the 1986-87 season marked the first year of an advertising and promotional program in Europe, a benchmark survey to determine consumer awareness of and attitudes toward Florida grapefruit was carried out before the start of advertising. Consumer research focused on determining how consumers evaluate the quality of grapefruit and the role of various fruit characteristics in selecting grapefruit.

Formulation and Implementation of Market Strategy

Following analysis of the market situation, a market strategy for a specific product can be developed, taking into account any changes occurring in the market.

Based on assessment of the market situation, the industry has been following a strategy of extending the uses of orange juice to occasions other than breakfast, using, for example, the slogan "it isn't just for breakfast anymore" and the midnight-snack theme for a television commercial.

Specific Action Plans

Once the strategy is developed, specific ads or promotions are prepared, designed for specific audiences such as working women 25-40 years of age or teenagers. The industry reviews these ads and test results extensively, conducting a final test with a group of consumers in the target market. Usually at least three separate ads are tested, and the most effective ad or ads are used in the promotion program. Pretesting potentially can save millions of dollars by preventing ineffective ads from being used.

Evaluation of Program Performance

Developing and implementing marketing programs would not be complete without evaluating program performance. Day-after recall surveys are an example of program evaluation to determine the effectiveness of specific advertisements.

The survey is designed to determine if the message is retained by the individual viewing it. While responses to individual ads are important, response to the overall promotional effort is perhaps a better indicator of program success, because most authorities recognize advertising and promotion to be long-term investments.

National advertising for Florida orange juice has been sustained since 1966. During that time, the image of orange juice has changed significantly. While orange juice is enjoying an improved image, the bottom line is sales. To monitor sales, the industry purchases data reflecting national supermarket sales from A.C. Nielsen Co. The Nielsen data show increases in both volume and revenue during the 1967-87 period. Volume increased 131 percent during 1967-87, and revenue increased 677 percent.

In addition to the Nielsen data, the industry purchases data on dairy expenditures to help monitor the impact of advertising and promotional efforts. Also, the citrus industry has used a mix of media, coupon promotions, merchandising, and public relations to achieve these gains.

Role of Research

Research supports the regulatory and promotion functions. Scientific research focuses on new product development and product quality improvement. Market research identifies changing market trends and appropriate market strategies, pretests ads to insure effectiveness before they are aired nationally, and conducts followup analysis to determine the effectiveness of specific ads.

Economic research plays an important role in the overall marketing effort. It evelutes short- and long-run supply/demand conditions; the implications of the supply/demand situation for the marketing activities of the industry; and the economic impact of programs, regulations, and changing competitive conditions of the industry.

Most of the economic research focuses on demand in the evaluation process with less emphasis on supply or the distribution of the benefits derived from the programs. Demand has become an increasing concern in Florida's orange-juice industry as a result of freezes and an increased volume of orange-juice imports into the United States, primarily from Brazil.

Florida's orange production is at about half the level that would have been realized without recent freezes. Imports, largely a supplemental supply at one time, are becoming more competitive in the U.S. market. Also, Florida growers and processors face competition from other suppliers who have benefited from Florida's promotion programs. This represents an important marketing challenge for Florida's citrus industry in the future and a unique measurement challenge for those evaluating marketing efforts. The orange-juice market highlights the need for considering supply as well as demand factors in the marketplace, if benefits to the grower from cooperative promotion programs are to be accurately assessed.

Economic research is designed to separate the effects of advertising from all other effects so that an economic value can be attached to the advertising activities. FDOC economic research in the area of advertising has focused on the longrun impact of promotional programs rather than evaluation of specific ads. Estimates of marginal returns from advertising provide useful guidelines in decisions about budget allocations for various markets and various products. Likewise, economic research has been useful in demonstrating that advertising cannot offset all other factors which affect the marketplace such as citrus product prices, price of competing products, population, and consumer income.

Keeping the Consumer in Mind

*Arnold E. Denton, senior vice president, and Ginny Marcin,
corporate relations, Campbell Soup Company, Camden, NJ*

In an increasingly competitive world, successful marketing of U.S. agricultural products abroad will, more and more, require a base of solid marketing research.

And whether they're trying to market in Austria or Australia, American agricultural product companies are going to have to accurately answer the questions: What does the consumer want? How can we translate those wants into desirable value-added products that are relevant to changing lifestyles?

Women in Work Force

One of the most important examples of changing lifestyles involves women in the work force, a phenomenon growing throughout the world. By 1990, about 62 percent of U.S. families will have two wage earners. And according to predictions, by the year 2000, 7 out of 10 women will be working.

In Japan, 47 percent of the young and middle-aged wives are now working outside the home, and Europe shows a similar pattern with a range of 25 percent in Italy to 45 percent in Belgium, the Netherlands, and the United Kingdom. Within all of the developed world, women now make up about 40 percent of the total work force.

So instead of expecting a meal cooked by mom, the family may eat out. By 1990, 45 percent of U.S. meals will be eaten away from home. Some meals eaten at home are prepared elsewhere. In fact, the fastest growing segment of the U.S. food industry is home-delivered foods. That segment amounted to $2.2 billion in 1985. Other changes are in shopping habits.

Growth of working women

Percent of adult women

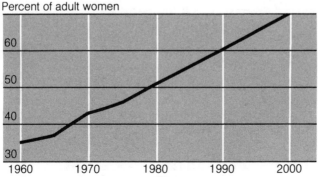

Source: Bureau of the Census (projections for 1990 and 2000 are those of Campbell Soup Company)

Changing Shopping Habits

With less time to spend in the kitchen, working women—in the United States and abroad—are shopping for convenience foods, but they're demanding more in the way of quality and variety.

The weekly shopping trip is becoming a thing of the past. More often, whoever is the shopper will purchase the makings of the meal on the way home from work. Sometimes, takeout food comes from the supermarket. The latest trend is to buy foods at a filling station, while getting gas for the car.

Meanwhile, teenagers have begun to play a part in family food shopping—but not just for snacks. In the United States, as stand-ins for mom, they may buy items like cereal, rice, frozen meals, and yogurt.

"Grazing" Lifestyle

Working women reflect another important feature of living in the 1980's.

In the past, a family might sit down together for one, two, or even three meals a day. But today, with family members coming and going on individual schedules, they often eat snacks or small meals whenever they are hungry. Perfectly suited to this "grazing" lifestyle and the passion for speed is the microwave oven. In the United States in 1988, more than 7 out of 10 households own a microwave oven, and Japan follows with 5 out of 10 households. The trend is growing with 40 percent of the households in Canada, 30 percent in England, 15 percent in Belgium, 15 percent in Sweden, 15 percent in Denmark, 10 percent in the Federal Republic of Germany, and 5 percent in Italy having them.

Lifestyles so busy and unstructured call for foods that don't require much preparation, can be prepared in small portions, come conveniently packaged, and require little cleanup.

Consumers Want More

Sophisticated modes of communication and convenient means of travel to foreign countries have spawned consumers with adventurous taste buds. In addition, consumers are seeking quality. "Fresh" is it. The salad, once just an appetizer or a show of self-control for a dieting debutante, now also appears on the plate of fitness-conscious males.

Hand in hand with "fresh," at least in the minds of the consumers, goes "nutritious." It's thumbs up for fiber and good fats, thumbs down for sodium, cholesterol, and sugar.

Chicken and fish are the new stars, as are nonwhite or specialty breads. Compared to 30 years ago, consumers now drink 257 times as much low-fat milk, serve up 47 times as many frozen potatoes; spoon 29 times as much yogurt; and sip 11 times as much apple juice. Seven times as much broccoli was consumed in 1988 as in 1968.

By the year 2000, European consumers will eat twice as much fresh and chilled foods, and 25 percent more frozen foods, but 25 percent less canned foods than they do today.

With these consumer preferences in mind, a marketer can begin to think about supplying the "value" a consumer—foreign or domestic—looks for.

Ways To Add Value

The Food Itself: Is it in the preferred form—fresh, frozen, canned, or dry? Is it something different from what the consumer has eaten? Does it have a flavor he or she seeks? Is it unique in texture or appearance?

Preparation Time: Does it have to be cooked? How long? Does it need to be stirred or can it be microwaved?

Point of Purchase: Is it on sale at a place that's convenient when the shopper needs it?

Packaging: Does the package draw the shopper's attention? Is it easy to open? Does it look like it is tamper-evident?

Cleanup: Does it require any?

Image: How does the consumer feel about himself or herself eating the product?

Many Approaches Needed

Marketing uses as many of these aspects as possible to differentiate the product and answer a consumer's need. When Campbell Soup Company set out to market a spaghetti sauce in the United States, it asked consumers what they wanted. When consumers said they wanted a product that tasted "homemade," the

When Campbell Soup Company set out to market a spaghetti sauce in the United States, it conducted surveys, such as this one in a shopping mall, to find out what consumers wanted. (Campbell Soup Company)

Growth of dual wage earning families

Percent of families

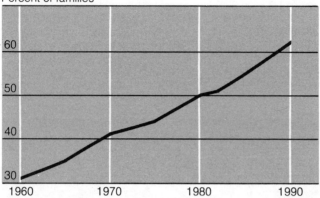

Source: Bureau of the Census (projections for 1990 made by Cambell Soup Company)

company had to explore what that term meant for the tasters. It took much testing and product research, but Prego spaghetti sauce didn't just win over existing consumers—it expanded the market.

Some examples of successful marketing show how "listening to the consumer" leads to sales in other countries.

In the early 1960's, Campbell was entering the Japanese market for the first time. The company studied the typical Japanese menu and spotted "corn potage soup." Campbell formulated several varieties and tested them in the marketplace. When the new convenience product was launched amid advertising and promotional support, it became the number one variety Campbell sold in Japan. An added coup was the fact that the new soup represented additional sales, rather than sales taken from existing varieties of Campbell soups in Japan.

Nearly 5 years ago in the United Kingdom, Campbell scored a success in the canned soup market by looking at its own consumers. At the time, Campbell's Soups had been there for

25 years, but the success of the product line had begun to erode. The company studied the lifestyles of those who were already consumers of its condensed soups, comparing them to consumers of the competition's ready-to-serve product.

The study showed that Campbell buyers were willing to get involved in the cooking process, and were possibly more affluent than the competitors' consumers. The resulting promotion, which made use of lush, tasteful ads with the theme "Soup for Cooks," invited the consumer to make more of the product by adding whatever he or she chose to. The promotion not only reversed a downward trend, it increased the sales by 3 percent a year, and has continued successfully since.

Adaptation Counts

Often, marketing the same product in a different country requires adaptation. In 1985, Campbell boosted its sales of soups in Hong Kong by 25 percent, just by making the labels better reflect what was in the can. The

Campbell Soup Company combined American-made equipment with mushroom technology from Holland for its newest mushroom farm in Hillsboro, Texas. Market research determined which mushroom strain would meet consumer preferences. (Ginny Marcin)

company knew that the Chinese valued the time-honored "Campbell" name, but it wanted Chinese consumers to be able to more readily discern what variety they could expect in the can. Campbell produced graphics for each variety, depicting not only the ingredients in the soups but the proportion in which they would be found in the products.

For instance, the label for Chicken Vegetable soup displays a picture of a plump chicken surrounded by piles of tomatoes, crisp carrots, celery, potatoes, and peas—in the proportion found in the product. This graphic took the place of the gold medallion usually found on the red and white labels. Campbell also translated the name of the soup into Chinese.

Adapting a product to a consumer in a different country may require more than a translation. That happened when Campbell's Canadian subsidiary set out to sell breakfast entrees and sandwiches similar to those sold by Campbell in the United States. The U.S. product's name was "Great Starts." In pursuing a bilingual package, the Canadian group learned that "Great Starts" did not translate into anything meaningful in French. So, instead, they capitalized on the already well-known "Swanson" brand name.

For a company that markets its products internationally and manufactures them wherever it's most practical, a look at the consumer can offer more of a clue to opportunity than any data on how much wheat, rice, or corn a country buys.

Selling U.S. Products Abroad

But for U.S. agriculture and the food industry here, the goal is to market products that make use of American-grown produce and American-made products.

For that reason, it's not enough just to think about what consumers want. Marketing U.S. agricultural products means going a step further and adding features that cannot be duplicated easily in another country if they're meant for sale there.

The most obvious "unique" feature an American product can offer is that it's American. Campbell recently garnered excellent success by marketing an upscale line of soups in Japan, under the name "American Classics." The soups are made in California, and the Japanese value them because they associate their origin with quality.

Likewise, a rich line of Pepperidge Farm cookies is finding success in convenience stores in Japan. The products are made using highly developed baking technology, with ingredients obtained from the United States such as pecans and peanuts.

Selling at Home

The U.S. agricultural industry can seek new markets in other countries keeping uniqueness in mind and producing value-added products. But it can also fend off the erosion of markets on its own turf. In other words, "it

can head off the competition at the pass."

Tying into the U.S. preference for fresh produce, Campbell Soup Company sought the world's best mushroom-growing technology and found it in Holland. The company imported much of the equipment for its first high-tech mushroom farm, but then it went a step further. It built a second farm, modifying it to use American equipment whenever possible. Both farms created jobs on our soil. Campbell then researched what consumers wanted in a mushroom, so that the products of the farm would be well received.

Capitalizing on Americans' love affair with gourmet and foreign items, Pepperidge Farm, whose cookie-making technology originally came from Europe, has joined forces with Campbell's Godiva chocolate plant in the United States to produce a new cookie that imitates one found in Europe.

Marketing U.S. agricultural products—at home as well as abroad—requires a great deal of ingenuity as well as energy. When the marketer keeps the consumer in mind, the product can benefit both.

Inventing and Testing New Products

Sylvia Schur, director, Creative Food Service, New Rochelle, NY

We've come a long way since people ate what could be caught, then what could be grown and harvested, thankful for availability. More recently, convenience or processing alone was reason enough for a product to succeed. Now we are in a period of food quality discrimination, breadth of selection, range of choice, and consciousness of nutritional quality, taste, and ease of preparation. These factors are all challenges to quality standards used in inventing and testing new products designed to win consumer loyalty.

Some 7,866 new food products were launched in 1987—a record number, according to Martin Friedman, editor of Gorman's *New Product News*, who writes a monthly report on new product entries in the marketplace. For each new product launched nationally, about eight or more fall by the wayside in the course of new product development and testing. Of those launched, only 2 out of 10 are likely to survive in the marketplace as lasting products.

Inventing and Testing

Successful products meet a consumer want or need, either for a broad universe of consumers, or for consumers in a specific niche, providing a unique consumer benefit. The food market, totaling almost $302 billion in sales in 1987, is second in consumer expenditures only to autos at $340½ billion. Some sophisticated methods of product development and testing vie with simple, appetizing ideas to spell success in multimillion dollar annual sales per product.

Let's examine some of the trends, successes, and has-beens of the past 40 years to understand the basic principles of food marketing success. Social, economic, and culinary factors affect success in a market which now includes more knowledgeable and sophisticated consumers.

Pizza—a Pattern for Product Positioning

Before examining the new disciplines of food testing and development, let's review the success of a product which now sells an estimated $2 billion a year in supermarkets alone, frozen and fresh. In 1943, when soldiers in upstate New York searched for satisfying foods quickly available in areas near cold-weather camps, enterprising vendors of Italian pizza offered "Hot Tomato pies" with cheese or sausage topping, sold by the slice. The tasty wedges of those first hot pizzas, a new experience to most Americans, spread in Chicago and New York, from carts to storefronts to restaurants—and now into homes nationally, as takeout or manufactured products sold in supermarkets. No major company invented this product, or plotted its success, although many now make it. Pizza is an excellent example of natural product positioning for success.

Positioning identifies 1) the target group, 2) the product, 3) a specific consumer need or needs met, and 4) the unique consumer benefits. For

Pizza started in 1943 in upstate New York but soon spread to Chicago and New York City where it was sold from carts to storefronts to restaurants and eventually into homes. Today, pizza is brought home fresh or frozen, unwrapped, and heated 2 minutes in a microwave oven, rather than 20 minutes in a conventional oven. (Pizza Hut, Inc.)

pizza, this positioning statement or concept might read: "To hungry, hearty-eating consumers (the target group) who want something satisfying and hot to eat in a hurry (the need), pizza (the product) provides a tasty, satisfying, and adventuresome quick meal, with gratifying flavor, texure, and aroma contrasts (the unique benefits)."

While takeout and home-delivered pizzas now reach record proportions, a new pizza area beckons for development. This pizza is brought home fresh or frozen, unwrapped and heated in 2 minutes in the microwave oven, rather than 20 minutes in a conventional oven. Tasty sauce bubbles under melted strands of cheese, zestily flavored and set off by a crust that shatters to the bite and chews tenderly. This at least is the expectation.

Technical Challenges to Product Development

The challenge in the development of a microwave pizza applies to many food products with dual texture. Moisture in one portion of a food migrates over time to another portion. The speedy microwave functions by heating the moisture within a food, thereby transferring that moisture to the crust, without permitting the drying and crisping that takes place in a conventional oven.

Soggy pizza does not satisfy consumers. Current research combines bakers' skills with technical study of moisture migration, fat impermeability, flour gluten strength, and engineering advances in microwave crisping, to deliver the microwavable pizza that succeeds.

Development Process

Food is our most lasting pleasure. For a drink or any other food product, pleasure—as delivered in appearance, aroma, flavor, and texture—is an important key to success. As lifespans increase, however, flavor must be accentuated for older palates. The testing and development of Clamato is a good case history of the product development process.

In early 1960, we worked on the development of a product called Clamato, a drink combining tomato juice (from concentrate), clam broth (the byproduct of a canned clam product), additional natural clam flavor, and seasonings. Our client was Mott's, a major fruit company, which had purchased a fish packaging plant that canned clams and generated quantities of byproduct broth. Flavored tomato juices showed healthy sales growth as a refreshing drink or appetizer, or as a base for Bloody Mary cocktails. Clamato, with its accent of clam broth, registered with consumers as a drink with additional benefits.

The four steps in this process were as follows:

1. *Identification of the area of interest* for development

2. Establishment of a *concept*—a consumer positioning statement and product illustration—to evaluate consumer reactions

3. Preparation of sample *prototypes*—kitchen-developed examples of the product for testing and tasting. For such preparations, we use commercially available ingredients, and simulated production methods, to indicate a reasonably accurate measure of success in the marketplace. We do such prototypes first as roughs, which we call *protocepts,* to provide products that look and taste like the end product. We compare the reactions to the taste with reactions to the concept, to determine whether the product lives up to consumer expectation, and whether it can be made better, or *optimized.*

4. *Optimization,* or improvement of the product in the course of development, takes place between test sessions, to bring the product closer to consumer expectations for product and packaging, and make it as good as it can be.

Passing the Test

Clamato tests indicated that consumers liked the concept of a tomato product with some clam flavor and content. Consumers also indicated that while they liked a trace of real clam flavor, "the kiss of the hops," they did not want this to be a heavy sea note. They also preferred a light refreshing texture to dense tomato thickness. All these characteristics were incorporated in Clamato, still popular in the marketplace.

A Consumer Focus

How do we gain these consumer reactions? We ask the consumers who might be the target audience for the product. Such testing is done first in small numbers for qualitative reactions, then in large numbers to measure quantitative chances of success.

The first small groups, called *focus groups,* judge a product and indicate to a manufacturer how consumers react. A focus group typically consists of 7 to 15 consumers who are potential users of the product being tested. To select panelists, demographic characteristics of target consumers are established—for example, half women and half men 24 to 55 years old, with family income of $35,000 or more a year or $20,000 a year if a single head of household. Other demographics might call for families with young children or teen-agers. Participants might include full-time homemakers at another panel and part-time workers at a third. Insofar as possible, we conduct three panels in one day to avoid variables in weather or mood of day, which might change the results.

Assembling and Conducting the Panel

To assemble panelists, a trained *recruiter* makes calls to locate appropriate consumer participants. A list of questions is used to screen out those who do not qualify and to find those who are part of the likely user group. Use of similar products is generally a requisite. Professionals or employees of food companies or agencies, people who have participated in a panel within the last year, and those who have special food restrictions are screened out.

A *moderator* conducts the actual panel discussion, following individual tasting and written responses. While panels are in session, clients and the development team might view the sessions from the *viewing room,* through a two-way mirror, or watch the process on closed circuit television, which also provides a VCR tape for review and checking.

Rating Results

In our system, panelists first rate product attributes on written forms, both for concept and taste reactions, using a scale of 1 to 10 (10 being highest), or sometimes scores of 1 to 5 or 1 to 9. We believe that a score average of 6, on the 1 to 10 scale, indicates a reasonable base for further testing; others accept a lower score of 5.2. A score of close to 8 or higher is considered a consumer mandate to go forward.

Following the written ratings, the moderator conducts a detailed discussion of the product, delivery in relation to concept, specific attributes, likelihood to buy, reactions to packaging samples, and price expectations. All this provides guidance for the development process.

In other focus group proceedings, consumers might interpret products using lifestyle photos for identity, or group similar products for point of identity. Panelists are paid for their participation.

Expanding the Tests

Following the initial tests in one location, focus groups might take place in three to six or more areas of the United States, to measure possible regional differences or likelihood to accept the product.

If the product succeeds in these focus discussions, it is then taste-tested with larger groups, frequently at a central location such as a shopping mall or a supermarket.

If central location tests confirm interest in the product, home placement tests follow, in which product samples are sent to homes, packaged with consumer directions. Home preparation will indicate family as well as individual reactions to a product and to its ease of preparation.

The product is next tested in a few stores in selected areas and closely monitored for consumer responses and repeat purchases. Following test marketing, the product might be "rolled out" in additional markets or across country.

Development Cycle

We complete this process—from concept through product development and testing to national rollout—within a year, if the concept is on target and the product meets consumer expectation. An example of this is White Wine Worcestershire Sauce, developed in 1985 for Lea & Perrins to meet the need for a light and flavorful seasoning sauce for chicken and fish. These are foods fast increasing in use. In the initial focus groups, tests defined the desired density, color, and flavor attributes, and the product went through production and marketing into national distribution within a year.

Complex products often take up to 5 years and cost millions of dollars in development and testing, before national roll-out.

No Guarantee of Success

Despite careful testing and painstaking evaluations, the failure rate for new products is high. A costly recent example was the new Coca Cola formulation. In test situations, sips of this registered as preferrable to tasters. In real life, it was reported that many deemed it too sweet and lacking in the effectiveness of what came to be called Classic Coke—the original product. Classic Coke was quickly rushed back into the marketplace, and now sells along with the new Coke formulation for a total gain.

Microwave Impact

With microwave ovens now in more than 60 percent of American homes, and expected to reach 80 percent by 1990, products designed for microwave heating became hot items in 1988. Microwave popcorn, which delivers a tasty, wholesome snack with consumer control of salt and butter, is a multi-million-dollar sales hit. Microwavable dough-encased snack products, which satisfy the need for small meals, or after-school snacks for children whose mothers work, are popular new product choices.

Meal Challenges

The most significant current challenge in new product development relates to the desire for freshness in prepared foods, and the need for individual meals, delicious and nutritious, packed in containers that can be used in microwave or conventional ovens, for range-to-table use. Social changes have removed the full-time homemaker from the kitchen and raised the standards of food quality for men and women. New product responses from major manufacturers include refrigerated meals and shelf-stable meals in plastic packages, being tested by General Foods, Campbell, Hormel, and other manufacturers as we write this. Like all plastic packages, these plastic packages raise new needs for techniques to salvage and rework the used package.

Reliance on either technicians or chefs for product formulation is no longer sufficient. Instead, a fusion of chef's skills and technical development is necessary. We call this a techni-culinary process.

Freshness Industrialized

Consumer quality expectations—including nutritional quality as well as taste, texture, and flavor—are higher than ever. To meet these expectations, new products must satisfy increasing demands for freshness, or for heat processing without destroying flavor and texture; for ease of preparation; and for gratifying eating experience. You might define this as the industrialization of home meal preparation. Packaging, directions for use, and serving ideas are part of this product presentation. Recycling of packaging materials becomes an added challenge.

New Quality Food Targets

We've moved in the last 10 years to a more knowledgeable appreciation of food and its nutritional values. Supermarkets have wider varieties of foods—from more varied whole grains, more quickly prepared, to salad bars and a new range of produce. More products have fewer of the artificial ingredients consumers complained of in the 1960's, 1970's and 1980's. More fish are farmed; more turkeys and poultry produced; more low-fat milk is used.

We are now at work developing "Meat-Like-Wheat" products, to optimize whole wheat protein and to flavor it as economical scaloppine, stir fry, chile, and wheat balls. This product line, like other U.S. products, may have an important impact on European markets, a counterpoint to the recent influx of European foods on the American market.

New product development now must be ready to fuse traditions of fine foods with advances in biotechnology, technology, and food testing. This will upgrade the uses of our vast food supply and allow us to develop food products that will help satisfy consumer expectations for a gratifying quality of life.

Part IV
New or Better Products to Meet Demand

ADAPT—Agricultural Diversification Spells Profit

Richard Krumme, editor, Successful Farming Magazine, Des Moines, IA

Since December 1986, *Successful Farming* magazine has treated nearly 10,000 farmers to more than 200 ideas for diversification. We did this through our popular Ag Diversification Adds Profit Today (ADAPT) conferences.

Numerous Possibilities

Our reasoning behind holding the ADAPT conferences, with their 100 diversification ideas each, is that even if farmers are inclined to diversify, they hardly know where to start. In the beginning we found that some farmers could only think of the obvious: a vegetable stand with garden produce, or cutting a few cords of firewood to sell out of a pickup. As the diversification concept has matured, we now know there are literally thousands of successful diversification possibilities.

The 10,000 farmers who came to our ADAPT conferences were out to take charge of their businesses again. Control of too many farms has slipped away—to lenders and to the Government. On too many farms the only "plan" is to wait for the next Government program. A third of net farm income will come from the U.S. Government in 1988. A cash grain farm will get two-thirds of its net farm income from the Government.

ADAPT ideas are geared to the idea that farmers want to receive more income from the market and less from the Government. A successful diversification program produces for a market—not a grain bin.

Low-Fat Meat Products

Consumers today are uneasy about fat in their meat. Is that a problem or an opportunity? We know stories of farmers who produce venison, which is low in fat and cholesterol. Or water buffalo...or rabbits. Or lite beef or aquaculture. If you are inclined to smirk at the impracticality of these possibilities, consider that until Thomas Jefferson ate one publicly, the tomato was considered poisonous, and not long ago the soybean was merely a Chinese oddity.

Quality Tomatoes

Did we say tomato? Here is a case of agriculture not responding to consumer needs. Everyone complains about hard, tasteless tomatoes in the stores. In some stores on the East Coast you can buy juicy, red, tasty tomatoes year-round. Where do they come from? Israel. What do they cost? Twice as much, side by side, as the hard, little, rubber balls that pass for tomatoes today. Consumers *will* pay for quality.

Salad Bar Crops

The fastest growing unit in most restaurants is the salad bar. And on that salad bar is something called sprouts ...alfalfa sprouts, bean sprouts. Do you know how long it takes to grow a sprout? Three days! Can you think of any other farm business which begins to pay off in 3 days?

Flowers

The fastest growing profit center in supermarkets isn't food at all, it's

The fastest growing unit in most restaurants is the salad bar. Many salad bars include bean sprouts or alfalfa sprouts. Sprouts take only 3 days to grow, making them one commodity that pays off quickly. (Marriott Corporation)

flowers. Demand for flowers is increasing 10 percent a year.

Mail Order Selling

Now maybe you live a long way from town. The U.S. population is on a mail order buying binge—$50 billion worth a year. Could you sell smoked meat, jerky, fruits, vegetables, preserves, wildflower seeds, popcorn, crafts, pets, hunting dogs, recipes, services, farm implements by mail?

Are We a Colony?

We believe these are the sorts of ideas American farmers must at least consider. Such new operations would remove some of our dependence on growing and selling bulk commodities like the grains—and, at the same time, *increase* our reliance on value-added products (those that have undergone some processing). Lee Iacocca writes, "What do you call a country which exports bulk commodities like cotton and steel and then imports products like textiles and automobiles.? A colony!"

Diversification Works

So what are some of the great diversification stories? We know hundreds. Here are just a few:

- The King Ranch in Texas has diversified from beef cattle into a shrimp growing operation.
- The Stobers in North Dakota farm wheat and sunflowers, and grow Sharpei dogs. They sell the puppies that have breeding potential for $1,500 each. Last year they grossed $25,000 with expenses of only $5,000. At our ADAPT trade show they took orders for $15,000 worth of dogs. Keep in mind that the idea is not to turn the entire farm over to the new enterprise, but rather to replace a money-losing enterprise with a new profitable one. We'd like to see the new enterprise account for about 20 percent of profits as a target.

- Sprouts are a low-investment diversification opportunity. You can buy a simple growing container for $2,500. You can sell sprouts wholesale for between $1 and $2 a pound, and your cost is 35 cents to 70 cents a pound. If the profit was 50 cents, you'd need to sell 200 pounds a week to make $100. The machines, which have the trays in them, will turn out 40 to 700 pounds a week and will fit in one small room.
- Our chemicals editor, Betsy Freese, claims a pick-your-own strawberry diversification saved her dad's hog farm in Maryland. He has 10 acres of you-pick strawberries and nets $800 an acre from them.
- Mark Becker from Illinois started growing specialty vegetables a few years ago. He grows napa cabbage and snow peas and sells them to oriental restaurants that pay him rather than a wholesaler from Chicago. Mark makes as much money from 2 acres of oriental vegetables as he makes from 400 acres of soybeans and corn.
- We hear mixed reports about llamas. One farmer we know generates $28,000 net income a year from a $100,000 investment. Clearly, these trendy enterprises call for getting in early, and, in this case, selling breeding stock. In this era of niche marketing, the niches are pretty small and by the time you hear about it locally, it may be too late.
- The next trendy enterprise is ostriches. A pair of ostrich chicks sells for $1,800. A mature pair brings $10,000. An ostrich lays 30 to 50 eggs a year and even an infertile egg can sell for $50 to be used as a decorative ornament. An ostrich lives for 40 years.
- An Indiana farmer grows and bags birdseed—corn, wheat, sunflowers, and milo. He gets an extra 1 cent to 6 cents a pound of grain. That's 50 cents to $2.50 more a bushel. He has a big operation and ships out three truckloads a day.
- Another big-time diversification is straw logs. A Colorado operation presses wheat straw into logs which are 12 inches long by 2.3 inches in diameter. They sell for less than competing products and burn cleanly. It is a high investment operation because the machine costs $150,000, but they claim to make $360,000 gross a year.
- An Oregon melon grower sells to the Japanese specialty market. He gets $40 for one melon! How? By turning it over each day so there is no flat or discolored spot on it.
- Several farmers are making good seasonal money with you-pick pumpkins. They put kids on hayracks and drive them out to the patch to pick their Halloween pumpkins.
- The U.S. consumption of mushrooms is only 2 to 3 pounds a year while it is 8 to 20 pounds elsewhere. That says there's room for growth. We know of three kinds:

1) *Shiitake.* When Buddy Hale harvested his first shiitake 5 years ago, he was one of just a few growers in the United States. They are grown by impregnating the oak logs with the spore. Today, the Madison, Va., dairy farmer has over 1,500 competitors, but the market isn't saturated yet. Hale sells his mushrooms to brokers for $5 a pound ($3 profit), who, in turn, sell them to 200 restuarants for $10 a pound;

2) *Oyster mushrooms.* These exotic mushrooms are grown on wheatstraw or cornstalk medium. They cost 50 cents to $1 a pound to grow and sell for $4 a pound;

3) *Morel mushrooms.* Finally it is possible to cultivate these wild delicacies indoors. Neogen Corporation

has the patent and will apparently be licensing a few farmers to produce morels. But they will require upwards of $50,000 in startup capital and will give preference to those who have experience growing mushrooms.

- A fish farmer from Missouri, Ron Macher, makes $200 to $300 per cage of catfish in his ponds. He says this confinement feeding causes faster growth, and they are easier to catch at market time.
- In Kansas, Sidney Corbin grows his fish in cages too, but because he has a free fishing operation (value added) he nets $900 a cage. He grossed $200,000 last year.
- Winnie Hawthorne in South Carolina grows crawfish in cages. The Hawthornes are grossing $1,500 a surface acre and can't keep up with demand, which is growing yearly with the growth of Cajun and country cooking.
- An Iowa family grew black and colored sheep for years. The owner began spinning wool and making a few sweaters. This has grown into a true cottage industry with five neighboring women carding and spinning wool in their homes. Other women come to the shop where they knit the wool into beautiful sweaters, mittens, scarves, and so on. She puts a nice label—St. Marys Woolens—on each piece and includes the story of their farm and how the sweater is made. The sweaters sell for more than $100 each at exclusive shops.
- We also know of two Colorado women who have a small-scale country catering business. When they found themselves with an empty dairy barn after their husbands sold off the dairy cows through the dairy herd buyout program, they installed a commercial kitchen and cater parties and functions. Last year they took in $26,000 and netted $7,500.

- An Iowan installed a trapshooting range on his farm. He takes in $300 some nights, which is the only time he's open.
- In South Dakota, David Maas spent $1,000 for cross country skis, and 500 customers flocked to the farm to rent skis and warm their toes in the granary. The family now hosts retreats throughout the year. Good skiing days can bring in $2,500. The Maas are trying to attract more meetings to the lodge they renovated from a barn.
- Finally, there is the granddaddy of all diversification enterprises— Booker T. Whatley's program to gross $100,000 from 25 acres of a you-pick operation. His concept is 10 high-value products that give year-round cash flow. He accepts up to 1,000 families who pay $25 for the right to pick fresh crops that are priced 40 percent less than the supermarket. His customers pay $40 if they want to fish his ponds while another family member picks vegetables.

A Useful Service

We tell farmers to keep in mind two rules for diversification: (1) If you don't like people, forget most of the enterprises, (2) If you don't like marketing, forget them all!

There is not one solution to what ails agriculture, there are 10,000 and 100,000 solutions. Those solutions are not in Washington or the State capitals; they are right there on each and every farm and ranch in the country.

An inspiration to our ADAPT and diversification efforts has been Thomas Jefferson's words, "The most useful service we can render a culture is to add a new plant to its agriculture." We believe one of the most useful services we can render our farmers today is to add a new and profitable enterprise to the business.

Oklahoma Farmers Try Alternatives

Janet Kim Kaplan, public affairs specialist, Agricultural Research Service, Beltsville, MD

Southeast Oklahoma—a place where people traditionally are in beef, hay, or oil. Southeast Oklahoma—a place in economic depression because beef, hay, and oil currently mean low profits.

But peaches, watermelons, cucumbers, strawberries, cantaloupes, tomatoes, broccoli, Christmas trees, and even catfish could change rural Oklahoma's dreary economic picture, giving ranchers and farmers an alternative to the tradition of cattle and forage.

To introduce new crops like these to the region and to diversify Oklahoma's agricultural economy, three groups in 1983 joined in a unique partnership—USDA's Agricultural Research Service, Oklahoma State University (OSU), and RedArk Development Authority, a State-created public trust intended to develop markets for new crops.

Introducing New Crops

Finding fruit and vegetable varieties that can handle Oklahoma's growing season, which has been described in many years as "too wet too late and too dry too early," is one of the main goals for ARS, according to E. Van Wann, ARS research leader at the South Central Research Laboratory in Lane, OK, about 150 miles south of Tulsa.

But the laboratory's plans to help establish new crops depend on more than just finding the right varieties. "We must demonstrate to people that problems with new crops are solvable," Wann says.

Many farmers are still sitting on the fence waiting to see how harvests turn out for pioneers in the new crops.

"Our presence here with this lab acts as encouragement," Wann says. "We can show them, for example, that with a tomato variety like Sunny or Mountain Pride, which the lab grew experimentally but under field conditions in summer 1987, you can harvest $6,400 worth of fruit per acre. The cost of the production runs $4,000-$4,400, depending on overhead. So an acre or two of tomatoes can be a nice supplement to a farmer's income."

Part of the objective is to convince people with no tradition of farming for market that there is potential for producing fruits and vegetables for wholesale. Many people in the area, even those growing produce for roadside stand sales, do not have the basic information about how to grow crops commercially.

"We try to introduce them to the best commercial varieties of crops and recommend ways to grow them here in southeast Oklahoma," Wann says. "For instance, we brought in supersweet varieties of corn last year, even sweeter than Silver Queen. Before, the only corn grown here was not particularly commercial."

In trials during the summer of 1987, agency scientists found that supersweet corn could yield just as much an acre as varieties more traditionally grown in the area. "And people love the taste. The patches of supersweet that people tried here hardly filled the local demand," Wann says.

Produce Finds Markets

To help farmers grow the produce and then develop markets for new crops, the Oklahoma State Government in 1984 created Three Rivers

E. Van Wann, ARS research leader in Lane, OK, is working to develop new crops, like tomatoes, for the southeastern area of the State. The additional income from tomato varieties, like Sunny or Mountain Pride, can mean another $2,400 an acre to the farmers of that area. (Bob Bjork)

Produce, a vegetable packing and marketing wholesale operation of RedArk Development Authority. The premise behind Three Rivers was that it would be easier to get farmers to try a new crop if they could start with a few acres and have some assurance of a buyer. Its markets are primarily grocery store chains.

Since Three Rivers began operations in 1985, the harvest of alternative crops has gone from 88,000 pounds of one crop—okra—to 2 million pounds of 6 or 7 different crops grown in 1987 by 22 farmers, according to its plant manager Jerry Sears.

"That kind of growth means many of the people around here on small places—2 or 3 acres—can make money," Sears says. "This is a very poor part of the country, and many of our young people have had to leave to find a job. The new industry is very welcome here."

For example, with Three Rivers' help, Bobby Pruitt, a local student, has made enough each summer from an acre of okra, one of the crops for which Three Rivers has opened a market, to pay his way through college.

But Three Rivers' marketing work cannot do the job alone. Just because you can sell tomatoes doesn't mean that any tomato will grow well in southeast Oklahoma.

That's where ARS comes in.

Researchers Seek Right Varieties

ARS scientists teamed up with researchers from OSU in 1985 to open the South Central Agricultural Research Laboratory and Wes Watkins Agricultural Research and Extension Center, named for Oklahoma Congressman Wes Watkins. One of the Center's assignments is to determine which varieties of fruits and vegetables grow in this area and their fertilizer and moisture requirements. OSU provided the land, and ARS built the facilities. Researchers from both work together on projects and on helping farmers with new crops.

"What to grow is pretty much chosen for its market potential by Three Rivers, but it is up to the research center to figure out how to grow that crop," says Wann.

Without that kind of data, people testing alternative crops could end up with expensive mistakes and no harvest. For example, in 1986 Three Rivers identified broccoli as a crop with a good potential market and signed up local farmers to grow a few acres. Unfortunately, much of it developed brown buds before the heads reached market size, according to plant manager Sears.

"So we'll be growing test plots of broccoli to find a variety and growing methods that will work here and can be grown at a cost that will help the farmer turn a profit," Wann says.

Sears counts on this type of research data to avoid mistakes for other new crops that Three Rivers wants to sell.

Complicating the picture in southeast Oklahoma is the area's large number of diverse soil types, according to Glen Taylor, Wann's counterpart at OSU. Such diversity means that researchers need to find a variety of each crop for each soil type.

"Eventually, all of the data will be entered into a computer data base. Then a person will be able to say, 'I've got 32 acres of these types of soil and this much water,' and the computer will generate a complete plan, with advice on how many acres of what crops to grow in which soils," he says.

ARS staff has also been directly involved in opening up some potential markets for Oklahoma farmers. For example, they have been testing carrots to find a variety that will grow orange enough in the Oklahoma climate and soil to qualify for use by Campbell's Soup.

"Campbell's has very strict requirements for how brightly colored a carrot must be before they will put it in a soup," Wann says. "Growing conditions, particularly temperature just before and at harvest, really affect a carrot's color.

The carrot varieties already tested were developed by Campbell's, themselves. At least one passed the color test, and Campbell's officials indicated they would buy carrots if local farmers grew them.

Wann is testing some ARS-developed carrot lines for color and yield in hopes of improving the economic potential of the crop to farmers and Campbell's.

Baby food manufacturer Gerber also has expressed interest in buying local produce, and asked if banana squash could be grown. At the research center they grew a test plot of the vegetable, but found that a powdery mildew attacks the crop. "We'll try to develop a management strategy that will let farmers grow the banana squash," Wann said.

Catfish

Another new potential revenue source for southeast Oklahoma is just getting underway—a projected 1-million-pounds-per-week catfish industry. The project is being developed cooperatively by ARS, RedArk, and the U.S. Fish and Wildlife Service.

ARS fisheries biologist Wendell J. Lorio is studying methods to help farmers raise catfish in ponds for RedArk's new fish processing plant, which opened in August. "The techniques for catfish farming were worked out years ago for Mississippi, but we need to adapt them for Oklahoma," he says. The biggest problem is maintaining water quality while keeping a high enough number of fish per acre of pond to be profitable.

Even the Army Corps of Engineers has helped out by providing expert advice on locating some of Lorio's experimental catfish pens in Lake Texoma.

In addition to his experiments to raise more fish in less space, Lorio also gives advice to farmers on getting their operations started. RedArk expects to pay about $1 a pound to the fish farmers, according to Gary Ainsworth, RedArk's catfish project manager. Costs of raising fish are about 50 cents a pound, according to Lorio.

Catfish are not only stimulating a new farm enterprise, but the RedArk's processing plant is also creating off-the-farm jobs. "We have 10 people employed right now in the startup phase and that will probably increase," says Ainsworth.

Phillip Howard and his son-in-law Troy Henry are not the first to try catfish farming in Oklahoma, but they are the first to do so with ARS guidance. "One guy down the road from here tried several years ago on his own and went broke," Howard says. "We depend on Dr. Lorio's advice to make our operation turn a profit."

Like many of those trying alternative crops, Howard is not quite ready to give up his cattle. "But raising beef here has become marginal. If the catfish work, we probably won't raise cattle at all," he says.

Revolution on Supermarket Shelves: The Value Added Is Convenience

Allen Bildner, chairman, Food Marketing Institute, Washington, DC, and chairman, Kings Super Markets, West Caldwell, NJ

Driven by new lifestyles that leave consumers with less time for cooking and shopping, a revolution is underway on the shelves of supermarkets. The food industry has developed a vast array of foods that put an accent on convenience: microwave products, both frozen and shelf-stable, and pre-cooked and refrigerated foods in every department of the supermarket—deli, bakery, produce, seafood, and meat. At the same time, these new foods deliver the good taste, nutrition, and economy that educated consumers demand.

The push for convenience extends well beyond the business of marketing food, as supermarkets broaden the concept of "one-stop shopping," saving consumers extra trips to other retail outlets. It is not uncommon at supermarkets today to find flowers, books, magazines, cosmetics, batteries, stationery, and postage stamps. Many services are now available: drug prescriptions, movie rentals, and photo developing.

Changing Lifestyles

These developments did not emerge as new ventures trying to create a market or stimulate a latent demand. They responded to basic lifestyle changes that coalesced in the 1980's. According to the Bureau of Labor Statistics, as many as 55 million women work in the United States outside the home today, representing 52.5 percent of all women, leaving little time and energy for ambitious cooking, except for a few times a week. In fact, both husband and wife work in 55.9 percent of the households, reducing the cooking time for both spouses. The Census Bureau reports another 23.9 percent of the households are occupied by singles, a hardworking and hardplaying group that by and large prefers to minimize time in the kitchen.

With everyone working, leisure time had diminished to an average of 2½ hours a day, according to a Rand Corporation study—down from nearly 4 hours in the early 1970's. Both men and women want to spend less time cooking, according to their 1987 survey of 2,000 adults. How much time would they like to spend per meal? For women, the ideal was 30 minutes, and for men only 15 minutes. Can you imagine such a response 10 or 20 years ago?

No wonder more than 65 percent of all households now have microwave ovens, and the number is projected to exceed 80 percent by 1990. According to the annual study *Trends: Consumer Attitudes & the Supermarket,* a national, projectable survey of 1,000 persons, conducted by the Food Marketing Institute (FMI), 69 percent of consumers have changed their cooking behavior over the last 3 to 5 years. Of those who have changed, 25 percent in 1987 and 17 percent in 1988 reported "more microwaving."

The push for convenience also is reflected in the growth of the carryout food market, which accounts for 15 cents out of every dollar consumers spend on food in restaurants and

Consumers like the time-saving convenience of microwave ovens.
(Magic Chef)

supermarkets, according to *Shopping à la Carte,* a 1987 study cosponsored by FMI and the Campbell Soup Company. By comparison, restaurants take in 19 cents out of every food dollar. Even among restaurants, the largest growth area is carryout food, reaching a new high of 44 percent of total traffic in 1987, reports *Restaurant Business* magazine.

The food industry identified these consumer trends through national surveys, surveys targeting special classes or ethnic groups, focus-group studies, and consumer advisory panels. Some of the most sophisticated methods use the data collected through the scanning of individual items at the checkout counter. All this research and the pressure of competition prompted the industry to meet the consumer's craving for convenience in a fast and furious manner.

Deluge of Convenience Foods

Food manufacturers have focused on convenience since the advent of canning more than a century ago. After World War II, frozen foods and

advances in processing brought cooking time down from 6 hours to 60 minutes. Today, with a deluge of microwave, refrigerated, and shelf-stable products and sophisticated packaging, we are closing in on the 60-second mark.

Consumers spent $760 million on microwave foods in 1987—up 64 percent from the previous year, according to the market research firm Selling Areas Marketing, Inc./Burke. Frozen foods in general are selling well, both for microwave and conventional ovens. Of course frozen foods always have offered convenience as an inherent value. The important change is their improved taste and quality and the addition of nutritional brands with reduced levels of calories, sodium, and cholesterol.

New Products
New microwave products are proliferating at an unprecedented pace— 284 new items in 1987, up 71 percent from 1986. Many of the newest dishes aim at more discriminating tastes: sweet and sour chicken, boneless beef ribs, linguine with white clam

sauce, coq au vin, manicotti in marinara sauce.

New Packaging

The packaging often doubles as the serving dish, eliminating the need for consumers to clean up after the meal. An increasing number of products are available in aseptic, shelf-stable packages. These may be stored at room temperatures in pantries for several months with no danger of spoilage. Consumers have not yet embraced the shelf-stable products because they are skeptical that these can be as fresh and nutritious as the frozen and fresh alternatives. These misconceptions should fade with time and education.

New Technological Developments

Manufacturers of microwave products have overcome technological obstacles in recent years—notably how to bake in an oven that does not generate the type of heat needed to crisp and brown foods. Several years ago, this barrier seemed insurmountable, but suppliers have overcome it with the "susceptor plate," a thin layer of powdered aluminum laminated under plastic that absorbs heat and radiates it onto the food. The plate is built into the packaging of pizzas and casseroles. For cake and brownie mixes, Pillsbury furnishes a reusable microwave baking pan that produces the same effect.

ConAgra, Inc. recently solved the problem of cooking time for microwave ovens of different wattages. Its "microready indicator," a thin strip on the top of the container, changes color when the food is ready. Manufacturers also are making microwave products convenient and safe for children—presenting the instructions in pictures and words.

A feature of the technology led to one of the more improbable products: the microwavable hot fudge sundae by Steve's Homemade Ice Cream. The two main ingredients, ice cream and fudge, are affected by microwaves over different lengths of time. The fudge is heated first, after only 30 seconds, and well before the ice cream. You can remove the dish after half a minute with *hot* fudge and *cold* ice cream.

Convenient Shopping

Supermarkets have responded to the craving for convenience in numerous ways. More than 150 products on supermarkets shelves can be prepared in less than 5 minutes, and many can be "microwaved" in just 2 minutes.

FMI's *Trends* survey asks consumers to report on the availability of new products and services in supermarkets. This measures the new offerings that have impressed consumers. In 1988, three of the top four items had a convenience value:

1. Food products designed especially for microwave cooking (93 percent)
2. Unbranded or generic products (85 percent)
3. Delicatessen or other carryout food items (80 percent)
4. Partially prepared foods that require less time to prepare at home (77 percent)

Other items on the list reflect the growth of one-stop shopping, saving customers trips to other businesses: photo refinishing (50 percent), video rentals (44 percent), automatic teller machines (35 percent), postage stamps (34 percent), prescription drug counter (27 percent).

Supermarkets are delivering convenience in quick and easy recipes on how to prepare foods. In-store videos and computers provide product and nutritional information in a concise and entertaining manner. Many grocers are reducing preparation time by selling foods already cut for cooking or consumption, such as pineapple sections and meats cut for scaloppine, stir-frying, and kebabing. A supermarket in Illinois installed a drive-through window where consumers can pick up groceries ordered ahead of time.

Grocers deliver convenience by cross-merchandising related products. For example, they position the ingredients needed for an entire meal in one place, such as putting beef round strips with fresh broccoli, mushrooms, and green onions for a quick and easy stir-fry dinner. Some have suggested the meat department of the future will become the "Entree Department."

Leave the Cooking to Us

While food suppliers create products suited for fast-cooking ovens, supermarkets do the cooking for consumers with a growing assortment of fully and partially prepared foods. Two-thirds of all supermarkets now offer prepared foods, and four-fifths of them plan to sell them by December 1989, according to the 1987 edition of FMI's *The Food Marketing Industry Speaks.* Individual examples abound of prepared foods among grocers:

- The deli departments in half of Safeway's stores offer precooked lasagna, pastas, barbecue chicken, salads, and desserts.
- Half of A&P's stores offer an extensive assortment of prepared foods.
- Grand Union of Elmwood Park, NJ, has its own recipe for lasagna, buffalo-style chicken wings, and baby back ribs.
- Giant Food Inc. in the Washington, DC, area is testing a breakfast bar in eight stores.
- Publix Super Markets in Lakeland, FL, has a deli specialist in each of its 307 stores who sets the menu of foods to be prepared each day.

At Kings Super Markets, the growing sales of produce, seafood, fresh meat, and other perishables prompted its move into ready-to-eat and ready-to-cook value-added foods throughout the stores. And for the first time, Kings created a deli, bakery, cheese, and prepared-foods store within a store, located at the entrance.

Marketing prepared foods, they found that their customers wanted foods for *dining out* at home. They didn't want plain prepared foods— they wanted restaurant quality. Kings sensed this about 6 years ago and began hiring chefs to help develop appetizers, entrees, and desserts— and to improve the quality of all its foods.

On an industrywide basis, the reception to precooked foods has been excellent. In a short period, supermarkets have captured one-fourth of the $62.4 billion takeout food market. Their success may relate to the fact consumers associate supermarkets with family meals, the source of food to be eaten at home. When they purchase precooked food at supermarkets, it is more a "take home" food than a "takeout" food. *Shopping à la Carte,* the FMI-Campbell Soup Company study, revealed three benefits to consumers in prepared foods:

1. These foods offer convenience—no cooking and little cleanup.

2. Consumers are too fatigued or rushed to cook, often because they came home late.

3. Consumers want to provide themselves a special treat as a reward for getting through the week.

Consumers perceive the foods prepared by supermarkets as fresh, of high quality, nutritious, tasty, and a good value for the money. By contrast, they perceive fast food restaurant items as too fattening. Still, the restaurants have the edge offering convenience and fun, especially for kids. Supermarkets are starting to improve convenience by placing checkouts in the departments that sell carryout foods.

One-Stop Shopping

One of the biggest time-savers has little to do with food: the many nonfoods finding their way onto supermarket shelves, saving consumers extra trips to purchase those products elsewhere. As much as 20 cents out of every dollar consumers spend in supermarkets today pays for something other than food.

The rising popularity of one-stop shopping is reflected in the remarkable growth in store size. The typical new store has grown by 50 percent over the last 10 years, according to the 1987 *FMI Industry Speaks* study—from less than 30,000 square feet to 44,000. Six in ten new stores in 1986 were either superstores or combos. Six in ten of the stores closed had the smaller, conventional formats—although conventionals still comprise the majority of the supermarkets standing.

Remodeling activity has remained strong, another sign of change that, in many cases, is moving in the direction of nonfoods. In both 1985 and 1986, nearly 10 percent of all stores were remodeled—many to add reading centers, movie-rental departments, cosmetic cases, and pharmacies. About 20 percent of all supermarkets today have pharmacies—compared with less than 10 percent a decade ago.

The largest example of one-stop shopping is the hypermarket, a French term for supercenters measuring anywhere from 70,000 to more than 200,000 square feet. In France, they account for 22.6 percent of all

food sales and 12.2 percent of nonfood sales. The trend began to sweep France in the 1960's and 1970's.

One of the first U.S. hypermarkets to open several years ago was Bigg's in Cincinnati with 40 checkout lanes, 75 aisles, and computers, designer clothes, pocketbooks, exercise bikes, color televisions, appliances, hardware—60,000 items in all—three times the size of the average supermarket. Nonfoods accounted for about 70 percent of sales the first year. Hypermarkets have opened in Pennsylvania, Louisiana, Oregon, Ohio, and California.

Future for Convenience Food

The push for convenience poses several questions for the food industry. Convenience foods are proliferating from the innovations of manufacturers and retailers. Who ultimately will become the supplier, and in what form or forms will the foods be sold—shelf-stable or refrigerated, service or self-service, prepacked or bulk, to name a few of the options?

All businesses will have to address the impact of the upcoming labor shortages. Where will we find the people to run the nonfood departments and the labor-intensive prepared food operations? Will these departments produce long-term growth and profitability to justify their existence financially?

The food industry will find answers to these questions as long as consumers demand convenience, an interest not likely to dissipate soon—if ever. It will not be the only feature that drives innovation and marketing, for quality, taste, economy, and safety are also important to consumers. But in an age where time is so precious and technology so fast, convenience will remain a central feature in the revolution on supermarket shelves.

Turkey Anytime

Barbara A. Schuelke, consumer information manager, Oscar Mayer Foods Corporation, Madison, WI

Since 1960, turkey consumption rose from 6.2 pounds to 15.3 pounds per person. Greater efficiencies in production techniques, resulting in increased supplies at prices favorable to consumers, contributed to more poultry on American dinner tables.

In addition to volume increases, the pattern of turkey consumption changed significantly. The majority of the product used to be consumed between Thanksgiving and Christmas. Now over 60 percent of the turkey eaten in the United States is accounted for during the first three quarters of the calendar year. Nearly all of this growth is attributable to further processed turkey products—turkey with any valued-added qualities beyond a whole ready-to-cook turkey, including fresh turkey parts and cooked items.

The following case history provides an overview of the Louis Rich Company. It reveals how a small poultry company became the world's leading turkey marketer, significantly influencing the types of turkey products that people eat and when they eat them.

New Turkey Products

The Louis Rich Company was born in the 1920's when Mr. Louis Rich began buying poultry and eggs from local farms and selling them to Rock Island, IL, area butchers and grocers. The 1930's saw the company expand to dressing poultry and shipping it to distributors in Eastern metropolitan markets. In the years that followed, their reputation for quality products brought in more and more customers, and the firm outgrew the Rock Island facility. Louis Rich decided to focus on the turkey segment and moved to West Liberty, IA, in 1958. There he established the Nation's most modern poultry processing plant.

Louis Rich and his sons Martin and Norman revolutionized the turkey industry in the 1960's. They began to cut up whole turkeys and sell individually packaged parts. Seemingly overnight, the traditional seasonal turkey became more convenient for consumers to purchase and enjoy year-round. The demand began to grow; a new product niche had been identified. By 1964, the Louis Rich Company had decreased emphasis on whole dressed poultry and was devoting most of its efforts toward producing and marketing fresh turkey parts and fully cooked turkey products.

The first major product entry was the oven-roasted Catering Quality turkey breast. This fully cooked, natural shape turkey breast provided the high quality appearance and taste that restauranteurs and deli operators wanted for their customers. Since it was a whole muscle product, not chopped and formed, another advantage was its true turkey texture. This product became so popular that a new outlet was needed for the remaining nonbreast turkey parts. Experimentation with spicing, cooking, and curing turkey led to the development of many new products—turkey bologna, turkey franks, turkey salami, turkey pastrami, and turkey ham.

The success of these products resulted in an expansion of the West Liberty plant, followed by the addition of plants in Newberry, SC, in 1972 and Modesto, CA, in 1974. Each of these facilities had access to nearby turkey farms. Such locations held transportation costs down and helped the firm maintain a competitive position as smaller regional companies began to enter the further processed turkey category.

Trends

The developing consumer interest in turkey products was consistent with nutrition and health trends as well as population demographics of the 1970's.

Low-Fat Content

The "fitness revolution" spread the appeal of jogging and aerobic dance; exercise and lean, muscular figures became fashionable. "White and Light" became key terms for food marketers. Better-for-you foods included an array of low calorie, low-fat, low sodium, and high fiber products springing up in the marketplace.

Turkey certainly fits the low calorie, low-fat profile. Compared to red meat products, turkey offers up to one-third less fat and calories. In addition, its small amount of fat is more unsaturated than fat from other meat sources. Many scientists believe it is the saturated fat content that contributes to heart disease risk. Its mild taste is as well suited to the unexpected (smoked sausage, turkey, and salami) as to the expected (oven-roasted turkey breast and smoked turkey). People were skeptical about these products until a taste proved that they were as delicious as the originals.

Convenience

Low fat and fewer calories are just part of what turkey has to offer. There has been a growing demand for natural foods and convenience foods during the 1980's. Turkey breast slices that cook in 5 minutes or tenderloins that are ready in 20 minutes have greater appeal than a whole turkey requiring 4 to 5 hours' roasting time. High quality convenience foods such as fully cooked turkey breast offer menu versatility with only brief heating times required. Adaptability of these products to microwave cooking or heating also has helped to create consumer interest.

Smaller Households

Not only is there less time to spend on meal preparation, but there are fewer people at home for whom to cook. The household size of mainstream America has diminished from four or five to one or two. Smaller 1- to 5-pound packages of turkey have greater appeal than 12 to 20 pounds of whole turkey. Louis Rich was a product line whose time had come.

Acquisition by Oscar Mayer Foods

During this same time, Oscar Mayer Foods took a hard look at its product line. That company commanded the number one position nationwide for cold cuts, hot dogs, and bacon and enjoyed excellent distribution. Still management realized that they could expand their business to include a wider selection of refrigerated meat products. They searched for a company which would be a good fit with their business and acquired Louis Rich in late 1979.

The acquisition proved to be mutually beneficial. Louis Rich provided a new avenue for growth and return on investment for Oscar Mayer stockholders for the long term. The benefits to Louis Rich were more immediate.

Marketing Advantages
Oscar Mayer had an extensive refrigerated distribution system which allowed Louis Rich to truly become a national brand. Oscar Mayer also had a direct sales force, widely regarded as the best in the meat industry, a definite advantage over the broker system used previously by Louis Rich. Oscar Mayer sales representatives had an established network of meat buyer contacts who believed in the quality and proven salability of Oscar Mayer products; soon they were convinced to give Louis Rich cold cuts a try. There was some resistance to fresh turkey parts, since retailers could cut up whole turkeys in the back room. But like tray pack chicken and, later on, boxed boneless beef and pork, fresh turkey cuts began to make inroads in the meat case because of labor cost savings and consistent quality.

Leadership
Louis Rich also was able to take advantage of Oscar Mayer's technology in both product development and packaging. One example is turkey franks. Soon they were being produced on Oscar Mayer's state-of-the-art "hot dog highway" and appearing on grocery shelves in Oscar Mayer's twin-pack packaging.

Promotional Expertise
In addition, Oscar Mayer had the marketing expertise and the working capital to educate the public about "today's turkey." National print and television advertisements aided public awareness; coupon drops and in-store demonstrations encouraged trial. Communication programs included media interviews, editorial features, and appealing recipes to support retail, deli, and foodservice product use.

Successful product introductions in recent years include oven roasted, hickory smoked, and barbecued breast of turkey; turkey cheese franks; turkey smoked sausage; and the first all-turkey cold cut Variety Pak.

Increased Demand Foreseen
Today, Louis Rich is the number one further processor of turkey and is the number two brand of all cold cuts, second only to Oscar Mayer. To meet increased demand, a new facility was opened in Sigourney, IA, in 1984, another added in Tulsa, OK, in 1987, with a third under construction in Tulare, CA, scheduled to begin operations in 1989.

Updated packaging graphics, new advertising creative strategy, and ongoing publicity programs will help Louis Rich maintain its strong position as "the turkey worth talking about." It is a brand that certainly will help propel turkey consumption to over 20 pounds per capita in the 1990's, as more and more consumers accept turkey as an anytime food.

How to Grow in a Maturing Foodservice Market

Kristin S. Ferguson, vice president of marketing, Food Service Division, Tyson Foods, Inc., Springdale, AR

Something different is happening in the foodservice marketplace. For the past 15 years, the market has experienced sustained growth. There were some periods, coinciding with a generally sluggish economy, when the rate of growth slowed from the previous period. But in no period was there an actual decline in business.

What we are beginning to see, however, is sustained change in the nature of growth in a maturing market. An example of substantial change in the market has been the growth of fast food, or Quick Service Restaurant (QSR). The overriding question is how does one deal with expansion and growth of one's products in a maturing market? To help understand the answer, we need to explore the product life cycle.

Product Life Cycle

The product life cycle has four distinct stages.

Market Development
The first stage covers the period from product conception through initial market introduction. Sales tend to be low, the product often has weak demand initially, and all the technical and production bugs may not be worked out. It is at this stage, though, where marketing works most diligently to "create" demand.

Market Growth
If Stage One efforts are successful, Stage Two is Market Growth. If Stage Two efforts aren't successful, the product dies a quick death. As the product gains customer awareness, demand begins to accelerate, and the size of the total market expands rapidly. This stage also is called the "take-off" stage, although it usually is a period of sustained and rapid growth during which customer acceptance, demand, sales, and profits all increase regularly. After some time, the product is a commonplace item before the consuming public: everyone who is anyone has one—or in our business, everyone eats it. Regularly. Perhaps even once a day.

Market Maturity
This is the point of transition from Stage Two to Stage Three. Demand is stable and strong, but growth usually weakens to the point, at the latter end, that it is nonexistent.

Market Decline
Then we see Stage Four. The product begins to lose consumer appeal and sales drift downward. Buggy whips died with the advent of the automobile; silk lost out to nylon. "I'm tired of hamburgers, period. Let's eat chicken nuggets."

Competition in the Life Cycle

Competition changes from stage to stage in the life cycle. In the beginning, a company may face no competition. It is a pioneer facing the task of developing the market for a new product. As the company succeeds, competitors enter the field, and as sales grow, the number of companies competing for the business increases to a point where it becomes more and more difficult to retain a satisfactory share of the market. Prices also change throughout the cycle. Frequently higher prices are charged at the beginning only to be lowered as competition enters the marketplace. The channels of distribution are also expanded over time. New products may enter a specialty house market, but later become available in general stores and discount houses.

The firm that pioneers a product may introduce it at high prices and high profits, but then withdraw after the saturation point seems to be reached. Alternatively, it may attempt to expand the life of the product by introducing new modes. The firm can also stretch or extend the market by promoting more frequent usage, more varied usage, new users, and new uses.

QSR's and Their Stages

In fast food or QSR's, we can see the stages of the cycle by looking at changes in real measurement of growth in QSR's: Average Unit Sales. In 1986, for example, the number of units increased at a rate considerably greater than did customer traffic growth. The result was an overall decline for the industry in average unit sales. Now, obviously, some companies did better at dealing with this than others. Some managed successfully to maintain their position, new products, and new users. Others did not and are now trying to figure out how to keep their position at the back edge of Stage Three from dropping off the edge to Stage Four.

Suppliers to these companies are influenced directly by these events. New products help, but as the market matures the opportunities for a supplier to present new products to the QSR, or to another segment of the market, are not as fruitful as before. The primary challenge for most suppliers, then, is how to sustain growth when your customers' markets are maturing—how, in effect, to keep your products moving and not sinking. Winning in the 1990's will require doing the foodservice basics better, by adopting modified strategies and programs. Overall, the marketplace will require more sophisticated marketing as competition and maturing markets stimulate operators to focus more aggressively on cost-effective purchasing, and distributors to focus more aggressively on item profitability.

A number of foodservice suppliers have already demonstrated that this challenge can be met. Tyson Foods is one of them. There are innumerable strategies and programs suppliers might follow, based on their own perceptions of relative risk and reward. Some will focus on new products, others on existing products, and still others on various combinations of both.

Achieving Growth

The seven steps for achieving growth in a maturing market go from low risk, with relatively low reward, to substantially higher risk with higher reward. The first *four* are strategies for capitalizing on an existing product; the last three for new products with new foods, new packaging, or new technology. In theory, the selection of a strategy or a combination of strategies would depend on how a company perceives itself as a risk-taker relative to the possible rewards, its market share in the business, and the internal resources available to develop new products employing sophisticated new technologies.

Steps for achieving growth in a maturing market

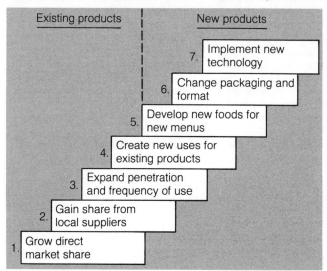

Existing products | New products

7. Implement new technology

6. Change packaging and format

5. Develop new foods for new menus

4. Create new uses for existing products

3. Expand penetration and frequency of use

2. Gain share from local suppliers

1. Grow direct market share

Tyson Foods as Example

Moving from the theoretical to the practical, now, let me take you through the strategies and programs that Tyson Foods pursued to ensure its continued growth in this maturing market.

We began by examining our entire line of products and where they were in the product life cycle. With over 300 foodservice products, individual products fell into each stage of the cycle—everything from appetizers in the embryonic or development stage, to bone-in breaded parts (otherwise known as fully cooked fried chicken) in the declining stage. With so many products, the process of analyzing each in terms of an appropriate strategy would have been enormously time consuming. We therefore looked at which combination of strategies would produce the best results for the foodservice product line as a whole, with each item evaluated individually as necessary relative to its position in its own life cycle.

Given this, we evaluated the four options for capitalizing on an existing product. After considering each of these four alternative steps for achieving growth in the maturing foodservice market, we decided to concentrate on the first option, growing direct market share.

Differentiating the Product

We look for the points of difference and capitalize on them. As a manufacturer and marketer of chicken products, what strengths do we have over the competition and what competitor weaknesses can we capitalize on? These strengths or weaknesses can be in the form of market share, distribution, brand recognition, etc. Differentiation can be something other than a new product. It can be customer assistance to enhance the buyer's own marketing efforts; it can be new forms of processing and packaging that blur the line between "scratch" and "further processed."

Currently, Tyson maintains a significant share in the poultry market with

Tyson Foods maintains a significant market share in poultry with more than 300 products in more than 30 lines. To stay competitive, Tyson had to capitalize on the rapidly expanding market for chicken in foodservice. (Tyson Foods, Inc.)

more than *300 products* categorized into more than 30 separate lines. And with these multiple product lines, Tyson Food Service needed an overall divisional program that not only helped *our* business grow, but also helped the overall markets grow and differentiated our products from the competition. We had to capitalize on the rapidly expanding market for chicken in foodservice. But, we also had to develop a cohesive marketing program from which all of this would follow.

The marketing strategy developed sounds quite simple: to help foodservice operators add more chicken to their menus. For example, by increasing the total market size—more people eating more chicken—Tyson, with significant market share, would benefit. And we could do this by giving them more ways to put Tyson chicken on their menus. We also wanted the operators to think that Tyson could help them become chicken experts and keep ahead of the latest food trends. We wanted them to know that we don't just *sell* chicken, we help the people who buy Tyson chicken *market* our products to their customers.

New Courses Program

We selected the theme NEW COURSES to unite the written and visual messages, and to communicate Tyson's ability to help operators keep on top of the latest trends. NEW COURSES relates literally to the "courses" of food pictured in ads, but figuratively we wanted to emphasize the courses—the new direction and trends—that drive the operator's menu.

The NEW COURSES program consists of three parts. First, a new advertising campaign to introduce the program, sign up members, and address various menu trends. The ads depict various serving suggestions for one or more of our product lines. The first trend—grazing rather than eating fixed meals—supports three lines: prime filets, wings and drummies, and breast tenderloins. The copy is informative, yet light. Here are some examples:

Timing. The right food at the right time. Tyson Wings and Drummies are sure fire appetite quenchers for happy hours, predinner appetizers, and small entrees. They come breaded and unbreaded, fully cooked or individually quick frozen. Prepare them as is. Or experiment with the help of our comprehensive menu planning program, NEW COURSES.

A Little Romance. For additional product, preparation, and recipe information, give us a call. You'll find that once you couple the right application with just the right lighting, Tyson wings and drummies will capture the taste of the moment. And maybe, just maybe, stir up a little romance.

Additional trends to be addressed are Cajun, American, and off-premise (takeout).

Second, operators who send in the postcard and meet various selection criteria become NEW COURSES members. They receive menu binders which include recipes of all products shown in the ad, recommendations on alternative Tyson chicken products to use in the recipes, and tips on proper handling of chicken. They also get a quarterly newsletter addressing each trend in depth and suggestions on how they can serve chicken in a variety of ways. Finally, tying it all together is an 800-4-CHICKEN WATS number. If an operator has a question regarding Tyson products or chicken in general, we will help the operator to solve the problem.

The NEW COURSES program shows the operator how to build a menu using chicken—the hottest growing protein food. Even if an operator uses a competitive brand, the risk is minimal. Since Tyson holds the major share, as the market grows, so does Tyson. Moreover, the NEW COURSES marketing strategy focuses on differentiating Tyson chicken from the run-of-the-mill commodity product. We anticipate that these strategic efforts will further Tyson's growth substantially.

Staying With Same Product

Success in the maturing foodservice market can be achieved without expensive new product development. By evaluating the marketplace *and* a company's product line, marketing strategies can be developed which incorporate current products with new programs.

Beef Makes A Comeback—by Listening to Consumers

William G. Fielding, president, Excel Corporation, Wichita, KA

The introduction of branded, vacuum-packaged, fresh beef is a major development in the beef industry. During the 1960's, industry innovators began selling boxed beef—5-to 20-pound cuts that were vacuum wrapped (in impermeable plastic bags) and shipped in cardboard boxes—which reduced shipment of bones and fat. With Excel's introduction of branded, individual beef cuts, retailers can now buy exactly what they can sell.

The marketing of boneless, USDA choice individual beef cuts also recognizes the importance of providing what consumers want. For too long the beef industry ignored consumers who wanted leaner, consistently high-quality cuts. Ignoring consumers cost everyone in the beef industry dearly, because consumers were able to find the consistent quality they desired in fish and poultry products.

Meeting Consumer Needs

By 1995, an estimated 85 percent of women will be working outside the home, up from 55 percent in 1988. Dual income families want products that are convenient without sacrificing quality. Meeting consumers' expectations will require the teamwork of packers, feedlot operators, producers, and breeders—all contributing their considerable skills to producing the type of products consumers want.

Branded beef does well when handled properly by retailers who are given the support they need by Excel, where we continually refine our consumer education and retailer-support programs.

Working with Producers Too

In addition to its branded marketing of beef, Excel has a complementary new cattle-buying system. Excel is showing cattle producers the types of animals that will yield beef cuts that suit consumers' expectations and paying cattle producers the first premiums ever offered by the packing industry. Producers who want to raise cattle suited for branded-product marketing will need to do more pen sorting of cattle and to select animals with the genetics to do the job, rather than aiming production at market-average cattle—or buying what grows quickest.

Excel's goal is to help the overall beef industry recapture a larger share of the consumer food market. If the industry prospers because of broader consumer acceptance, Excel expects to earn its share of that increased consumer spending.

The Excel Brand line of 38 boneless beef products was developed with those thoughts in mind. The cuts were test-marketed in conjunction with The Kroger Co. at its Charlotte, NC, stores in June 1986. Success there led to expansion into other Kroger test markets, and during 1987 the products were introduced at other retail supermarkets in 14 States.

Excel Brand beef cuts are now available in about 750 supermarkets. Within 10 years we expect that 60-70 percent of all beef marketed in this country will carry a brand name.

Research Prompts Branding

Branded, individual beef cuts were developed in response to consumer research done in 1985. The National Consumer Retail Beef Study revealed that consumers regard closely trimmed beef as a high-value product with the flavor they prefer. That research also determined that consumers want and will buy new beef products that are leaner and more healthful. It also revealed that they judge leanness primarily by external fat cover—not marbling within the muscle tissue.

Since then, breakthroughs in packaging technology and greater consistency in the type of cattle needed to produce branded products enabled Excel to put its name on individual cuts of beef. Meat-science research at Ohio State University confirms that vacuum packaging of fresh beef extends shelf life and maintains high quality. Studies there found that even after 35 days in a refrigerator, Excel Brand beef ranked higher among trained taste testers for tenderness, juiciness, and flavor than traditionally packaged beef products.

In focus-group marketing research, we found that consumers resent opening conventional tray-packed beef cuts to discover fat or gristle on the other side of their purchase. So we use a clear vacuum package that gives consumers a view of entire cuts of fresh, USDA Choice beef.

Consumer Benefits

The convenience, quality, and shelf life of vacuum-packed, fresh beef appeal to consumers and retailers. For consumers, vacuum-packaged beef cuts can be taken home, put in the refrigerator, and cooked on a moment's notice or kept refrigerated for as long as a week. When properly refrigerated at home, Excel Brand beef stays fresh without freezing for at least 7 days. The beef is ready when the consumer is.

Another advantage for consumers and retailers is that quality control and sanitation are better from processor to consumer. Excel Brand products are cut, trimmed to one-quarter inch or less of external fat, and vacuum packaged in the strict, hygienic atmosphere of a food plant, which greatly reduces the risk of contamination. The oxygen-free environment of vacuum packaging prolongs freshness because bacteria that attack conventionally wrapped beef cannot grow.

We have found that many consumers recognize the freshness and other advantages the packaging offers. They seem to like it because it doesn't leak, it lets them see the entire piece of meat, and it provides better protection from freezer burn than conventional wrap if they ultimately decide to freeze a beef cut. Printed information and a point-of-purchase videotape explain to first-time buyers that once the vacuum seal is broken and oxygen reaches the beef, it changes from deep red to the rosy red color they expect.

Retailer Benefits

Retailers like the products' 30-day shelf life and freshness dating, which enable them to assure freshness without freezing for at least 7 days after consumer purchase—a big improvement over the 3-day shelf life of traditionally wrapped products.

Economics also favors Excel's branded products, even with the more expensive package. Branded meat reduces in-store production costs and product shrinkage. Meat departments can be assured of consistent, high-quality beef cuts without the added cost or inconvenience of packaging those cuts and disposing of

*Consumers and retailers appreciate the consistent high quality and
extended freshness offered by vacuum-packaged Excel Brand beef cuts.
Consumers can see the entire cut of meat before buying and no "buy-
freeze-thaw" routine is necessary to keep beef choices fresh. (Excel
Corporation)*

excess bone and trim that result
when they have to cut boxed beef
into individual tray-packed cuts.

With Excel Brand beef, meat-
department personnel simply open a
box and stock the display case. Excel
preweighs and preprices individual
cuts at the processing plant according
to price-list directions from individual
markets. This gives butchers more
time to answer consumers' questions,
merchandise products, and prepare
value-added cuts like stuffed pork
chops, beef Wellington, stuffed sole,
and other specialty items offering
consumer convenience.

Another major retailer savings is in
freight costs. Instead of paying shipping costs for carcasses weighing
about 650 pounds or boxed beef
equal to 430 pounds, retailers now
can buy the 230 pounds of marketable, boneless products they could
cut from the other forms.

Lean Cattle Needed

Our branded-beef program focuses
on providing consumers what they
want, and we are paying cattle growers a premium for raising cattle that
have the muscling, tenderness, and
flavor consumers seek. Producing

consistent-quality, leaner beef cuts will require increased cooperation from cattle producers. We need leaner cattle without sacrificing the internal marbling that produces the flavor and tenderness consumers desire.

In the past, the beef industry sold what it produced. From now on, if beef's share of the consumer dollar is to increase, the industry must produce what consumers want.

By instituting a new specification system for purchasing cattle, we've taken the first steps toward achieving the quality of cattle needed to consistently market the beef consumers prefer. Since September 1987, Excel cattle buyers have been using a muscle-scoring system based on an 8-month study of beef specifications that was designed and administered by meat scientists at Kansas State University.

Based on that study, we developed a premium and discount system of buying cattle. Excel is the first packer to pay a designated premium for the cattle it prefers. We are working with cattle producers and breed associations to explain how the specifications will help meet consumers' demands.

Striving for consistency in beef production helps processors and cattle producers in their competition with other sectors of the meat industry. The animals earning premiums have the following characteristics:

1. Hanging carcass weight averaging 600-800 pounds, with 625-725 pounds being the range used for Excel Brand beef.

2. A minimum of 0.2-inch and maximum of 0.5-inch 12th-rib fat cover

3. A minimum rib-eye area of 1.8 inches long per 100 pounds carcass weight, and a maximum rib-eye size of 15.5 inches.

4. Carcass composition in the upper half of the No. 1 USDA feeder-grade

muscle score, which will meet specifications for rib-eye size per 100 pounds of carcass weight.

The buying system scores carcass muscling on a scale of 1 to 5, with USDA quality grade also considered in pricing. Producers marketing live cattle with muscle scores of 1 and 2 are paid a dressed-weight premium of $2 per hundredweight above the base market price Excel pays for cattle with a score of 3. Number 4 cattle are discounted $1 per hundredweight and number 5 cattle are discounted $10 per hundredweight.

Promoting this approach to cattle production and pricing will help fill branded-beef packages with cuts consumers desire. It also will help reinforce in consumers' minds that they can rely on beef to provide a consistently satisfying eating experience.

Learning from the Past

Excel initiated the branded-beef and beef-specification buying programs to prevent going the way of the old-line packers. Those packers were not attuned to consumer demand and did not adopt new industry technology, so they were forced to reduce beef processing or give it up entirely. When feedlot operations developed away from large cities, packing plants that moved near them saved in transportation costs and developed more efficient facilities and packaging such as boxed beef. The beef industry is just recovering from that lack of foresight, which contributed to the loss of markets to poultry processors who branded their products much earlier.

If the beef industry works as a team to meet consumer demand, the Nation's feedlot operators, ranchers, cattle breeders, processors, and retailers can meet the challenges of the future successfully. Otherwise, the business is going to be taken by others who are more in tune with the public demands.

Frieda's Finest—Promoting Specialty Produce

Karen Caplan, president and chief operating officer, Frieda's Finest/Produce Specialties, Inc., Los Angeles, CA

Thanks to my mother, Frieda Caplan, I can cook! Her method was unique. I was just over 3 months old when Frieda went to work in the produce business. She wanted a job with flexible hours so that she could take care of me. She got a job with relatives on the Los Angeles Produce Market in the accounting department. Nearly 2 years later, in November 1957, she began to "dabble" in sales. California Brown Mushrooms were the first items she sold. And by June 1958, my younger sister Jackie was born, and my career in "cooking" began.

Produce Specialties, Inc.

In April 1962, with the encouragement of her growers, Frieda opened Produce Specialties, Inc. on the Los Angeles Produce Market. As the first woman there, she began attracting new growers offering new produce items, and her career in specialty and exotic produce was launched.

As a 9-year-old, I remember getting up with my mother at 1 a.m. to eat breakfast. She had to be at the produce market at 2 a.m. to sell her goods. She'd drive off at close to 1:30 a.m. to downtown Los Angeles. Jackie and I would call her as we left for school and when we got home. She'd get home after 5 p.m. each afternoon.

So I began my cooking career at an early age. First, it was breakfast for Jackie and me before school. Then, as we got older, Dad and Mom expected dinner on the table when they got home from their respective jobs. Business was always *the* topic of discussion at the dinner table. Dad talked about his labor relation clients. Mom listened intently and planned visits to the mushroom farms near Ventura, CA.

What a promoter and an opportunist my mother was! When we moved into the house we grew up in, my father planted orange trees, pomegranate, and guava bushes—and nepal apples were in between the hibiscus bushes.

Frieda marketed our first crop of guavas and pomegranates at the produce market (we'd pick them in the afternoon after school and she would transport them to work in the back of her station wagon). Jackie and I would go door-to-door selling 5- and 10-pound sacks of fresh picked oranges.

We ate everything that mom was selling. We always sliced up kiwifruit in fruit salads whenever we had guests. We each got our own big, brown paper shopping bag to set next to our chair when we ate artichokes dipped in butter. Most of my friends had never *heard* of an artichoke, much less eaten one for dinner.

Spaghetti squash, sugar snap peas, sunchokes (Jerusalem artichokes), alfalfa sprouts, mangoes—these were the foods that we ate regularly at our house. So, as the official family cook (by default), I quickly learned what to do with these "strange" foods.

Company Name Changes

When I graduated from the University of California at Davis in 1977 with a degree in Agricultural Economics and Business Management, I came to work full time for Frieda's Finest/ Produce Specialties, Inc. (we had changed our company name). One of Frieda's trusted business associates had convinced me to come into the business with my mother—to offer continuity to our business, and to our vendors and customers.

We were still on the produce market, occupying five doors between two of the biggest houses on the 7th Street Market.

My directive from Frieda was clear at that time. She allowed me several years to learn every aspect of the business. I sold produce on the floor starting at 2 a.m. each morning. On Saturdays, I filled orders and delivered them. I took product inventory every day (in 36° coolers—where your pen freezes up if you don't write fast enough).

By that time, consumer letters were flowing in at a steady pace. In March 1972, because of extra room on the back of a label, we had established our famous "Dear Customer" offer. We encouraged shoppers (and still do) to write to us and tell us what they bought and where they bought it, and to ask any questions they had, and we promised to send them free recipes.

Part of my job was to answer any unusual complaints or questions. These inquiries from consumers allowed us to find out the answers to many questions we had ourselves. And because of our interest in finding out the answers to *any* and *all* questions that came to us, we became a friendly and frequent contact for many Government agencies, research facilities, and universities, not to mention cooking schools, food editors, and seed companies.

My next assignment was to "Get to know every food editor in America...personally." I had never taken a public speaking class in my life, yet by age 23 I was speaking to a group of prestigious food editors at a national conference in Southern California. Enoki mushrooms, shiitake mushrooms, wheatgrass, and spaghetti squash were some of the items I talked about. My experience in cooking really came in handy by this time. At my apartment in Hollywood, I developed and tested recipes for all our new products. When I spoke with the food editors about questions from their readers, I was well prepared to answer them with real life experience. How to choose one, how to store it, do I cook it? What does it taste like raw? Cooked? If I didn't know, I found out.

By 1979, things had changed in our office and I was suddenly thrust into sales. I had never taken a psychology or sales class. But there I was, calling retailers all over the United States and Canada. And what did they tell me? "That stuff won't sell in our city!" "The price is too high," "I don't like your shipping containers."

Packaging Redesigned

After a trip to Super Duper, a supermarket in Erie, PA, I saw firsthand what our containers and our packaging looked like at their destination. As I set up my first produce department, I learned about eye-catching packaging and how to group products.

That's when things really began to change and evolve at our company. We redesigned our shipping containers with our retail distribution center customers in mind. We used bright white boxes with purple printing; big, clear lettering with proper storage information on every box; proper ventilation holes; and adequate stacking strength.

As the pioneers of shipping produce by air container in wide-bodied planes, we had already concluded that offering "specialty produce" in smaller than "normal units such as individual trays or bags made it much more affordable to ship by air.

We did the same thing with our consumer packaging. All of our packaging was designed and priced to be sold under $1 at retail. Of course, with inflation and increased retail margins, we now aim to sell under $2 a package.

Our consumer packaging included bold, easy-to-read lettering; purple labels, stickers, and headers; recipes on every package (by 1983 we hired our own home economist to develop our recipes under my guidance and direction); and UPC bar codes (as retail scanning became a reality).

Moving Saves Money

In November 1982, I approached Frieda with a rather outrageous idea. Let's move *off* the produce market and consolidate our operation at our distribution center. Thanks to a Dale Carnegie seminar and one of the men I worked with at Frieda's Finest (who later became my husband), I pointed out that we could save more than $134,000 annually by moving. Well, dollars talk. On August 26, 1983, we moved into our present facility where things started changing more quickly than ever before.

Our sales staff had grown to five people besides myself (when I first joined Frieda in 1977, most sales were done by Frieda, assisted by someone taking care of national sales and another handling local sales).

We began innovating like no other wholesale distributor had ever done before. We hired a director of field services to visit some of our growers when they needed help or advice. We established our Consumer and Information Services Department to

handle all the consumer and media inquiries that we were now getting daily (by December 1984, we had received 100,000 letters).

We were packing most of our own products at our facility starting at 4 a.m. By packing daily we were able to offer our retail accounts the freshest possible products, longer shelf life, and hand-inspected quality.

As one of the first wholesalers to exhibit at our industry trade shows, we began traveling several times a year to "show our wares" at Produce Marketing Association conventions. We designed and constructed a 20-foot-long booth to showcase more than 150 items we had to offer retailers.

With no real retail experience, we began training retail produce managers on how to properly merchandise specialty produce to maximize their in-store traffic, sales, and profits, and to reduce shrink. We campaigned to get store owners to build and expand their produce departments. Studies were beginning to show how profitable produce was, and its real contribution to gross margin.

Our publicity is impressive. Just about every week we get a phone call from a writer doing a story for a national publication. Or a radio or television producer calls to do a segment. If it has anything to do with cooking, I take it, since Frieda can't cook.

We are now faced with a new challenge. Many farm advisers, researchers, farmers, and even politicians see "specialty" produce as a solution to the economic dilemma facing many farmers. "Grow specialty crops and your troubles will be over" seems to be a popular—and *scary*—decree.

Since our company has spent 26 years building produce departments, advising farmers, developing recipes, marketing programs, and answering consumer concerns, I can assure you that to overproduce a product for a somewhat limited market can guarantee disaster.

More than 10 years ago, a large farming concern owned by a large oil company came to us asking about thousands of acres of bare farmland. They wanted to plant 50 acres of anything we thought would have potential in the future. Fifty acres? When we talk with our small groups of farmers we suggest 5 *rows* of a new item. Because of our convincing story, the large farming concern backed off and went into other, more well-known crops such as grapes and tree fruit.

Beware Overproduction

How many farmers can make it selling 100 cases a week of Baby Gold Beets? Or 5,000 cases a week of Belgian Endive? Because of the high retail prices and attractive returns, we see the next few years as a real challenge as we watch many farmers and conglomerates getting into the spe cialty produce business.

And we expect to watch them get out, too. Just this past year, a large grocery concern started a venture with "snacking vegetables." After a year in test-marketing, they dropped it—not enough volume.

We welcome new products to evaluate. We now have a plant pathologist and a Grower Relations Department; Frieda and I work closely with both to evaluate new products and seek new items to market. Our home economist comes in several times a month and together we evaluate, test, and develop new recipes.

We're very selective now. And very challenged. And very lucky! In the retail business, produce directors, vice presidents of perishables, and owners of companies call us daily to help them make their stores more profitable and to give them the edge over their competition. And in between calls—I'm still cooking!

Fruit and Vegetable Varieties: New and More Marketable

Howard J. Brooks, national program leader, Agricultural Research Service, Beltsville, MD

The abundance and variety of fruits and vegetables in grocery stores and roadside markets is the result of several centuries of plant introductions from Europe, Asia, and Central and South America, and of several decades of scientific plant breeding. Earliest inhabitants of North America found only a few fruits, such as blueberries, blackberries, and strawberries, and none of the vegetable crops grown for market today. Most of our important fruit and vegetable crops were imported early on by the Indians from Central and South America and by the European colonists.

In recent years, agricultural scientists have extended the number and variety of fruits and vegetables we take for granted in the marketplace. They carefully select plant parents, apply pollen from one plant to another, and patiently evaluate millions of hybrid offspring in search of better plants. These plant breeders, who work for USDA's Agricultural Research Service (ARS), State universities and experiment stations, and private industry, have made tremendous improvements during the last 85 years using the tools of modern genetics. Today, our fruits and vegetables are flavorful, nutritious, pest-free, and essential to our health. We consume more and more of them each year—now about 400 pounds per person.

Consumer Determines Varieties

Of course, it is today's consumer who ultimately determines what kinds of varieties the plant breeder develops and the wholesaler and retailer make available for sale.

The farmer grows only what will sell. Color and appearance are important characteristics to the consumer, but more important are flavor, nutritional quality, shelf life, and food safety.

Meeting Producer Requirements

The public and private fruit and vegetable breeders also must serve the producers. New varieties are needed that have high yields, ship well, and have tolerance to insects, diseases, nematodes, and air pollutants. Tolerance to cold, heat, and drought are equally important, and many of our new varieties have these characteristics.

New Vegetable Varieties

Potatoes

Today's potato varieties are good examples of scientific achievement through plant breeding. By collecting wild relatives in Peru where potatoes are thought to have originated, we now have varieties adapted to specific production areas in the United States and specific uses—for baking, french fries, chipping, and dehydration. Potatoes and potato products have become increasingly important in our diets. On average, each American now consumes about 140 pounds of potatoes per year.

Carrots

The carrot, which originated in Afghanistan, is now considered an essential vegetable in our diet and is the leading plant source of vitamin A. New varieties with greatly increased vitamin A content have been jointly developed by ARS and State scientists. These new carrot varieties are freely available to developing countries worldwide, where vitamin A deficiency is much more common than in the United States. In addition, carrots are an important source of fiber that reduces cholesterol in the bloodstream.

Lettuce

Varieties introduced from the ARS lettuce-breeding program at Salinas, CA, now account for about 60 percent of U.S. lettuce acreage. Lettuce was introduced from the Mediterranean area, but our present varieties bear little resemblance to the original wild types that were nonheading and bitter. Fortunately, our breeders were developing improved lettuce varieties long before the recent year-round public interest in fresh salads.

Cucumbers and Onions

The cucumber introduced from India and the onion introduced from Afghanistan also have been greatly improved through breeding techniques. We have fresh and pickling cucumber varieties of different shapes and sizes and an equal array of onion varieties. Resisto, a new, high-yielding sweet potato variety developed from the ARS Vegetable Laboratory at Charleston, SC, is resistant to 14 different insect, nematode, and disease pests. The germplasm used originally came from Central and South America. The Charleston Gray variety of watermelon introduced earlier from this laboratory has long been the standard of excellence, but breeding research continues to develop even better varieties.

Beans

Bean breeders at Beltsville, MD, have introduced many new snap bean varieties resistant to the bean rust fungus that causes unsightly blemishes and makes the beans unsalable. They also have recently introduced high-yielding, highly flavored, drought-tolerant lima bean varieties.

Other Vegetables

With ARS breeding programs on tomatoes, peppers, okra, asparagus, cabbage, broccoli, and sweet corn and many State and private industry programs on these and other vegetable crops, the U.S. farmer and consumer have reasonable assurances that new, improved high-quality vegetable varieties will continue to be marketed to satisfy the ever-changing needs of consumers.

New Fruit Varieties

Our fruit breeders have had an even more difficult assignment. All of the tree fruit crops originated outside the United States and had to be introduced and adapted to this country's diverse climate and soils. These crops include apples, pears, peaches, nectarines, plums, apricots, cherries, wine grapes, figs, oranges, grapefruit, bananas, mango, papaya, avocado, and dates. One parent species of our commercial strawberry came from Chile, but the other parent species was the small, highly flavored wild meadow strawberry still found growing in abandoned fields in Northeastern States. Blueberries, cranberries, and certain blackberry, raspberry, and grape species are native to the United States, and it is appropriate that ARS and many individual States have active breeding programs.

Blueberries, Blackberries, and Strawberries

ARS at Beltsville has had a long history of breeding small fruit crops—blueberries, blackberries, strawberries, and raspberries. The Northern highbush blueberry program started in 1910 using the largest of small berries from the wild. Through careful selection of parents, and saving only those hybrid seedlings with good flavor, color, size, and shipping quality, consumers now have improved varieties that exceed 1 inch in diameter, are highly flavored and attractive, and have excellent shipping quality. While wild blueberries are soft and unsuited for shipment, these new varieties ship well, and some fruit is now being exported to Europe for the fresh fruit market. This export market is expected to increase as world markets expand to include U.S. fruit not previously exported.

Many State universities have been involved in the ARS breeding program on Northern blueberries and now new cooperative programs are improving the native rabbiteye blueberry for the Southern States. One might wonder if those big delicious blueberries available in our markets today need any improvement at all and if the breeders have not already reached the ultimate in flavor, appearance, and shipping quality. But the breeders see other opportunities through continued breeding. They are sure the size can be increased further, if that is what the consumer wants, but they also see the potential for plant adaptation to different soil types and increased tolerance to cold and insect and disease pests. Such improvements would further reduce the cost of production and market prices to consumers and would encourage an expansion in home gardening as well.

The ARS breeding programs for blackberries and strawberries started about 1920 and have been continuous ever since. The blackberry is not commonly found in the eastern marketplace as a fresh fruit, largely because of the disease problems, so this wonderful fruit is now used primarily for jams, jellies, and juice. However, after many years of research, ARS breeders at Beltsville have developed disease-tolerant, high-quality, high-yielding varieties without thorns on the canes. The absence of thorns is especially good news for growers and pickers. These varieties are particularly well suited for fresh market uses and juice and have led to renewed interest in home garden and commercial production.

Unlike many fruit crops, each strawberry variety is adapted to a rather restricted geographic area. For this reason, ARS and State scientists have worked closely together to jointly develop and introduce varieties for each production area. Emphasis has been on the maintenance of flavor found in the wild strawberry; good firmness and general appearance needed for the marketplace; resistance to disease, insects, and nematode pests; tolerance to frost, cold, and heat stress; and, of course, yield and adaptability. The University of California has had a particularly successful breeding program, and large, beautiful fresh strawberries are now available from California for about 11 months of the year. Contrast this market availability to earlier years—when fresh strawberries were available for only 2-4 weeks in the early summer.

Peaches

Much progress has been made in the quality and availability of fresh peaches (and nectarines which are genetically the same as the peach but without fuzz on the skin). The peach is thought to have originated in China and been introduced into the United States from Europe. The wild peaches in China ripen in late summer and have small, hard, hairy, nearly inedible fruit with white flesh. Plant breeders have used this poor plant material as parents and developed the many large, yellow-fleshed, high-quality, early-season peach varieties we now expect and find in our produce markets nationwide. It is a considerable achievement, yet additional improvements are expected. Current objectives of State and Federal breeding programs include breeding for increased tolerance to cold and resistance to many disease, insect, and nematode pests. Environmental stress and pests greatly reduce efficient production by the farmer and increase costs to consumers.

Grapes

Consumers have also benefited from ARS research on improved table grapes. Since most people prefer seedless grapes over seeded varieties, a long-term objective was to develop seedless varieties that could be shipped long distances. Though it is extremely difficult to develop seedless grape varieties, research at the USDA Horticultural Research Station at Fresno, CA, resulted in the Flame Seedless variety, introduced in 1973. This new red variety, sometimes sold as Red Flame in the market, has been extremely well received by both growers and consumers. It is well flavored, attractive, firm for shipping, and individual fruits stay on the bunch rather than shattering. The Fresno station has introduced 42 improved varieties of grapes, peaches, nectarines, plums, and apricots.

Citrus Fruit

The origin of citrus, particularly grapefruit, is not well established. It is known that Southeastern Asia is the center of origin and that citrus has been under cultivation for several thousand years. Oranges were introduced in Florida in the early 1830's but were killed by a freeze in 1835. The grapefruit was introduced in the 1880's, and the value of citrus as a new crop was soon recognized. California and Florida, as well as USDA, initiated citrus improvement programs about the turn of the century.

Primary objectives in citrus breeding are to develop varieties that are more tolerant to cold, diseases, and insects and have increased consumer acceptance. Important fruit characteristics are interior fruit color, juice color, the sugar-acid ratio, the absence or reduction of seeds, and of course flavor. Collectively, these characteristics equate to market quality. The ARS citrus breeding program at Orlando, FL, has cold hardiness as a primary objective. A citrus species known to survive as far north as Pennsylvania is one species used as a cold-tolerant parent even though the fruit is small, sour, and inedible. Some of these citrus hybrids have survived cold temperatures as low as 7 °F. During the 1983 Florida freeze that killed or severely damaged 25 percent of commercial plantings, these hybrids survived and will continue to be used as parents in the breeding program.

It may be many years before more cold-hardy, high-quality citrus varieties can be commercially introduced. It should be reassuring to growers and consumers, however, to know that such a long-term Federal breeding program exists and that progress can be made. ARS has already developed 21 new improved citrus varieties, 3 during 1987, but these recently introduced varieties still do not have all of the cold tolerance desired.

Other Fruits and Nuts

Other ARS tree fruit and nut breeding programs are underway on pears, apricots, plums, avocados, mangos, carambola, passion fruit, pecans, and walnuts. This is long-term research to provide improved varieties that are needed for our expanding markets.

Marketing Ben & Jerry's Equals Fun

Jeff Durstewitz, franchisee, Ben & Jerry's, Saratoga Springs, NY

Several years ago at a meeting of Ben & Jerry's Ice Cream franchises in Vermont, one of the store owners raised his hand and addressed a comment to Ben Cohen, president and cofounder of the fast-growing company. Cohen had just given an overview of the company's history and was relating his own business philosophy to the franchise experience.

"You're forgetting the major thing, Ben," the franchisee said.

"Oh, really, what's that?" asked Cohen.

"Marketing, marketing, marketing, marketing," the franchisee said.

The comment served to emphasize one of the key concerns of all retailers: How does the company present its products to the public?

But although Cohen had not been discussing the subject specifically, Ben & Jerry's always has been a keen marketer of its products since its inception in a refurbished gas station in downtown Burlington, VT, in May 1978. But where other companies have used the services of professional marketers, Ben & Jerry's has had a more integral approach—marketing by the seat of its pants.

That approach has always centered around the basic appeal of the product—which is, after all, ice cream. It's cold, it's delicious, it's fun,

Ben & Jerry's, which began in a refurbished gas station in downtown Burlington, VT in 1978, has gone from sales of under $1 million in 1983 to about $30 million in 1987. They now sell 34 flavors of ice cream. (Lynn Jarvis)

Ben Cohen, left, and Jerry Greenfield use simple marketing strategies—bold, funny graphics, free ice cream—to encourage word-of-mouth advertising, and lots of community support through donating ice cream for charity benefits. (Gary Clayton Hall)

and that's what Ben & Jerry's has always sought to stress. Another major theme is the "all-naturalness" of Ben & Jerry's, plus the fact that it is the first major brand of superpremium ice cream in the United States without a foreign-sounding name. And the fact that it is made in Vermont with all Vermont milk and cream products. As Cohen says he discovered early on, "Vermont has a very positive image."

In the beginning, when Ben Cohen and Jerry Greenfield set out to build a modest ice cream business in Burlington, they had a few basic goals in mind. The first was to make a living, of course, since they had put their life savings, about $8,000, into the venture. The second was to have fun at it, an aim they were well positioned to achieve, since they were their own bosses and were selling America's favorite dessert. The third was perhaps a bit more altruistic: They would produce superior-tasting ice cream and give a substantial portion of the profits back to the community.

Their Marketing Strategies

From the first, their marketing strategies were simple. The graphics at their store had to be striking enough to distract attention from its furnishings, which were mainly hand-me-downs purchased at used-equipment sales. And the graphics, designed and executed by a young artist named Lyn Severance, did the job perfectly: They were bold, colorful, funny, and told stories. To this day, customers at Ben & Jerry's stores (which now number more than 50) still comment on the great graphics—usually right after commenting on the great ice cream.

With virtually no money for advertising, Ben and Jerry's second major marketing strategy was to give away copious amounts of the product. This way, they reasoned, people would have even more fun when they came to the store; they would not only spread the word about how good the product was, but also would sing their praises as well. Anything to get the word out! Just about any excuse was good enough for Cohen and Greenfield to give away ice cream. When Jerry was scooping, pretty girls got free cones as long as his girlfriend wasn't around; on Mother's Day they gave away cones to anyone who conceivably could be a mother and double scoops to anyone who visibly had conceived; on the anniversary of their first day in business they staged a "Free Cone Day," during which the cash register was closed and customers could keep coming back for as many freebies as they could hold.

Being children in the 1960's, they also had a strong feeling that their business should be involved in a positive way with the community. So they supported as many community events as they could, giving away hundreds of pounds of ice cream in the process. Most of the events they took part in were festivals or other types of celebrations, which again reinforced one of their basic thrusts: Ben & Jerry's equals fun. It is probably true that scarcely any celebratory public events happened in and around Burlington, VT., without the participation— usually personal—of Ben and Jerry.

Another element of the "fun" theme was the names of the flavors themselves. Ben and Jerry turned the familiar Heavenly Hash into their own devastating "Dastardly Mash." The huge sundae sold at retail outlets is called, fittingly, the Vermonster. Since it weighs in at about 6½ pounds, the name is hardly an exaggeration. And suggestions from their customers are always appreciated. Both "Cherry Garcia" and "Chunky Monkey" flavors were submitted by fans of Ben & Jerry's ice cream.

The Right Graphics

The company's main logo is a primitive but striking picture of a round, bearded man—presumably Ben

himself—making ice cream in an old-style rock salt freezer. The company still uses that image on its pint containers and in other applications, in addition to the picture—now familiar as well—of Ben and Jerry themselves sampling their product. The picture, which seemed to sum up the ideas that Ben and Jerry were two real people who believe in making great ice cream and having fun in the process, has been replicated hundreds of thousands of times on pint lids, posters, and postcards.

What effect have these images had? It is impossible to gauge precisely, but the figures speak for themselves. Ben & Jerry's has gone from sales of under $1 million in 1983 to about $30 million in 1987. And that growth has occurred with an advertising budget that most other companies of similar size would find downright embarrassing.

Good Copy

Another major element in the Ben & Jerry's marketing story has been the tremendous amount of favorable publicity the company's activities have generated.

Most of this has occurred of its own accord—Ben & Jerry's simply makes good copy. But beyond that, the company made a conscious decision to serve up all kinds of news, not just glowing self-congratulation, in order to get the attention of the media. The reasoning was that editors and news directors would sit up and take notice if a company occasionally poked fun at itself. A striking example was the burning of the first "Cowmobile" in 1986.

The Cowmobile was a large old converted mobile home, its sides painted with cows, that was set up to provide free scoops to people in new market areas. Ben and Jerry themselves set off across the country on a "scoopathon," spreading their ice

In addition to ice cream, Ben & Jerry's operates a retail store that boasts one of the largest collections of ice cream and cow-related gifts anywhere. Also sold are Ben & Jerry's T-shirts with "Vermont's Finest" stenciled on the back. (Lynn Jarvis)

cream and good cheer wherever they went. Unfortunately, the engine caught fire on the way back to Vermont from Cleveland, and the Cowmobile burned to scrap, ice cream and all, in about 5 minutes.

Of course, Ben & Jerry's put out a press release. The first sentence was, "It was kind of like a giant baked Alaska." Newspapers and radio stations all across the country picked it up.

Growth Continues

A period of tremendous growth for Ben & Jerry's came in 1985. In June of that year, a new manufacturing plant was brought on line; unfortunately, surging demand made it obsolete, in terms of production capacity, from the day it opened. Ben & Jerry's has been expanding the plant ever since, and today is in the process of opening a second plant to handle its growing novelty business, including such treats as brownie ice cream sandwiches.

A unique feature of the main plant, located in Waterbury, VT, near the Stowe ski resort area, is that it was designed not only as a production facility and corporate headquarters but as a tourist attraction as well. The plant's retail store, which boasts one of the largest collections of ice cream and cow-related gift items anywhere, now does a thriving year-round business. Plant tours (with free samples, of course) draw throngs of visitors, making the Waterbury plant the second most popular tourist attraction in Vermont.

Do It Yourself Marketing Pays

To sum it up, the Ben & Jerry's approach to marketing is a total approach. Today, all marketing and advertising operations are handled in-house.

The message, Greenfield says, is that "When you're really involved on a day-to-day basis with the products you're making and selling, there's no better marketer than yourself."

New Product Development: The Ocean Spray Way

Tom Bullock, vice president, Business Operations, Ocean Spray Cranberries, Inc., Lakeville-Middleboro, MA

New product success is not a haphazard "shot in the dark." It is the end result of carefully laid plans and a deliberate set of goals.

For Ocean Spray Cranberries, Inc., well-known for taking the tart-tasting cranberry and marketing it into a popular beverage, quality and innovation have made it the number one brand name in the canned and bottled juice category.

Perhaps the success of Ocean Spray in bringing new products to market reflects the ability of the cranberry-based cooperative to build new business opportunities from the business it knows—a strategy inherent to the Ocean Spray philosophy—as well as the swiftness with which it turns out and markets new products.

In comparison to that of many food companies, the Ocean Spray approach to new product development employs recognized marketing theory in a very streamlined process. All in all, the making of a product can take 18 months or more from conception to implementation.

"It takes more than a successful brand name for products to make it on the supermarket shelf," says Steve Dinsmore, director of marketing services. His new product development group molds a new product idea into a positioned product concept.

"At Ocean Spray, we do our homework with consumer and technical research before we ever go to market. By the time we go into the marketplace, we've already determined a solid product positioning and we've tested the product as well as the communication message with the consumer."

"Positioning the product correctly in the market is important," says Dinsmore. "Positioning means establishing a clear image and understanding about a new product in the consumer's mind."

This new product development process is based on five successive stages—exploratory, early development, criteria measurement, advanced development, and, finally, test market introduction.

"First, we identify the short- and long-term business needs of the cooperative in terms of new product development," says Dinsmore. "We identify where the greatest opportunities are in the marketplace and develop product ideas that are aimed at addressing those opportunities."

Exploratory Stage

This first stage is broken down into two substages: idea generation, and idea sorting and acceptance. **Idea generation** develops an ongoing program of newly generated product ideas. New product ideas come from a variety of sources, including Ocean Spray employees, formal idea generation sessions, and market trend surveys. "There may literally be hundreds of ideas generated during the exploratory stage," explained Dinsmore.

Several important internal resources are involved early in the exploratory phase of a new product: marketing, research and development

(R&D), and sales. Outside idea consultants also help to develop and narrow down a broad array of ideas to those that are most promising.

According to Dinsmore, the concerted effort of both the new product development team and the R&D team during the inception of new product ideas creates a spirit of partnership and cooperation between both groups.

In the **idea sorting and acceptance** sub-stage, the product development group tries to secure early consumer evaluation of basic core ideas—simple one-line descriptions of the product idea. The object is to narrow the field down to a few truly viable ideas, and try to understand the target audience by further defining consumer receptivity.

Core idea screening studies determine how well the concepts survive when evaluated by a large sample of potential consumers. These screening studies also help to define the competitive frame of reference of the idea and the demographic, psychographic, and lifestyle habits of those consumers most interested in it.

Identifying the target audience helps to determine the consumer frame of reference—the set of products that will be competitive. The team then determines the point of difference—that quality that will make the product different from others within that frame of reference.

At this point, money and capabilities available to develop, produce, and market a given new product concept are assessed. Combined with the research data collected on the targeted consumer audience, the new product development group can set priorities for further development of new product ideas.

Early Development Stage

The second stage also is broken down into two substages: concept

Cranberry harvest in Wisconsin. Some of these cranberries will go into a popular tart-tasting beverage developed by Ocean Spray Cranberries, Inc. (Ocean Spray Cranberries, Inc.)

development and concept evaluation. In the **concept development** substage, the new product team works to execute the core idea into a hypothetical product that is both understandable and relevant to consumers. Several conceptual executions may be developed. These executions, taking the form of a simulated introductory advertisement complete with copy and artwork, must communicate the competitive point of difference or special quality that makes the product different from its competition, uncovered in the exploratory stage.

One point of difference, for example, that Ocean Spray discovered for its Mauna La'i™ guava juice drink product was the "taste of Hawaii." According to Dinsmore, Hawaii is a special, almost magical place in the minds of the American consumer.

"In trying to come up with a point of difference for guava, we tried several other approaches before settling with the Hawaiian motif. The first point we explored with consumers was that guava has five times the vitamin C of orange juice. However, when we tested this point of difference in consumer groups, the idea didn't seem to spark much interest. Another point of difference we tested was that guava is high in natural fiber content. Again, the idea didn't work. It wasn't until we hit upon the imagery of a uniquely Hawaiian fruit variety—the taste of Hawaii—that the concept struck pay dirt."

To develop potential product positioning, Ocean Spray may conduct several focus group sessons. Consumers look at an artistic drawing of the product concept to determine whether the concept communicates its intended message and elicits strong interest.

The new product group may go back to focus group sessions several times to redefine the positionings again and again until they feel they have consistent executions of the "positioned" product concepts.

The early development stage also involves the first "hands on" research and development in the form of rough product prototypes. These prototypes may be shown to consumers for feedback, or they may stimulate further development and even more consumer feedback.

Quantitative concept evaluation, the second substage among large numbers of consumers, determines which, if any, of several alternative positionings offers the greatest business opportunity. Such information will determine if the fully positioned concept is worth pursuing from a business standpoint. If it is not, the new product team may return to the concept development substage to redefine the product concept. The process of new product development is driven by the strategy. The strategy may change; therefore, the process must change to fit it.

"You have to do a lot of thinking before the product is developed, not after the product is in the marketplace," says Dinsmore. "Because once it is there, the marketer loses the power to change the product positioning. Once the consumer has a product positioned in his or her mind, it is difficult and expensive to change that perception."

Criteria Measurement Stage

This third stage evaluates new product concepts that have survived all hurdles so far against specific Ocean Spray new product criteria. This critical assessment evaluates a strong potential new product concept against Ocean Spray capabilities and several strategic and financial requirements. Additionally, management commitment is sought, and greater amounts of resources are deployed against the product.

Once this assessment is made and

consumer needs and product concepts identified, the R&D group begins to develop the product based on the concept developed and tested by the new product team. R&D product development determines the flavor, color, and texture in response to consumer testing. New products are initially developed in the laboratory and are constantly guided by employee and consumer taste testing.

Advanced Development Stage

The fourth stage is the advanced or "report card" stage. The concept/product Home Use Test is commonly used to answer three critical questions: Does the product satisfactorily deliver to consumer expectations of the positioned concept? Can the product sustain usage over time? What are the volume potential and the risk factors surrounding the product?

Test Market Introduction Stage

At Ocean Spray, test marketing is the final stage in the development/research process, not the first stage of national product rollout. This is an important distinction which, if not fully understood or embraced by the organization, could lead to costly mistakes on a national level.

Not until a product has successfully completed the test market evaluation phase is it ready for introduction. The business operations group then markets the product, again using a predetermined formula.

Formula for Success

The Ocean Spray marketing formula is simple: Take the product story directly to the consumer early in the introduction of the product and often. Followup programs include cooperative merchandising, couponing promotions, and merchandiser support.

"The trade gives us a lot of support, because they know that we will reinforce their efforts with television and point-of-sale materials," says Kevin Murphy, director of business operations. "After a product is up and running, we continue to support it with TV advertising."

Ocean Spray continues to be a strong advertiser and was the leading advertiser of canned and bottled beverages in 1987.

According to Murphy, the nine Ocean Spray juice products introduced between 1981 and 1987 were successful. All nine applied the same product development process, including newer product introductions such as CRAN•RASPBERRY® and Pink Grapefruit Juice Cocktail.

Other Major Roles

Working side by side with the manufacturing and product development departments is the Packaging Engineering Department. The packaging group tries to identify a package that satisfies not only marketing objectives but also technical, manufacturing, and purchasing objectives.

The key areas that play a major role in the making of a new product, in addition to the new product development and R&D group efforts, are the law department, graphic services, manufacturing, and logistics groups.

At the same time, advertising and packaging are being developed to determine the best way to inform the consumer and to deliver the new product to the consumer's table.

Look at the Record

It takes a lot of time, energy, and money to consistently introduce quality products in a competitive marketplace, but Ocean Spray has been doing it—and doing it well. With sales of $735 million in fiscal 1987, Ocean Spray's success in the food and beverage industry cannot be ignored.

Commercializing Promising Technologies

Paul F. O'Connell, deputy administrator, Special Programs, Cooperative State Research Service

Many people think that new ideas flow easily from the research bench to the marketplace. Nothing could be further from the truth. Scientific laboratories and libraries are overflowing with alternative techniques for producing, processing, and marketing agricultural products. Some of these techniques are ready for adoption and others are not. Sorting out the most promising ones is difficult and time consuming.

An estimated 90 percent of the cost of research and development is development. Development—demonstrating the usefulness of a promising technology—includes growing and harvesting technology, raw materials handling systems, processing and extraction technology, market identification and promotion, business planning, and formation of grower cooperatives and associations. The purpose of development is twofold: to prepare the farm sector to grow and sell a material for a new use and to prepare industry to buy, process, and market the product.

The weakest link in the U.S. economy is transferring promising technologies from "Idea Generation" to "Interim Manufacturing" stages. There is little strategic planning or investment in phasing out obsolete technologies and developing new ones that satisfy changing markets.

Loss of Markets

Public-supported agricultural research and education have always had a close working relationship with producers of food, fiber, and forest products. Most of the effort has been on production—increasing yield per acre, animal unit, or hours of labor. That was fine when the United States fed, clothed, and sheltered its own citizens and exports were continually expanding. We now must compete with other producers. We import $20.1 billion of agricultural products plus $13.3 billion of forestry products, $4.8 billion of edible fish and shellfish, and more of imported industrial feedstocks that could be obtained from U.S. farms and forests. For 1987, the value of agricultural, fish, and forest product exports was $36.3 billion, down 31 percent from 1981.

On April 4, 1987, Congressman Larry Hopkins told his constituents in central Kentucky, "Farmers must diversify into alternative enterprises." Gross income from tobacco sales in Kentucky was cut in half between 1984 and 1986, and corn income was down 40.5 percent. Hopkins continued, "The question isn't whether our farmers can grow nontraditional crops or begin new farm enterprises—they can. But will they? Are they really convinced they won't always be able to count on tobacco and corn and livestock? And if they do go into supplemental crops, where will they sell their harvest? Where will they store it? Where will they process it, or freeze it, if necessary? How will they move it to market?"

Similar questions are being asked by sugarcane farmers in Hawaii

Agricultural, Fish, and Forestry Products
(Changing Trade Balance for U.S.)

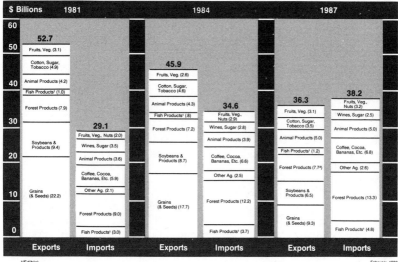

¹(Edible)
²1986 figures

February, 1988

(world price of sugar is now one-third the domestic price), corn producers in Nebraska, wheat farmers in Kansas, and many others. Given uncertain market situations, especially in the international arena, what can the United States do to expand the market base for its farmers?

Tapping Our Own Market

One possible solution is to put promising technologies for farm products in the hands of private investors to provide these markets. We need to explore domestic opportunities—especially where we depend heavily on imports. Every other country is anxious to target U.S. markets. Why shouldn't U.S. scientists, technical specialists, processors, material handlers, venture capitalists, and marketers put their heads together and find a way to tap one of the best markets in the world. This doesn't mean that export markets shouldn't

be aggressively pursued, but let's also explore opportunities within our own borders.

Public/Private Partnership

In the United States, private and public institutions have often mistrusted each other. An entrepreneur sees public institutions as tax collectors or regulators, unaccountable for the bottom line. A civil servant sees business as having a short time horizon, focusing primarily on making money, and having inadequate concern for broad public interests such as environmental and social issues. These stereotype images are common enough to prevent needed bridge building.

Many research programs are funded by universities and the Federal Government because payroll is too long term and uncertain for the private sector. Commercialization of promising technologies has similar incentive problems, but is not quite as elusive. Therefore a partnership is the answer. Joint private/public ventures are needed because very little happens without a combined effort. A joint partnership helps share the risk, especially in the early stages. And we must recognize the significant costs and market uncertainties associated with technology adoption.

The private sector has a key role to play in the process because people experienced in buying and selling goods are best able to identify the market. The private sector also should provide a product champion, that is, a firm or individual that believes in the ultimate commercial success of a particular product. A project should be based on solid analysis, but the success of any given venture most often depends on someone who strongly believes in the final outcome. Industry members of a commercialization team have the knowledge and experience to identify the best market opportunities and the most useful knowledge and technologies to meet changing competitive conditions. They also understand why private sector initiative provides the most flexible and efficient mechanism for producing, processing, and marketing agricultural products.

Government/academic partnerships can provide well-trained researchers and technology transfer specialists with a long-term view; a network of State and Federal Government contacts who can reduce regulatory red tape; and seed money. They also can bring production, processing, and marketing sectors together. Often not enough incentive is present in any one sector to adopt promising technologies, but together the incentives can often be sufficient.

A commercially successful and profitable enterprise does not always require a joint effort. Private sector initiatives frequently create new markets for farmers. In many instances, however, the barrier to commercialization is management of resources with which to link agricultural production to the processing and marketing sector. When appropriate, a catalyst organization can provide that linkage by actively organizing and promoting the final stage of product development with a relatively small public obligation. Time is of the essence for developing promising ideas. If the appropriate moment is not seized, the advantage of early adoption will occur elsewhere, most often by a foreign competitor.

Active Demonstration Projects

In recent years the Special Projects Unit in the Cooperative State Research Service has been bridging the gap between research results and commercialization with demonstration projects. These projects are short term, usually 3 to 5 years, with public/private partnerships established through USDA cooperative agreements. Capitalizing on decades of public research—generally by the Agricultural Research Service or State Agricultural Experiment Stations—the demonstration projects are designed to build, within the private sector, a base on which to sustain new agricultural industries. The kenaf, guayule, and hybrid striped bass projects demonstrate the success of this approach.

Kenaf Project
Kenaf is an annual, nonwood fiber crop that grows from seedling to 10 feet in less than 5 months and can be transformed from seedling to newsprint in less than 7 months. It grows across the southern tier of the United States. Newsprint is normally made from wood such as northern spruce and southern pine. The United States imports about 60 percent of its newsprint supply from Canada at an annual cost of $3 billion.

The Kenaf Demonstration Project began in March 1986 with a cooperative agreement between USDA and Kenaf International—a venture capital firm and the product champion for kenaf. This agreement marked the reopening of research and development for kenaf in USDA after an 8-year hiatus. The project's principle objective was to gain acceptance for kenaf as a source fiber for the manufacture of newsprint. To accomplish this objective, a Kenaf Task Force was established involving participation of a venture-capital company, private laboratories, processing and pulping plants, equipment manufacturers, and the American Newspaper Publisher's Association—a prime mover in the search for a substitute newsprint fiber.

Initial results showed that kenaf has distinct price and quality advantages. For example, it uses less ink, is stronger, results in whiter paper, and requires less energy for processing. Kenaf International and CIP Forest Products already have announced plans to build a $300-million kenaf newsprint mill in South Texas for operation in 1990. The anticipated acreage needed to fill the mill's annual needs is 40,000 acres of unsubsidized kenaf.

And this is just the beginning. The newsprint industry estimates that it will need 19 new mills of similar size by the year 2000 to meet estimated demand. If one-half of these were kenaf mills, U.S. farmers would have a market for 375,000 acres of kenaf.

Guayule Project

The United States is totally dependent on imported natural rubber—a commodity of critical importance to the Nation's defense position and the economy. Approximately 750,000 metric tons are imported at an annual cost of $1 billion. Natural rubber has performance specifications not available in its synthetic alternative, and is preferred in applications that require elasticity, resilience, tackiness, and low heat buildup. Natural rubber is indispensable for automobile, bus, truck, and airplane tires; it has extended the lifespan of radial tires. Natural rubber constitutes 30 percent of the total domestic rubber market.

Of some 2,000 plant species known to contain rubber, only a few have ever produced sufficient quantities for commercial use. The two most common sources are the rubber tree (*Hevea brasiliensis*) grown principally in Southeast Asia (where 90 percent of the world's supply of natural rubber originates) and guayule (*Parthenium argentatum*) native to semiarid regions of North America. In contrast to the rubber tree, guayule is a small desert shrub averaging 3 feet tall.

Under a 27-month guayule domestic rubber project signed in 1986 with USDA, the Defense Department is providing $11 million to build and operate a prototype processing plant in Arizona that will process 275 acres of guayule shrub into 50 tons of natural rubber, 100 tons of resin and low molecular weight rubber, and 1,600 tons of plant residue. Also cooperating on this project are the Firestone Tire and Rubber Company, Gila River Indian Community, and four southwestern land-grant universities—located in Arizona, California, Texas, and New Mexico. Over this same period, USDA plans to invest about $4.5 million in guayule research and development.

With today's technology and current prices for natural rubber, a domestic industry is not economically viable. An economic model indicates a farmer growing guayule would have positive cash flow in 1995 if the following technological improvements could be realized: 1) doubling per-acre yields of rubber and byproducts,

Extension agricultural engineer John Hoccheimer measures two hybrid striped bass at the Walnut Point Farm near Chestertown, MD, where a field trial demonstration project for raising these fish began in the fall of 1986. The project includes fingerling production ponds, growout ponds, water supply wells, and a combination hatchery, storage, and Extension education building. (Norman E. Pruitt)

2) developing direct seeding capability, 3) establishing markets for byproducts, and 4) reducing production and processing costs by one-third.

Research, development, and demonstration projects indicate that these improvements can be attained and a viable industry established by the mid-1990's.

Hybrid Striped Bass (HSB) Project

A field trial demonstration project for raising HSB in farm ponds began operation in the fall of 1986 at Walnut Point Farm near Chestertown on Maryland's Eastern Shore.

HSB is a cross between the female striped bass, or rockfish, *(Morone saxatilis)* and the male white bass *(M. chrysops).* It has the same flavor and general appearance as a striped bass but is more disease-resistant and faster growing than either of its parents.

The 3-year development phase includes construction of eight 1/2-acre fingerling (young fish) production ponds, four 2 1/2-acre growout ponds, six water supply wells, and a combination hatchery, storage, and Extension education building the first year; it will include two additional 5-acre growout ponds the second year. At maturity the project will encompass 24 surface acres of water, 4 dedicated to fingerling production and 20 dedicated to the production of market-size fish.

The increasing demand for and decreasing supply of fish and fish products have resulted in a dramatic jump in domestic product cost and foreign imports. The U.S. seafood consumer now pays 64 cents of every seafood dollar to foreign suppliers. These imports amounted to over $4.8 billion in 1986, an historic record, and contribute to the Nation's balance of payments deficit. Since the harvest from our wild fisheries is not growing appreciably, the increasing consumer demand for fish can only be met by foreign suppliers or by a

strong domestic aquaculture industry. Through joint ventures, U.S. aquaculture can develop to offset these escalating imports.

The market potential for HSB appears promising. Because of the moratorium on striped bass fishing in the Chesapeake Bay, there is an immediate market shortfall of 14 million lb. Private and government marketing experts estimate a beginning market of 52 million lb—equal to that for trout. At that production level, producers' gross income would be about $182 million.

The margin between $1.00-$1.50 estimated per pound costs and current New York price of $4.50-$5.00 per pound appears adequate to attract private investment, but there are technical and market uncertainties. Will the fish overwinter in commercial size ponds? What is the best feed mixture? How are striped bass ponds harvested? What regulatory approvals are needed? Who will process and market the fish? These are some of the questions to be answered by the project.

Other Potential Demonstration Projects

Several other potential opportunities for expanding the market base for farmers include expanded uses for traditional and new farm crops such as industrial oils from soybeans, meadowfoam, crambe, and winter rapeseed; absorbents and biodegradable plastics from corn; carbon char from hardwoods; and red drum fish farming.

A renewed push in commercializing promising technologies for the American farmer will not solve the immediate supply/demand imbalance. However, it represents a positive market-oriented response and a more effective long-term solution than subsidies for agricultural production in surplus.

Commodity Boards Help Develop New Products[1]

J. Patrick Boyle, administrator, Agricultural Marketing Service

Over 7,800 new food and fiber products were introduced in 1987, making it a record-breaking year. New food and fiber products have almost doubled since 1983, causing an "explosion" of new products, according to Marty Friedman, editor of Gorman's *New Product News.* "In one year, new products replace an entire aisle at the supermarket," says Friedman. Approximately 21 new products are introduced each day.

These new products expand the demand for agricultural commodities, create new jobs, and provide a wider range of product choices for consumers. Research and development play a critical role for manufacturers in

[1]Part VI of this Yearbook contains several articles written by individual commodity board and industry representatives.

understanding consumer trends and demands, and in creating marketable and successful new products. In fact, without research and development, the explosion of new food and fiber products would not be possible.

Consumer Trends

In the 1980's, the trend in new food and fiber products has included few major technological innovations; however, there has been a surge in the introduction of new products, which includes new brands, products with new ingredients, and products with new packaging—especially those designed for microwave cooking.

The surge of new products is due to the manufacturers' efforts to meet

New products replace an entire aisle at the supermarket in one year. About 21 new products are introduced each day. (Giant Food, Inc.)

the demands of the increasingly sophisticated consumer.

Consumer tastes and needs have been undergoing fundamental changes during the mid-1980's, including more health and nutritional concerns; an interest in gourmet, ethnic, and weight-conscious foods; and the "grazing phenomenon"— eating smaller but more frequent meals and snacks. Manufacturers have developed new products to meet these specialized consumer demands. In 1985 the keywords describing new food and fiber products were "healthy" and "exotic," according to *Advertising Age*. In 1988 the list of keywords includes convenience, single-serve, light, fat-free, fiber, microwave, cholesterol-reduced, and calcium-enriched, according to Gorman's *New Product News*.

Commodity Research and Promotion Boards

Food and fiber commodity research and promotion boards are the result of congressional legislation; most of them were created in the 1970's and 1980's. They are monitored by the USDA's Agricultural Marketing Service (AMS), and assist the food and fiber industry in developing new products through their research programs. They know that their ability to increase demand for their products depends on their ability to work with industry, academia, and government to develop new products and new uses for their commodities. By staying tuned to changes in consumer needs, and by disseminating their research to food technologists and manufacturers, these boards contribute significantly to the development of new food and fiber products.

There are boards for cotton, dairy, pork, beef, potatoes, honey, and eggs. Members of these boards are nominated by their industries and appointed by the Secretary of Agriculture. The work of the boards is fully funded by producers and growers through a deduction, called a checkoff or assessment. For example, the checkoff rate for beef is $1 per head of cattle marketed. AMS monitors the collection and expenditure of these research and promotion funds, which will exceed $440 million in 1988.

In 1988, new products under development financed by the boards include a prototype new beef product, called beef surimi, that has a potential market of $70 million a year; a prototype all-cotton disposable baby diaper which, when produced and marketed, could be worth $240 million in additional annual sales to cotton growers; and an innovative dairy product with cultures that actually consume and remove cholesterol from fermented dairy products, such as sour cream.

Here are some examples of what the commodity boards are doing to monitor consumer trends and help industry introduce new products that can meet consumers' demand and manufacturers' needs.

The Potato Board

The Potato Board assists companies that develop new food products by providing them with statistical information about potato production and consumption trends. It also furnishes companies with information about consumer attitudes and the nutritional benefits of the potato.

This Board explores new ways in which the potato can be used. For example, the potato can be used in food processing as a binding agent in cereal and pasta. Potato products, such as starch and flour, may be used by food technologists as an ice crystal retardant in ice cream, as an emulsifier in salad dressings, as a fat extender in dairy products, and as a nutritional supplement in processed

Commodity Research and Promotion Boards	Industry and Producer Organizations
The American Egg Board 1460 Renaissance Dr., Suite 301 Park Ridge, IL 60068 Congressionally enacted by the Egg Research and Consumer Information Act of 1974	
Cattlemen's Beef Promotion and Research Board P.O. Box 3316 Englewood, CO 80155 Congressionally enacted by the Beef Promotion and Research Act of 1985	Beef Industry Council of the Meat Board 444 North Michigan Ave. Chicago, IL 60611
The Cotton Board 5350 Poplar Ave., Suite 210 Memphis, TN 38119 Congressionally enacted by the Cotton Research and Promotion Act of 1966	Cotton Incorporated 1370 Ave. of the Americas New York, NY 10019
National Dairy Promotion and Research Board 2111 Wilson Blvd., Suite 600 Arlington, VA 22201 Congressionally enacted by the Dairy and Tobacco Adjustment Act of 1983	
National Honey Board 9595 Nelson Rd., Box C Longmont, CO 80501 Congressionally enacted by the Honey Research, Promotion, and Consumer Information Act of 1984	
National Pork Board P.O. Box 9114 Des Moines, IA 50306 Congressionally enacted by the Pork Promotion, Research, and Consumer Information Act of 1985	National Pork Producers Council P.O. Box 10383 Des Moines, IA 50306
The Potato Board 1385 S. Colorado Blvd. Suite 512 Denver, CO 80222 Congressionally enacted by the Potato Research and Promotion Act of 1971	

foods. The Potato Board funded and developed an information campaign for manufacturers and consumers alike.

In addition to working with industry to develop new uses and products, the Potato Board is helping to develop new markets. With the assistance of $2.5 million from USDA's Targeted Export Assistance Program, the Board has successfully expanded its market in the Far East. The market share of American frozen potato sales in Japan increased from 53 percent in 1985 to 75 percent in 1987.

Cattlemen's Beef Promotion and Research Board
A new type of 100-percent beef product, called beef surimi, is being developed and processed into high protein surimi hot dogs, bologna, beef nuggets, finger food, even a new ready-to-eat snack beef chip. The Cattlemen's Beef Promotion and Research Board contracts its research work to the Beef Industry Council of the Meat Board, which is currently developing the new beef surimi products.

Beef surimi gets its name from a Japanese food process, now widely used, for making fish sticks and fish patties. Beef surimi has high-bonding qualities and will contain about 5 percent fat, much less than currently found in such beef products as hot dogs. Prototypes for the beef surimi hot dog and snack chip already have been developed.

The National Honey Board
In a typical supermarket, 40 to 50 products contain honey. Honey is increasingly in demand because today's consumers prefer natural tasting foods without added chemicals or preservatives.

The National Honey Board has developed a list of new product applications. For example, honey attracts moisture and can reduce shrinkage in hams, cured meats, and baked goods. Honey also can clarify wine, and is being tested as a seasoning on corn chips. The Board, which was a year old in 1988, will continue to encourage food manufacturers to expand their use of honey in future products as an alternative to other sweeteners, including artificial sweeteners.

The Cotton Board
Research funded by cotton growers has assisted the textile manufacturing industry in developing new cotton fabrics and products.

Since 1984, research supported by the Cotton Board and conducted by its subsidiary, Cotton Incorporated, has produced new cotton products now used extensively in clothing and in the home: cotton-wool blends for year-round clothing, high-loft resilient cotton for all-cotton pillows and mattress pads, and all-cotton stone-washed denim for jeans and jackets.

A major area of research and development has been with nonwovens, which are non-spindled cotton materials made of cotton fibers held together by a bonding agent or meshed together by water. Nonwovens have been used in new, all-cotton medical/surgical wipes, dressings, and hospital apparel. Advances in nonwovens also have made a nonwoven, all-cotton disposable diaper possible. In preliminary testing, this prototype diaper appears to be comparable to the nondisposable cloth diaper both in hygiene and comfort. Currently, disposable diapers are a $3.3 billion annual market.

The American Egg Board
Through its research programs, the American Egg Board has developed several new products, such as frozen egg crust pizza, egg dip, egg sandwich loaf, and egg-filled burritos.

In assisting industry, the board's primary objective is to stimulate ideas among food scientists and marketing planners about developing new products using eggs. The Board promotes both the nutritional and functional properties of eggs, which can be used to bind, leaven, thicken, emulsify, glaze, and clarify, and to retard crystallization.

The National Pork Board

The most significant research currently being funded by the National Pork Board is aimed at creating trichinae-safe pork. The industry has developed two distinctly different methods for safeguarding pork: irradiation and testing. Irradiation of fresh pork at a low level has been approved by USDA and the Food and Drug Administration. While trichinae can be rendered harmless by freezing, curing, or cooking at a high internal temperature, these two new methods of irradiation or testing would provide fresh, trichinae-safe, raw pork.

In addition, a new pork chop called "America's Cut" was introduced into the retail market in 1987. It is a premium boneless, center, single-cut chop, and the first cut of fresh meat ever to be trademarked.

National Dairy Promotion and Research Board

Since 1984, the Dairy Board has increased its annual product research budget to $4.4 million to support work at U.S. universities and laboratories. In 1987, 25 percent of the research budget was spent on new product research.

In the next few years, the Board believes that research in biotechnology and genetic engineering can potentially revolutionize the industry. Studies now underway indicate that applied use of biotechnology could result in cultures that consume and remove cholesterol from fermented dairy products. Research also is being conducted on cultures that can extend the shelf life of many dairy products.

High on the new product research agenda are the expanded use of whey protein concentrates in more foods, increased use of nonfat dry milk in baking, and introduction of shelf-stable carbonated milk products.

New Products Create New Opportunities

The commodity boards have often succeeded in either creating new product prototypes or in disseminating information to producers and manufacturers, assisting industry in developing new products.

Some of the new products already introduced, such as "America's Cut" pork chops and cotton-wool blends, are worth millions of dollars to their respective producers and growers. In the long run, new product development helps ensure continued demand for agricultural commodities. The boards work to promote their commodities to both retailers and consumers and make a significant contribution to the economic health of U.S. agriculture.

New products also are an important opportunity for consumers. Consumers are demanding more variety and convenience, and these demands and needs are reflected in the increasing number of new food and fiber products being manufactured and introduced. The result is that consumers have more and more choices.

Part V

Delivering Quality Goods

001000045172

Productivity in the Food Industry

John R. Block, president, National-American Wholesale Grocers' Association (NAWGA) and former U.S. Secretary of Agriculture

Productivity is more than a philosophy. It is a way of life for the food industry. In an intensely competitive industry, productivity and efficiency are vital. Questions of cutting costs and improving ability to deliver are not academic questions. Even incremental changes can influence or finally decide the financial future of both small and large businesses.

Productivity has several components. As always, it depends on one's perspective. To the human resources manager, employee morale or solving substance abuse problems may be critical to boosting productivity. To the warehouse operator, it may mean a new racking system. A transportation manager might cite improved vehicle maintenance or more stops per delivery route. An executive may worry about increased labor costs and might muse, "How is the company going to get more return on the dollar?" Accounting officials worry about monitoring cash flow. Others wish they had a better handle on inventory management or "shrink"—lost merchandise from waste, spoilage, or damaged packaging.

All of these people have legitimate concerns. Whether examined from producer, processor, distributor, or retail level, productivity is an overriding concern. It is not just a few in one company trying to increase productivity. Their competitors across town and even across the world are worried about the same things: How can I compete better?

How can I be more productive? These are the two most important questions American business must answer today. Because the food industry is consumer driven, the urgency of becoming more productive permeates everyone's thinking from an Illinois farmer to a Temple, Texas, food distributor to a grocer in Spokane to a homemaker in Brooklyn.

Productivity—a Total Commitment

How can the industry be more productive? The answer lies in an understanding that there is no radical leap that will transform a business overnight. Productivity results from numerous changes in everyone's operation. It is not just buying a computer or investing in a new trade fleet. It's not installing an employee assistance program. It is all these things and more. Each department in a firm must understand how its contribution fits into the whole, and each department must resist the tendency to parochialize (my department is essential but not yours). This is not an easy task. It takes a commitment by management to realize that productivity must be a theme in every facet of the firm's operations. Only a high-level management decision will make the difference.

Once the business makes that total commitment, productivity increases. Driven by a need to stay competitive, many things happen.

There is a great deal of political rhetoric in these times about American competitiveness, or the lack of it.

I believe the food industry already is competitive. We grow the best food in the world—and efficiently too. Our food transportation system is well developed. Efficient distribution of food and grocery products keeps 152,000 U.S. grocery stores fully stocked with an average of 20,000 items per store. This includes 30,600 supermarkets with over $2 million in annual sales each. Total grocery sales in 1986 were a staggering $350 billion. And we can't forget the 64,000 convenience stores that sell an additional $54 billion. Product selection is better in the United States than anywhere else in the world. And food is a bargain here, unlike elsewhere. Because competition is the rule, so is productivity.

Changes in Wholesale Distribution

What changes have occurred to give us today's food industry? Here are a few highlights:

- As a boy, I milked cows by hand and we took the nonpasteurized milk to the direct retail outlet. This was also true for eggs and produce. Are things different now? They are, both in scale of operation and in the increased efficiency of the food distribution system.
- Consider the tremendous difference in the size and operating capacity of full-size farm equipment since my youth.
- Wholesalers used to confine themselves to a narrow geographic area but no more. Now, because of economies of scale, one distributor covers hundreds of square miles. On a recent drive around the beltway in Washington, I saw no fewer than 10 grocery distributor trucks from out of the DC area delivering goods to local stores.
- Productivity is up because of computerized truck routing which plots schedules.

- Warehouse operators no longer have 100-pound cases of canned goods with no outside marking except for maybe a stencil. Now, thanks to reduction in size of packaging to 35 pounds or less, and computer scanning, we know how much product we have and we can distribute it far more effectively than before.
- The warehouses themselves used to be five to six stories with low ceilings, handstacking, and rail sidings outside the buildings. Only a finite number of cases could be stored in them. Now we have high ceiling warehouses with palette racks, standardized palettes, and fork lifts as a norm. Different size cans used to make it difficult to distribute food efficiently, but now standardization has established certain size cans.
- Until just a few years ago, retailers had to keep huge inventories on hand. This tied up tremendous capital and held down expansion. Now with "just-in-time" delivery, a grocer can replenish fast-moving stock quickly with little notice. Such speed would have been impossible until just recently.
- Thanks to computers and shelf scanning, a business can keep track of its inventory quickly and often immediately. What a far cry from the old days when stores and warehouses had to shut down for days at a time to take inventory.

These changes did not happen overnight, but the pace of change has increased dramatically. Although some of these changes are small in and of themselves, they build on each other, create momentum, and have transformed the face of the wholesale food industry in less than two decades.

Changes in Packing and Processing

Although some of these examples relate specifically to wholesale distribution, changes in the packing and processing industry are also remarkable.

Information technology has led the charge, but pause to consider, once again, the cause. A consumer-driven industry fosters competition. Competition creates a climate of innovation where technological advance can reduce cost and increase productivity.

Where will all this lead? No one knows whether the accelerated pace of change will moderate. We have seen a massive influx of new ideas and techniques. For the next few years, we will see some settling-in as the food industry concentrates on adapting and applying these changes. Change will continue but at a slower pace.

The Human Challenge

Up to now, food industry change has concentrated on "hard" measures of productivity in transportation, processing, warehousing, and information technology. Now, with an almost full-employment economy, employers are refocusing on the human element as an integral part of productivity.

On the positive side, what will management have to do to attract and retain workers? Pay of course will be competitive, but such issues as working conditions, health benefits, and pensions will be in the forefront of worker-employer relations.

On the down side, the food industry is just now coming to grips with drug abuse and the resulting loss of productivity from user-employees. The trend is toward education and employee assistance programs to restore an employee to productive potential rather than termination. The National-American Wholesale Grocers' Association developed a model substance abuse program to aid business managers spot alcohol and drug problems and to help rehabilitate employees.

Another issue is acquired immune deficiency syndrome (AIDS). Although not seen as a major food industry problem now, it is only a matter of time before a food employee is stricken with the disease and there are alarms from consumers who will ask if the food chain is safe. All the medical experts agree that the Nation's food supply is safe from contamination by someone with AIDS who works with food. The labor and productivity issue is the reaction of fellow employees and unwarranted consumer fears.

Lost productivity, absenteeism, and even wildcat strikes are a real possibility. Insurance and health benefits costs, as well as AIDS (and drug) employment screening tests, will soon be major concerns. Employers will develop and implement education programs to help employees understand AIDS and how it is transmitted. That will be the human challenge of our time.

A Jewel of a Market for Blue Diamond

Walt Payne, vice president, marketing and sales, Blue Diamond Growers, Sacramento, CA

Blue Diamond Growers found a jewel of a market for its almond products in Japan, which is now second to West Germany as the biggest importer of California almonds. And almonds are now California's number one food export. Sales of almonds to Japan ran from 22,000 pounds in 1955 to more than 40 million pounds in 1985.

In addition to selling in Japan, Blue Diamond has cracked 90 foreign markets so far and has scored record sales in the United States, Europe, Asia, and, most recently, the Soviet Union.

In 1975, U.S. consumers were eating about 75 million pounds of California almonds a year. Today, that number has doubled. Consumers outside the United States were eating about 123 million pounds of California almonds in 1975, and today that number has tripled. Eastern and Western Europe and Asia consume more than 90 percent of the total exported California almonds.

The California almond industry production is valued at more than $1 billion. The Blue Diamond cooperative of 5,300 growers produces over half the State's supply and, in many years, as much as 40 percent of the total world supply.

To boost Blue Diamond® brand recognition and sales, the almond processor and marketer recently launched custom-tailored advertising campaigns for branded products in Australia, Canada, Europe, Asia, and the Middle East.

Patience and perseverance are required for any export company to understand the idiosyncrasies of a new foreign market. Breaking into the Japanese market and producing almonds to please the sophisticated, quality-conscious Japanese consumers was not easy. Unlike many companies that tried to market in Japan and failed, Blue Diamond concentrated on the reasons why it was possible to develop the Japanese market.

Distribution is Key to Success

Our first sale of 10 tons in 1955 was made through a trading company to the Japanese chocolate industry, because of a European crop failure that year. It was an "opportunity" sale and an impetus to keep unraveling the mysteries of a complicated distribution system in Japan.

Experience soon taught us that an exclusive supply arrangement with a trading company in Japan was not the way for us to develop the market. Taking a direct approach was an impossible option in the Japanese market at that time. So, several trading companies representing us were appointed to gain broader exposure for almonds, create some friendly competition, and expand the use of Blue Diamond almonds in the market. Today, the group consists of nine trading companies, all of whom specialize in similar food areas.

This technique was adequate for servicing existing market sectors but did little to further expand the market. In 1967, when almond exports to Japan were about 6 million pounds, we decided to open our own market development office in Japan. Within 4 years, almond exports to Japan doubled. Today, Blue Diamond offices in Japan consist of nearly 60 Japanese staff members, charged with increasing Japanese almond consumption.

Overcoming Trade Barriers

Japan produces no almonds. As a result, political problems have not been a hindrance to trade. During the early years, however, it was sometimes difficult to pass a container through customs at a specific port on the first attempt. Phytosanitary questions, as well as other red tape, made the passage of shipments a tedious and frustrating experience.

But we quickly discovered that these same types of delays with customs did not occur when the goods were shipped to a second port. So, we shipped everything to the second port until passage of goods through customs in the first port ran more smoothly.

Today, we distribute almonds in the industrial sector through trading companies. Blue Diamond personnel make all sales calls (usually in combination with representatives from the trading companies). They make the sale, generate new product interest, and use trading companies for financing, documentation, warehousing, and distribution.

We export the raw product to Japan where it is custom processed under Blue Diamond's supervision and specifications for the snack consumer market. The forerunner to this arrangement was an operation jointly owned by Blue Diamond and a Japanese partner. This arrangement was another false start that did not prove to be as efficient as the current arrangement.

Innovative Promotions

In the snack area, we bypassed the multitiered distribution system that would make the cost of packaged nuts prohibitive. To service this market, Blue Diamond, over 10 years,

Raw almonds are shipped in bulk from California to Japan where they are custom processed under Blue Diamond's supervision and specifications for the snack consumer market. (Blue Diamond Growers)

In the snack area, Blue Diamond distributed its snack products in Japan through agreements with Coca Cola. This system eliminated 2 or 3 layers in the distribution system and allows more money to be used for advertising and sales promotion. (Blue Diamond Growers)

forged 17 separate agreements with the 17 Coca Cola Bottlers in Japan to market and distribute Blue Diamond snack products. This system eliminates two or three layers in the distribution system and allows more money to be used for advertising and sales promotions.

We also learned that many young Japanese women attend cooking school before marriage. So we made almond cookery a part of the cooking school curriculum by adding several cooking school demonstrators to our payroll. These almond cookery specialists teach classes on cooking with almonds, free of charge, at many of Japan's 700 cooking schools. We also educate young customers by introducing almonds to Japan's school lunch program and providing almond recipes to the program.

Traditional advertising and promotion techniques such as print, billboard, and radio and television advertising are used. We also sponsor the Miss Universe Contest in Japan and bring the winner and two runners-up with the top Japanese Coca Cola/Blue Diamond salespeople to Sacramento each February during almond blossom time for a plant and almond-growing-area tour. The group is accompanied by several members of the Japanese and U.S. press, who cover the visit and broadcast it back to Japan, where millions of dollars in free publicity are generated for almonds and Blue Diamond.

Market Development Vital

Part of Blue Diamond's initial overall export strategy was to develop the Japanese market and not to simply get rid of surplus. If, when supplies get tight and everything can be sold in the domestic market, a corporation decides to continue to supply the foreign market, then that corporation is dedicated to developing the

market, which separates it from peddlers just looking for an opportunity sale.

We export to more than 90 countries worldwide during good crop years. In poor crop years, almonds are still offered to the same 90 countries, but on a pro rata basis. Only Japan and the United States, which are treated equally, have first call on whatever supplies they need, provided, of course, that customers are prepared to pay the fair market price.

The cost of developing a market such as Japan is expensive. It takes commitment to continue spending over a long number of years and much faith that the payback will come someday. Exchange rates create a sword that cuts two ways. The cheap dollar makes it easier to export almonds, but the cheap dollar also makes the cost of operating an office in Japan much more expensive. Fortunately, if you get far enough along in development, you will probably be in a position such as ours, which enables you to generate substantial sales in the host currency. These sales afford Blue Diamond a portion of the benefits that the Japanese realize with a strong currency.

Success Takes Time and Effort

Although Pacific Rim nations sometimes seem more export than import motivated, Japan is searching for American "success stories." If your product fits the right niche and you are effective in conveying your story to the Japanese Government, you will find a ready and willing trade facilitator. While this obviously is not true for all products, it may be true for yours.

U.S. business firms can penetrate the Japanese market, but don't forget that success in this case calls for a marathon, not a sprint.

They Chose to Fight

Tom Jurchak, county extension director, Lackawanna County, PA

The buzz word in agriculture today is "alternatives," most often translated to mean new crops or enterprises. If farmers aren't making a profit at what they're producing, then switch to something else. This may be the appropriate decision for many producers, but too often the questions "What's wrong with what we're producing?" and "How can we do it better to compete more effectively or reach new markets?" are not addressed vigorously enough. Sometimes we are too quick to abandon enterprises in which we have developed skills in favor of something that seems to offer better profit opportunities. Before we switch, we should consider being more competitive and finding new markets for what we know how to produce.

Call it market penetration or market development or market expansion, but it means taking a share of the market away from others when we learn to be more competitive. It means making the best use of the resources we have to penetrate markets already served by others. It means making changes in what we are now doing, rather than changing to unfamiliar enterprises that present new and different problems. It means fighting rather than switching.

Fruit and Vegetable Farmers Face Problem

This was the choice facing farmers in Lackawanna County, PA, long before marketing became a national issue in agriculture. Thirty years ago fruits and vegetables were produced on nearly every farm in the county along with small grains, hay, livestock, and dairy—typical of agriculture in northeastern Pennsylvania. All of the small grains and hay were fed to livestock and dairy cattle, but the fruits and vegetables were sold to wholesale produce buyers chiefly in Scranton and Wilkes-Barre but also at terminal markets in New York and Philadelphia.

The principal vegetable crops grown were tomatoes, sweet corn, cabbage, and peppers. Much of the tomato crop was sold mature green to brokers from Florida who would grade them locally for repackers in the major cities on the East Coast.

An early sign of change was the suburbanization of rural areas in the county caused by the migration of young families from Scranton in the 1950's and 1960's. Considering a population of 80,000 in Scranton and 225,000 in Lackawanna County, changing land uses were inevitable. In addition, urban renewal in Scranton eliminated the "wholesale block" of markets and with it nearly all the buyers. Also during these years supermarkets expanded, selling 60 percent of away-from-home food purchases. Product assembly was through company warehouses, eliminating local farm-to-store markets.

The mature green tomato profits began to shrink as local growers paid the brokers grading and packing costs that cut sharply into their returns. California growers became more competitive in Eastern markets with the help of cheaper transportation and a massive Federal interstate highway program in the 1960's.

Because of the increasing pressures from land use, the loss of wholesale markets, and disappearing profits from mature green tomatoes, local farmers had to make some choices between fighting or switching long before national dietary habits began favoring fruits and vegetables or retail marketing was a standard topic at winter farm meetings.

Solutions

Producers of fruits and vegetables had tough choices. They could get bigger and try to penetrate wholesale markets in metropolitan areas, or produce a variety of crops and penetrate retail markets without increasing in size. Entering wholesale markets meant crop specialization and large volume. Retail markets required diverse crops and all the marketing services to consumers provided by the supermarket chains.

Of course, the choice for some was leaving commercial agriculture, selling the land for commercial or residential development, or finding off-farm employment.

First Retail Markets

The fruit and vegetable growers who made the first move were those who saw the retail marketing opportunity near a large population center such as Scranton, while recognizing the trend toward consumer services provided by the supermarkets. Growers knew they would have to go to the consumer rather than expect the consumer to come to the farm. A few of the more daring producers in the 1950's tested the waters with curbside markets in Scranton, parking on any street that the city would let them use at hours when they would not interfere with traffic. Quickly they saw the

need to concentrate farmers in one area to offer consumers a wider selection of products, regular hours, a permanent location, and parking space.

These were the days before downtown businesses recognized the appeal of farm markets, and municipalities had no interest in subsidizing the effort by providing space or facilities. So growers rented vacant land from the city, the school district, or private owners, and the market expanded with more producers and more customers. The location of the market was still at the mercy of the landowner and kept changing every few years.

Cooperative Formed

At this point the need for a permanent location was widely recognized, and the Cooperative Farmers Night Market was organized and incorporated to purchase 4 acres of land in the heart of Scranton. The deal was financed with certificates of indebtedness purchased by the farmers and paid off over 15 years. Buildings were constructed to shelter producers and their customers. Even a food booth was included where nonprofit organizations provided hot meals for customers for fund-raising projects.

Marketing experience had shown that best customer response was on Monday, Wednesday, and Friday from 2 to 8 p.m. This provided shopping opportunities in the afternoon for homemakers, on the way home from work for employees, and in the evening for the entire family.

Cooperative Marketing

As their marketing skills developed, the cooperative members produced a wider diversity of crops (sweet corn, cabbage, broccoli, melons) and products, offering them in a range of quantities and packages to meet the needs of one couple for one meal or large amounts for canning and freezing. Many began to sell jams and relishes made from their fruits and vegetables. Product lines expanded to include flowers, honey, meats, and even home-made pastries. Members have become adept at promotion and advertising, using all the media available in a metropolitan market. In recent years, billboards have been added to supplement newspaper, radio, and television, along with special "customer appreciation" nights when consumers can sample farm products.

Today the uniqueness of the market is that the members own the physical facilities and pay their own taxes, insurance, and advertising. They regulate the market operation and insist, as they have from the start, that members sell only what they themselves produce. This strategy eliminates other participants in a marketing system so that all revenues from retail sales go to the producer. Under the leadership of J. Wilfred Richards, who has been president of the cooperative for 15 years, the market has provided the opportunity for farmers who did not expand production to stay in agriculture and enjoy an adequate income from limited resources by meeting the desires of the last link in the marketing chain—the consumer.

The Mature Green Tomato Industry

This industry was slower to change. Acreage declined steadily as growers chose dairying, retail sales, or leaving agriculture. A crop produced on 1,000 acres in the 1950's shrank to one-tenth of that by the 1970's. The only remaining producers were those few with the skill and foresight to pack their own tomatoes. Cheap transportation for California tomatoes had

taken its toll and beaten us in our own markets. There wasn't much left to save and little time to save it if mature green tomato production was to survive in Lackawanna County.

Although we were within a day's drive of a third of the Nation's population—an advantage that should have guaranteed profits—the marketing system had changed and we had lost our markets because we didn't stay competitive. To penetrate wholesale markets, radical changes were required.

Energy Crisis Fuels Rebuilding

The energy crisis of the 1970's, when diesel fuel prices increased 114 percent between 1976 and 1980, helped growers decide to rebuild the mature green tomato industry. Two-thirds of that increase occurred after June 1979, and that's when we felt that the comparative advantage might be in our favor. We reasoned that continuing increases in fuel costs would raise costs for California considerably in Eastern markets.

We knew that California had a reputation for providing the best product in Eastern markets and that penetration would be difficult. We also knew that the technology for mature green tomato production in other areas was not entirely transferable to Pennsylvania, and we would have to do our own research and development. But we felt we had the skills, soils, and climate needed to grow quality mature green tomatoes.

Although mature green tomatoes had been grown in Lackawanna County for many years, an evaluation of the production methods indicated that changes would be needed to lower costs, since some of the practices were borrowed from other States without testing in Pennsylvania. As a result, everything, including varieties, fertilization, plant density, pest control, rotations, and soil management, was evaluated to find the most profitable method for local conditions. Profits became the only goal, and every practice had to pass the test.

Production Changes

The variety grown almost exclusively in 1980 for eastern mature green tomato markets was too small to be profitable locally, since tomatoes are priced on size as well as grade. Extension variety demonstrations provided larger tomatoes with acceptable quality and higher profits. After some resistance, buyers finally were convinced that newer could be better.

Fertilization provided the most radical change in production practices. Using research results from Pennsylvania State University, a program was developed and tested. It showed that the previously recommended amount of fertilizer could be cut in half if calcium and magnesium levels were adequate and all the fertilizer was placed in bands at planting time.

Similarly, the effect of plant density was checked. Two years of research showed that the number of plants per acre could economically be increased threefold over the old standard, getting increased production per acre with the same amount of fertilizer.

With available land limited, soil management practices and rotation were critical. Old rotations—planting hay and grains in the fall after the tomatoes were harvested—became unprofitable on rented land. But the "living mulch" (sod-forming crops of annual or perennial grasses grown with the tomatoes) developed by Extension allowed tomatoes every other year on the same field while controlling diseases, maintaining soil condition, controlling soil erosion, conserving nutrients, and suppressing weeds.

Band spraying the plants with pesticides where control was needed, and not the soil, saved up to 30 percent in pesticide use; this practice cut costs and was environmentally sound.

These are but a few examples of the many changes in production practices that made local growers more competitive at current market prices.

Secretary of Agriculture Richard E. Lyng, left, buys fresh sweet corn at the Cooperative Farmers Night Market in Scranton, PA, from Roy Thompson, a charter member of the cooperative. With Secretary Lyng is Keith Eckel, president of the Pennsylvania Farmers Association. (Ike Refice)

Because of a growing season much shorter than most other production areas, which often allowed only one picking, we had to devise methods for reducing costs per box, rather than being driven by yield per acre. We eliminated some practices used in other areas that were not cost effective for us.

Harvesting and Packing Methods Improved

As with production practices, harvesting and packing methods were changed to improve efficiency. The old field crates used in the past were replaced by 18-bushel bulk bins or gondolas that hold 10 tons of tomatoes, usually made of fiberglass. Chlorinated water dumps were added at the packing house to minimize damage and to control soft rot organisms on the fruit. Automatic box fillers speeded up the packing to 1,200 boxes an hour in some houses. Handling efficiency was improved by using pallets and fork lifts. Glue was used instead of plastic bands to hold 80 boxes on a pallet, and trailer capacity increased from 1,400 boxes to 1,700 boxes.

To stay competitive, all the marketing services and conveniences expected by the buyers were included. Salespeople familiar with the mature green tomato market were hired to seek out new buyers and get the best prices. Growers provided seasonal farmworker housing, and labor contractors provided the crews and supervised the harvests. Truck brokers were contacted to provide transportation anywhere in the country for the tomatoes sold f.o.b. (free on board) at the packing house. As the acreage increased, grounds buyers (who go to the packing house to buy) were attracted and are now a permanent part of the marketing scene in Lackawanna County from August to October.

Need for Records

From the beginning of the effort to resurrect the mature green tomato industry in the late 1970's, it was apparent that a practical recordkeeping system was needed so growers, individually and collectively, could evaluate their performance in production, harvesting, packing, and marketing. Profitability was the criterion for every practice, and the only way to determine profitability was with good records. The problem was that the pace of work growing and marketing the crop never allowed enough time for recordkeeping. In addition, the need for records was not apparent to the growers who had not used them for business analysis in the past. Profit and loss were only a matter of how much money was left after the bills were paid.

The answer was computer programs easy enough for growers to use and fast enough to provide answers while there was still time for adjustments. Everything from programmable calculators to mainframes was tried, and simple programs provided quick answers to growers who met and evaluated the relative profitability of changing any of a dozen different variables. In the beginning none of the growers had their own computers. Today nearly all of them do, using similar programs.

The principal data base for evaluation now comes from Extension programs, which compile information from all the growers and evaluate the performance of each in relation to the others. Now growers have a record that shows not only the financial results for the crop but also what they did right or wrong to warrant the profit or loss. These records are examined at grower meetings and in individual sessions with the Extension agent. Information gathered is shared among the growers so everyone benefits from the exchange.

There can be no excuses for failure when everyone had the same growing and marketing conditions.

Staying Competitive

As a result, the mature green tomato acreage has expanded from 200 acres and two packing houses in 1979 to 1,500 acres and six packing houses in 1988, spilling over into another county as new ground was needed. One of the lessons learned from the 1960's was the need for growers to own the packing facilities and market their own tomatoes. The risk of weather-related losses in production and the volatility of market prices have to be hedged with the ownership and control of the marketing facilities. This requires risktaking and management skills that not every farmer possesses. But for those who can learn and are willing to commit themselves to meeting the market competition, success is achievable.

Increases in transportation costs from California never reached the highs expected in 1979, and today real costs are only slightly higher and California is still competitive. In addition, tomato growers in other Eastern States were watching the same developments back in the 1970's, and they expanded production for some of the same reasons.

The Pennsylvania Farmers Association, through its president Keith Eckel, has helped growers to adjust to changes in State and Federal regulations, as well as to the demands of groups and agencies concerned with seasonal farm laborers.

Costs are under constant scrutiny, and marketing services are still being added to attract new buyers. The addition of degreening rooms (where the temperature is controlled to obtain the degree of redness wanted by consumers) is already underway in anticipation of direct sales to supermarket chains rather than through repackers.

Economic Impact

Gross income has now reached $5 million in the county, rivaling milk production for the top spot—not a large amount in some counties, but a significant contribution to Lackawanna's economy. The growing and distribution of 7 million tomato transplants alone has produced a $300,000 industry. The purchase of 882,000 boxes to ship the crop to market has generated spirited bidding for the $660,000 worth of business. Harvest labor for more than 30 million pounds of tomatoes provides payrolls of a half millon dollars in addition to packing house labor of $335,000. Production costs of $1.2 million are going to local dealers of farm supplies and machinery, and 40 percent of this goes for local labor. Hauling costs for shipping 580 trailer loads of tomatoes to markets between Boston and Miami provide more than $600,000 of revenue to local truckers. Nearly all of this is new business in the county because growers, with the help of Penn State University, Pennsylvania Farmers Association, the Pennsylvania Department of Agriculture, and USDA, decided to fight to regain lost markets and establish a new industry.

The produce growers in the county, other than tomato growers, had to find new markets when old ones were lost or changed. They adapted production to retail sales and captured part of the supermarket business. The mature green tomato growers penetrated existing markets at the assembly stage in the marketing chain while the members of the Cooperative Farmers Night Market reached the consumer. Both are examples of farmers who chose to fight rather than switch to other crops or leave agriculture.

Marketing on a Central Illinois Cash-Grain Farm[1]

Darrel Good, agricultural economist, and Bob Sampson, communications specialist, University of Illinois Cooperative Extension Service, Champaign, IL

Surrounded by deep, rich black topsoil about 10 miles southwest of Champaign, IL, the farmstead of Bill and Debbie Klein appears, viewed from the country road that passes it, far removed from the competitive, fast-paced world of commodity marketing. The well-kept buildings and machinery bring to mind the traditional, romantic view of a farm family linked to the soil.

But inside one corner of a heated machine shed where a paneled office has been constructed, the Kleins keep in contact with the world of commodity trading. They monitor and use that knowledge to best advantage to insure that the lifestyle of three generations of Kleins on this land remains an option for their children.

Bill Klein, who attended Champaign's Parkland College and the University of Missouri, has been farming since 1975. In 1981, he took over full responsibility for the operation when his father passed away. He rents part of the 1,500 acres farmed, but Klein markets all the corn and soybeans produced on the acreage for his eight landlords.

Bill Klein serves on the board of a large grain cooperative with a 12-million-bushel storage capacity and is involved in buying and selling machinery. He markets his grain through this cooperative as well. He is also a distributor for a computer

market information service.

Debbie Klein, who graduated from the University of Illinois in 1979 with a degree in Agricultural Industries and worked for a time with a Production Credit Association, handles financing, bookkeeping, tax management, and credit. She helps make most of the business decisions.

"When Bill's father died 6 years ago, it was a very difficult time. Bill's mother hadn't paid that much attention to the business side of the operation and I decided right then that wasn't going to happen to me. If anything happened to Bill, I wanted to know what was going on and what needed to be done," says Debbie.

The Kleins Are Innovators

In 1972, with the help of the Agricultural Engineering Department at the University of Illinois, they designed grain storage facilities to accommodate natural air drying. Today, Bill Klein continues to make extensive use of information and assistance through the Illinois Cooperative Extension Service.

Like other farm families in these times, the Kleins are always looking to diversify. They've discovered one excellent method.

"Last year, we cooperated with six seed corn or chemical company experiments," Klein explains. "Some people around here call me a professional cooperator. This place is getting to be like a research park."

Such an arrangement with one

[1]See article, *Marketing Strategies and Alternatives for Individual Farmers,* by John (Jake) N. Ferris for explanation of specialized marketing terms and strategies.

seed company has resulted in a new building on the farmstead that will be leased to the research project, paying the cost of construction and eventually providing Klein with a "free" building.

"It helps diversify our operation, and the income it brings in is something you can always count on," says Debbie.

But the heart of the couple's approach to farming is marketing. Marketing is critical for us," explains Debbie. "Bill spends more time marketing than he does planting and harvesting. Even when we go on vacation, he follows the markets, frequently calling back home to check on price developments."

For clear evidence of this commitment, just drop by Klein's office any weekday morning around 9:30 a.m. There you will find him closely monitoring the two computer screens on his desk that carry price information. One is that of a commercial advisory service to which he subscribes.

And while the telephone rings frequently, Klein's attention rarely strays long from the screen.

In addition to monitoring futures prices, Bill watches the cash market for corn and soybeans. The changing relationship among cash prices, futures prices, and the posted county price for corn have become especially important for implementing the strategy of repaying Commodity Credit Corporation (CCC) loans with certificates.

Rapidly changing basis levels for soybeans also make access to current cash prices necessary to complete a hedging or contracting arrangement. Timely cash price information is available through numerous pages of market-related information at the punch of a key.

While there are no secret formulas for a successful marketing program, Klein has implemented all those measures that are necessary to do the best job of marketing possible.

"You can have all the advisers you want," he explains, "but ultimately it's the producer's responsibility."

His marketing plan begins with a careful evaluation of planting decisions, including participation in Government acreage-reduction and paid-diversion programs, which he has been part of since 1983.

Next, he painstakingly assesses the supply and demand fundamentals for

Debbie and Bill Klein are a close-knit team and believe marketing is critical for them. (David Riecks)

the marketing year and settles on a projection of the season's average price for corn and soybeans.

"When I try to forecast a price in my mind, I'd rather be pessimistic than optimistic," he says.

Still, the projection changes often during the 2 years in which a crop is marketed. To keep those projections current, Klein follows USDA reports and other sources of information.

Historical records and projected input prices can serve as the basis for cost of production estimates.

"But because of little land debt, most of my eight landlords have such a low cost structure that the cost of production is not an especially useful price target," he explains.

Yield projections, too, are made and updated as the planting and growing season progresses.

Klein has developed a working knowledge of the major marketing alternatives available to him.

"I'm not a big fan of commodity options because of the premiums associated with them," he relates. "I've used options on occasion just to become familiar with that market. And I've taken advantage of the futures market during the growing season to lock in a price on expected production. Routinely, I use basis contracts to lock in a favorable basis."

Marketing corn and soybeans over a relatively long period of time—from before planting until the summer following harvest—is advocated by Klein. He has, however, sold as much as 50 percent of expected production before the crop was planted.

"I realized that by using the futures market I could reverse that decision if price or crop prospects changed dramatically," he says.

Technical Analysis Important Too

In addition to becoming familiar with and staying current with market fun-

damentals, Klein uses technical analysis in timing his pricing decisions. For a few years, he kept daily bar charts in order to obtain a working knowledge of the role of that tool.

"Now I rely on technical information provided through a marketing advisory service and my commodity broker," he says.

Realizing the importance of detailed and accessible information, Klein also keeps records of his marketing decisions. He uses a daily calendar on his desk to record the quantities of corn and soybeans sold, the pricing method used, and the price or basis level locked in.

"I find this record to be an excellent source of information for reviewing the season's decisions and looking for ways to improve those decisions," Klein says.

He also observes and records the corn and soybean basis levels at the two buying stations he uses. These records provide a benchmark for forecasting basis and recognizing unusually good basis levels.

These include three major factors, according to Klein: "First is the amount of time you spend and the second is the people you draw from. Experience is the other factor."

Experience helps a farmer separate useful information from that which is merely confusing. Klein has stopped going to marketing meetings because he feels too many opinions can muddy rather than clarify a situation. Instead, he relies on the views of a few people whose opinions he values.

Has it worked? Klein says he is generally satisfied with his ability to meet his goal of pricing most of his crop in the top one-third of the season's price range.

"You have to say we've been successful," Debbie adds with a laugh. "We're still farming."

Quality in Marketing Grain

Mack N. Leath, agricultural economist, and branch chief, Crops Branch, Commodity Economics Division, Economic Research Service

Quality means different things to different people. Quality in grain is seen differently by grain producers, grain marketing firms, domestic processors, and foreign buyers. They all have an interest in grain quality, but it is diverse indeed.

Quality is generally considered to be at its peak when the grain matures in the field, and it is seldom maintained through the harvesting and marketing process. Decline following harvest is due to many factors—including drying and storage practices, breakage in elevator storage from rapid handling, micro-organism and insect damage, mycotoxin contamination, and inventory management practices.

Harvested grains are intermediate goods that require marketing services before being processed into a wide variety of products for consumers. Different quality characteristics are therefore important to different users—producers, handlers, merchandisers, and processors—which complicates the establishing of grades and standards. Standards have historically been developed to describe the physical and biological condition of the lot of grain represented by an official sample. Having been developed mainly to aid the marketing process, the standards often do not measure chemical properties important to processors and other end users, for example livestock feeders, feed manufacturers, dry corn millers, and flour millers.

The need to define and identify quality factors for grain and to develop improved drying, storing, and handling methods may require changes in (1) varieties planted, (2) methods used in drying, handling, and storage, (3) management practices, (4) equipment that measures quality, and (5) grading standards that describe quality.

The quality of grain is also determined by the value of various characteristics in alternative end uses. Consequently, the worth of improved quality must be balanced against the added costs to obtain it.

In addition, some quality characteristics relate to health and safety. The tragic instances of dust explosions at grain elevators and mycotoxin contaminations have aroused public concern.

Although the United States is a major grain exporter, competition from other exporting nations is expected to remain strong. As a result, quality will remain important in determining our competitive position.

Quality Preferences in Various End Uses

Researchers concerned with quality factors for end users can identify how structural, chemical, and physical properties of grain relate to product yields and values. Once these quality factors are identified, plant breeders can then develop varieties and hybrids having those attributes.

Varietal effects on quality—
Researchers select varieties or hybrids that are not susceptible to breakage during drying and handling operations, while providing the maximum yield of higher valued products when processed. Dry millers who make products such as grits and corn flour prefer a corn that has a high yield of total endosperm (the inside of the kernel or starch portion) products. Corn kernels that are more dense are desirable, but these high-density types also tend to be more susceptible to breakage. Broken kernels must be separated from whole kernels before milling and cannot be used in processing high value products.

Drying for quality—At harvest, corn is usually too moist for safe storage and must be artificially dried. High-temperature drying reduces kernel density, causing the kernel to absorb more moisture from the air, which adversely affects dry milling characteristics. It creates stress cracks in the kernels. The stress cracks and breakage contribute greatly to microbial growth and insect activity.

Breeding for quality—Plant breeders have long been trying to raise crop yields, develop plants that retain their grains to harvest, and speed or regulate maturity. The addition of complex quality objectives may slow the progress in those areas. The dry milling industry is concerned with removal of the grain's outside layer in a way that will maximize the yield of endosperm products with a low-fat content. The larger endosperm particles are more valuable, but recovery is hampered by the presence of broken corn. Consequently, kernel density and breakage susceptibility should be addressed in plant breeding programs.

Food and feed manufacturing companies, concerned with mycotoxins, would like to see mold resistance emphasized. Breeding programs represent one long-term approach, but the genetics and environmental effects are complex. Therefore, improvements in grain quality through better handling and storage methods may be more easily achieved.

Quality Related to Safety and Health

Dust explosions, mycotoxins, and mold contamination represent serious threats to both human and animal health. There are several areas where grain quality relates to these problems.

Dust and explosions—The mode of ignition of grain dust in grain elevators is the same as that of coal dust. Most grain elevators near urban areas are required to have dust collection systems. Dust, generated when grain is handled during loading and processing, is a serious problem for the grain handling and storage industry.

An alternative to collecting dust is to reduce and control it. A promising method is suppression by the application of edible oil. A process was patented in 1980 that involves the addition of 0.02-0.06 percent edible oil to a grain stream when it is handled. Tests indicate that good dust suppression is achieved at application and after several months in storage.

Mycotoxins and molds—Although a variety of molds grow on stored grain, much of the attention has been focused on aflatoxin produced by the fungus A. flavus. Aflatoxin problems have been prevalent in several southeastern States in the past decade. A severe outbreak occurred in 1977 and a number of research projects were developed as a result. Plant stress during development of the corn ear seems to be associated with the higher levels of aflatoxin in the corn kernels at maturity. Plant stress may be induced by temperatures in excess of 90 °F., drought conditions, inadequate fertility, and weed competition.

Feeding grain contaminated with aflatoxin to farm animals reduces feed efficiency, increases susceptibility to diseases, interferes wtih immunization, and reduces reproductive performance. Feeding products with high aflatoxin concentration can sicken and kill livestock.

Drying, Handling, and Storing Methods to Reduce Quality Losses

Little benefit comes from improving harvested grain quality unless drying, storing, and handling methods can be developed to help preserve it. The potential for quality deterioration during storage has increased in recent years as a result of the buildup of U.S. grain stocks. A sizable proportion of

these stocks are stored on farms under the farmer-owned reserve program, in structures where it is difficult to monitor the condition of the grain.

Insects do a great deal of damage to stored grain. Insect problems appear to start on the farm, and they can be economically controlled there through better storage management.

Commercial warehouse operators constantly monitor the temperature of stored grain. When hot spots are detected, they may turn the grain by moving it from one bin to another to condition the grain. Many commercial operators also use aeration to protect the quality of stored grain. The circulation of air cools stored grain and this minimizes mold growth and insect activity. Insect fumigation can be done through an aeration system. Aeration also can prevent moisture movement from warm grain to cool

Proper drying, handling, and storing methods are essential to maintain grain quality. Farmers and commercial grain warehouse operators must constantly monitor stored grain to detect changes in the grain's condition. (Farmland Industries, Inc.)

grain in the grain mass, which is usually associated with mold growth. The presence of broken kernels, as well as foreign material such as dirt, weed seeds, and dust in the grain mass reduces the effectiveness of aeration systems and creates a favorable environment for insects. The exposure of the internal starch portion of the kernel and the presence of cracks are believed to increase susceptibility to mold growth. Mold growth is a frequent source of heat and moisture, and provides a good environment for insects. So it is a major contributor to quality losses during storage.

The greatest potential for reducing quality losses in storage is probably in improved drying methods, particularly for corn, but adoption of improved drying methods will be gradual because existing drying equipment represents a substantial investment by farmers and warehouse owners. Improved methods will likely be adopted only when existing equipment becomes obsolete. However, adoption could be accelerated if the marketing system provides incentives to deliver a product to the marketplace that has less breakage susceptibility. A sizable research effort is underway to develop instrumentation and analytical procedures to measure breakage susceptibility in corn. The regional research project, *Marketing and Delivery of Quality Cereals and Oilseeds in Domestic and Foreign Markets,* is a collaborative study underway to evaluate the measurement of corn breakage susceptibility using a number of devices designed to measure breakage susceptibility. If a reliable device can be identified, breakage susceptibility may become a grading factor in the future.

Measuring Quality

There should be incentives to maintain the original quality of grain as it matures in the field. However, current discounting practices used by country elevators reflect biases in the methods normally used to measure quality. For example, test weight (a measure of grain density) is a factor in U.S. standards for corn, but it cannot be justified on the basis of value in end uses, since it has no effect on the feeding value of the corn. On the other hand, it measures density of the grain kernel, which is important to dry millers. Thus, there appear to be conflicts between grading standards that are based on end-use values and those that encourage quality maintainence.

Improved Grading Standards Needed for Processors

Many of the chemical and physical properties of grain that are important to processors are not measured by current grading standards for U.S. grain. Soybean processors, for example, are interested in the oil and protein content of the soybeans they crush. Current grading factors are only indirectly related to the quality of oil and meal that can be produced from the soybeans. To provide processors with the desired quality, we must identify those factors that are important to the economic profitability of their operations.

In the case of corn, the characteristics that influence value in dry milling, wet milling, and feed manufacturing are not reflected in the grading standards. Processors need information on oil content, starch content, breakage susceptibility, and nutritional value in order to make informed purchases. Pricing on the basis of some of these factors would have an influence on the hybrids selected by producers. Price premiums for selected quality characteristics would also provide marketing firms with an incentive to segregate high quality grain in the marketing channel.

New quality factors may not need to be incorporated into the grading standards; however, they must be standardized so that buyers can specify the quality characteristics that are economically important to their operation. Manufacturers of corn food products often obtain grain that meets their special needs through contracts with producers. They provide growers with a list of acceptable hybrids and specify how the grain is to be dried. They offer premiums for high quality grain and producers respond accordingly.

Quality as a Competitive Tool

The recent change in the procedure for certifying dockage (nonwheat material such as chaff, wheat seeds, and dust) in U.S. wheat is an example of a change designed to enhance buyer satisfaction with U.S. grain. In 1987, the Federal Grain Inspection Service began reporting dockage in wheat to the nearest one-tenth of 1 percent rather than to the next lowest one-half percent. This change is significant for large-quantity buyers, and it should lead to greater satisfaction on the part of our customers. Before this change, cleanliness of U.S. wheat had become a major issue.

The export market has become more competitive in recent years. Retaining our market share will require us to meet the competition head on. It may require changes in U.S. grades as well as developing new contractual arrangements that will permit foreign buyers to specify quality characteristics that are economically important to them. Being price competitive will not assure us of a market for our grain, since other exporters can easily match our price. We need to identify which chemical and physical properties are important to our customers. Once these preferences are known, we can provide producers with incentives to produce grain that meets our customers' needs. More attention to quality will improve our position in the highly competitive world market.

Value-Added Packaging: An Edge in the Marketplace

Susan B. Bassin, principal, King-Casey, Inc., New Canaan, CT

Today's food marketing is more competitive than ever. Developing an innovative, value-added package can capture the busy consumer's attention and help gain a real competitive edge.

Hundreds of new products are introduced every year, all fighting for shelf space in crowded supermarkets. Some departments are growing—delicatessen, bakery, and fresh produce—while others are shrinking. With this squeeze on space, supermarket management has become more sophisticated. More and more chains have instituted direct product profitability measures, and now supermarket managers know before suppliers which products are selling best.

At the same time, consumers have changed shopping habits. Ten years ago the average supermarket shopping trip took 1 hour; today, 20 minutes. Consumers are so busy, they do not even plan these trips according to the 1987 report by the Point of Purchase Advertising Institute. It stated:

- 69 percent have no shopping list
- 75 percent do not read newspaper ads
- 90 percent do not read store circulars
- 80 percent do not redeem coupons

It is no wonder that fully two-thirds of supermarket purchase decisions are made at the point of sale and half of the purchases are unplanned!

Unfortunately, many food marketers have not kept pace with these changes. While most of the purchase decisions are made *in-store,* most of the marketing budget is allocated to "out-of-store" advertising, coupons, sweepstakes, and even direct mail programs. While we do not mean to minimize the importance of advertising and public relations, agricultural marketers often overlook the power of packaging—the only element of marketing communications that is always on duty, selling the product at the point of sale.

To be effective, today's package must do more than just contain and transport a product through distribution to the supermarket. Here are five other functions that can add value for both consumers and producers.

1. Brand Identification

Branding agricultural commodities has helped to increase sales and profits in meat and fresh produce. If you deliver quality products dependably and build a brand image, consumers will rely on your quality product time and time again.

The package can establish brand identification with both graphics and structure. Graphics can express your brand name, the key benefits of your product, and your market positioning, that is, what you want to represent to the consumer.

With consumers in a hurry, just the brand name itself may not be enough to catch their eye. The total look must be recognizable. So, package shape is another way to add to brand identification. The objective is to help consumers find your product in a cluttered environment quickly and confidently.

2. Advertising at the Point of Sale

Television and magazine advertising are less effective than they once were. Audiences are fragmented. Consumers are bombarded with thousands of messages a day and channel hop or flip through the pages of their magazines.

But when shoppers are in the supermarket, your package is there in the store when they are ready to buy and need information. They want to select the best product for themselves, and the package is the best and only source of information available at the point of sale.

3. Transport of Product With Less Damage

The busy consumer has only a few minutes to stop off at the supermarket to pick up a few things and run through the eight-items-or-less check-out line. To be sure, supermarkets will provide a bag to carry the items home.

But how about fresh produce? Many stores have expanded this department. It *is* nice for consumers to pick out exactly the tomato or fresh peaches they want, but unfortunately only a plastic bag is offered at the produce department to carry these products home. How often have consumers been frustrated at the checkout counter when these plastic bags filled with ripe fruits and vegetables are dumped in the bottom of a paper sack where they get crushed by heavier products? Why not a new value-added package innovation that will help protect and transport the fresh produce picked out by the consumers themselves?

4. At-Home Storage

Many opportunities exist to create demand for your products through careful attention to their use and storage at home. One of the most recent successes has been the application of aseptic packaging to fruit juice—compact, shelf stable, easy to transport, single-serving containers with straws packed—ideal for lunch boxes or taking on picnics. Opportunities also exist to package produce in more convenient serving sizes, especially for snacking.

Why not add convenience at home for other products? A recent King-Casey study of consumer problems with food packaging identified leaking fresh meat packaging as the No. 1 problem—experienced by 76 percent of female supermarket shoppers.

Our study also showed considerable frustration among consumers about packages that do not adequately reseal—flour, cookies, cereal, crackers, cheese. Many consumers say they have to repackage their foods at home to keep them fresher longer.

5. Task Assistance

It was probably the TV dinner that started it all—it was convenient and allowed busy families to meet different meal preferences. Today, many food manufacturers are providing this task assistance and taking advantage of the microwave process. More and more manufacturers are offering frozen foods in dual-ovenable packages. Others are formulating their foods strictly for microwave oven cooking, targeting their brand toward the busy consumer. Here we find many efforts to make these packages more convenient.

For example, packages that go directly from the supermarket to the freezer to the microwave oven to the table add tremendous convenience and value from the consumer's point of view.

Pasta sold in flow-through plastic bags make it much easier for consumers to drain the cooked product.

This preschooler is enjoying an apple drink from aseptic packaging. The packages are compact, shelf stable, easy to carry, and come in single-serving containers. (William E. Carnahan)

Squeezable containers were a natural for catsup but haven't worked quite as well for jellies. It's crucial in developing your value-added package that you understand clearly consumers' habits and needs.

Involve the Consumer in the Development Process

Looking for an edge in the competitive marketplace and recognizing the important role that packaging can play, how do you go about developing an innovative value-added package? A disciplined, careful process—test, design, retest, refine—can lead to the outstanding development you are seeking.

Test the Market.
Identify your target customers and understand thoroughly how they use your product, their likes and dislikes, and their problems with current packaging. It is important to understand alternative products that consumers may choose when dissatisfied with your product; that is, what are their options?

A variety of consumer research techniques may be used, such as individual interviews, focus group discussions, in-home use tests. Thoroughly understanding your consumers and their problems leads to your objective—namely, to solve those consumer problems.

Design New Solutions.
With the design objectives set on the basis of information collected, a wide range of creative concepts should be generated. Draw on your own staff, your packaging supplier, or an outside consultant as resources.

Then visualize these concepts in sketch form, discuss them, and measure these concepts against the objectives you set. Toss out the ones that are impossible or do not really solve

the problems. Estimate costs, and select the best alternatives.

Retest—Check the New Concept With Consumers.
Now is the time in the process to go back to consumers, and through market research, expose them to the new product or package concept. Again, outside consultants can help you organize and conduct the research. Let the *consumers tell you* which is the best solution to their problems from *their* point of view. We like to keep this focus on the consumer because, in the end, it is the consumer who pays for the product at the cash register and determines its ultimate success.

Refine the New Idea.
You must now interpret the consumer input collected. You may have a clear "winner" among your concepts, but, more often than not, even the winner can be strengthened through refinements indicated by the research. Here, it is critical to apply design expertise to translate this consumer input into real and practical packaging structure and graphics for market success.

Packaging Important for Marketing Success

When putting together your marketing plan for your agricultural product, be sure to consider the important role that packaging can play in your success.

But above all things, know your consumer and his or her problems. Then: test—design—retest—refine— and use a disciplined process to create those new package solutions. If packaging lacks appeal or practicality, the consumer may never be tempted to look inside, no matter how fine a product you offer.

Moving the Farm Harvest

Martin F. Fitzpatrick, Jr., administrator, Office of Transportation, USDA

In business, there is an old saying that "nothing happens until the sale is made." In agriculture, a sale cannot be made if the products cannot reach the marketplace. Farm products stored at the farm gate are of little value to consumers. Physical distribution operations add value to the farm products by virtue of the transport, storage, packaging, and handling services performed.

Last year, American consumers spent about $17 billion, or nearly 6 percent of their food dollars, for transportation. If agricultural transportation were considered as an industry, it would equal the combined farm value of the wheat, swine, and commercial vegetable industries. Moving millions of tons of farm commodities and food products at the right time and to the right place is an essential and costly activity. Some recent approaches to improving how we move the farm harvest follow.

Modern Business Management Approach

Today, managers are sharply aware of costs of transportation and physical distribution, as they search for a greater share of the market and more profits. Look, for instance, at the dramatic switch in the form and manner of marketing and distributing fresh meat. Today, almost all fresh meat is shipped to retail markets in boxed form instead of as the traditional hanging carcass. Costs of handling are lower, transport equipment requirements are reduced, and freight rates are lower for boxed meat shipments.

The marketing and physical distribution system must react promptly to serve a continuously changing consumer mix. It must maintain the ability to move, handle, and store various-sized packages of products, and be flexible enough to supply both domestic and world markets. The transportation and distribution system must respond to market needs by locating storage facilities and freight terminals at the right places.

Cost Tradeoffs

Most successful distribution executives no longer make shipping decisions based solely on a comparison of transportation rates. Rather, they evaluate, in addition to transportation costs, the total cost of the several individual physical distribution components. This evaluation procedure involves cost tradeoffs. For example, it is possible to select a freight mode, such as air transport, with a higher freight rate that still is cheaper door-to-door than shipping by surface carrier with a lower freight rate. In this case, there is a total cost saving if the tangible costs of packaging, crating, insurance, distribution warehousing, and so forth are reduced sufficiently to offset the more costly rates of air transport. In sum, before shipping decisions are made, a careful analysis of all of the physical distribution costs—plus customer service considerations—must be made.

Just In Time

Cutting costs in important ways has simply become essential. Among the innovative concepts now emerging in the marketplace is a practice called "Just-In-Time" supplier deliveries. A few years ago, when interest rates skyrocketed to double-digit levels, agribusiness and other industry leaders began to ship items as they were needed and thus reduce or eliminate large and costly inventories. Managers controlled the amounts of various materials used in manufacturing within more tightly defined boundaries by receiving items as needed for their plant production line. The idea is to stock only what will be needed or sold in a predictable period of time—no more, but also no less. Essentially, the shipping process becomes an integral and dependable extension of the product assembly line.

The higher levels of customer service resulting from a zero or nearly zero inventory business has put greater pressure on providers of transportation services—tighter scheduling and assurance of reliable transportation. There is no margin for error. But, numerous processors and retailers are finding they can reduce storage requirements and eliminate the loss of goods from aging through "Just-In-Time" programs.

Improved Shipping Techniques

Also, as the distance from farm to final market increases, as market territory enlarges, and as competition intensifies, the development of better shipping techniques greatly influences the fraction of the sales price netted back to the farmer. Within the last few years, the accelerated pace of foreign competition and the many abrupt changes in the farm economy have prompted American farmers, agribusinesses, exporters, and transportation companies to focus even greater attention on productivity improvements in physical distribution and transportation activities.

Double-Stack Container Trains

As the volume and value of U.S. imports from the Far East grew rapidly during the 1970's, their high unit value made them unusually well suited to containerization. And, as the use of containers grew, maritime liner companies developed several options to deliver containers to U.S. receivers inland. Motor carriers and the use of special container trains for more distant markets were options, but more often it was simpler to keep the container on the West Coast and merely transload the containerized product into another carrier's equipment. The container was then immediately available to be shipped back, sometimes empty, for more Asian cargo.

The growth of intermodalism (e.g., freight containers placed upon railroad flat cars) has spurred the unveiling of a specialized railroad freight car designed for container traffic. To make fuller use of the protective container and eliminate costly transloading, ocean carriers invested in the development and production of a "welled" rail car that could accommodate one container stacked on another. This special car was needed because ordinary cars stacked two containers high would not fit through standard rail tunnels. With the new double-stacked cars, however, more containers can be placed on each car, and more containers can be carried on each train. The economics were evident and the practice mushroomed. The volume of double-stacked container movements, which amounted to only 30,000 moves in 1984, expanded to over 400,000 moves in 1987.

Double-stacked container rail cars mean that more containers can be
placed on each railroad freight car. Thus, more containers can be
carried on each train. Such container movements expanded from
30,000 in 1984 to more than 400,000 in 1987. (June Davidek)

Intermodal rail car design

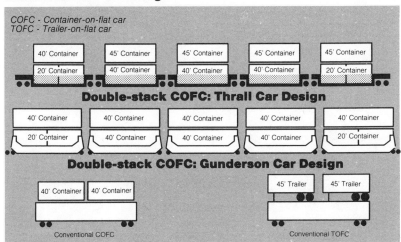

COFC - Container-on-flat car
TOFC - Trailer-on-flat car

| 40' Container | 45' Container | 45' Container | 45' Container | 45' Container |
| 20' Container | 40' Container | 40' Container | 40' Container | 20' Container |

Double-stack COFC: Thrall Car Design

| 40' Container | 40' Container | 40' Container | 40' Container | 40' Container |
| 20' Container | 40' Container | 40' Container | 40' Container | 20' Container |

Double-stack COFC: Gunderson Car Design

| 40' Container | 40' Container | | | 45' Trailer | 45' Trailer |

Conventional COFC   Conventional TOFC

Source: Department of Transportation Staff Study, Effects of Ocean Carrier
Double-Stack Container Train Services on Domestic Rail Freight Services
SS-42-U-41 June 1986

Today, over 50 special, double-stacked container trains leave West Coast cities weekly, bound for hub centers like Chicago, Memphis, Atlanta, New York, Houston, Columbus, and Cincinnati. Still the containers often return empty to westbound locations because of lack of loads. At the same time, cotton, tobacco, hay cubes, food-grade soybeans, seeds, special wheats, and other food products are often trucked or railed to the West Coast to be loaded in containers for export. This is an opportunity for many agricultural shippers to lower freight costs and improve market competition. Testing and evaluation of containers for the movement of perishable farm products continue—but no consensus as to a best new design for double-stack refrigerated containers has yet emerged.

Furthermore, in anticipation of future international business growth, some maritime companies are investing hugh amounts of capital in vastly larger container-carrying ocean vessels. Applying state-of-the-art shipbuilding technology, such ships stretch the length of three football fields, are nearly 130 feet wide, and have a container capacity of up to 3,900 TEU's (20-foot equivalent units). Improved fuel efficiency, speed, reliability and other economies of size could result in substantial cost savings per container.

Unit Trains

A popular method of achieving improved productivity in transporting bulk agricultural commodities over considerable distances is by unit train. A unit train usually consists of 25 or more jumbo-covered hoppers (rail grain cars) between 4400 and

Unit trains, like the one at the left, usually consist of 25 or more jumbo-covered hopper cars. They are capable of moving large quantities of grains to terminal facilities such as this one where barges are being loaded. Most agricultural commodities transported by rail for export move in unit trains.

4800 cubic-foot capacity hauling a single commodity between two points.

Shippers of corn, wheat, barley, and other whole grains are using these trains to move one commodity between one or several origins and destinations, but through recent technology, jumbo-covered hoppers are being developed for dual service—so that two commodities, such as wheat and rye, can be loaded side by side in the same car. This versatility allows for both merchandisers and receivers to tailor their requirements in domestic markets for what they need—raw commodity or finished product. In addition to grain, unit trains are widely used to move perishables, canned foods, coal, chemicals, and ores.

Unit trains of 25 or more cars further contribute to the marketing of agricultural products since railroads often encourage their use because of efficiencies gained over single or smaller multicar shipments. These efficiencies may be realized through the limited number of origins and destinations, automation, better turnaround time (in some cases half that of single car movements), and maximum crew and equipment utilization. Another advantage to the railroad industry is the ability to keep better track of its equipment. As one rail industry official put it, "cars are not scattered all over the country."

Most agricultural commodities that are transported by rail for export move in unit trains. Export elevators are designed to handle 100-car trains. One major Western railroad, the Nation's largest carrier of grain and grain products, transports 60 percent of its whole grain traffic in unit trains. The carrier has a fleet of 27,000 jumbo-covered hopper cars available for its use, consisting of its own cars as well as those owned by grain cooperatives and private grain companies that have purchased or leased the rail cars.

A major benefit to the cooperatives and companies who use unit train services is lower freight rates. Volume rates associated with larger capacity equipment and unit trains create a major incentive for grain marketing organizations to streamline their collection and distribution practices. As a result, farm-to-market price differentials have declined and farmers have benefited.

Improved Information Systems

Greater intermodal transportation (combining the advantages of different modes of shipment) and unit train movements will result in a greater need for timely information of all types. Complex applications of communications lines that link both voice and computer data of the many transportation users and providers could inevitably lead to totally paperless documentation of shipments by substituting electronic communication for today's mail systems. Efforts are underway to tie together customers, carriers, and the several U.S. Government agencies through computers to handle the increased information workload without significantly adding to staff.

Advances in computer-based information systems also enable transportation and physical distribution managers to evaluate a host of options quickly and more thoroughly than ever before. The availability of computerized problem-solving programs that produce simulations of vehicle routes and schedules, return on investment, and cost analyses, plus other "what if" solutions are increasingly valuable tools for agribusiness management in the quest for profit improvements and greater efficiencies in moving the farm harvest.

Convenience and Competition in Food Marketing and Distribution

Drayton McLane, Jr., president and chief executive officer, McLane Company, Temple, TX, and chairman, National-American Wholesale Grocers' Association, Falls Church, VA

The American food industry is consumer driven like no other. Although agricultural production of certain commodities is constant, processors, distributors, and retailers cater to customer desires. To see whether this is true, one has only to enter a supermarket and compare it to a store 10 or 15 years ago. One would see:

- Almost a 50-percent changeover in new products
- In-store bakeries and full-service delicatessens
- Fresh seafood departments
- Salad bars generous enough to make most restaurants jealous
- An increase in variety and selection in the produce section
- The rise of sections with hot food to go

These changes show some larger demographic and social trends in our society. A two wage-earner home is now typical in the United States. Because of this, food buying has changed. Instead of buying items that involve significant preparation time, the typical shopper looks for quick preparation items. Microwaving is, for many, the preferred mode of cooking. (Ignore for the moment the rise of gourmet cooking which, by definition, requires investment of time as "an art form.")

Another reason for the grocery changes is competition from fast food outlets and from restaurants. Since one meal out of three is eaten away from home, a supermarket must be prepared to compete for the food dollar. The trend generally points to faster preparation time (or none at all) for food, a greater variety of products, and an emphasis on healthful, nutritious—and fresh—foods. "Healthy" fresh foods also should be easy to prepare.

Convenience Drives Consumer

The common denominator for all of these consumer wants is convenience. For example, convenience stores (which we call C-stores) increased from 51,000 in 1982 to 64,000 in 1986. These stores are usually about 5,000 square feet or less and sell items which consumers need in a hurry. Sales for the same period climbed 50 percent from $35.9 to $53.9 billion. McLane Company distributes mass merchandising products such as candies, tobacco, and perishables as well as import specialty items to 18,000 convenience stores in all 50 States. More traditional stores have tried to make themselves more convenient with in-store fresh or fast food features.

Another structural response to the demand for convenience is store size. Interestingly, store size has taken two distinct paths. One road leads to smaller convenience-type stores with perhaps 3,000 square feet. The other leads to the opposite extreme. Hypermarkets with 300,000 square feet and 40 checkout lanes make the supermarket of 10 years ago look primitive by comparison.

Are these roads leading to the same destination? At first glance, they do not appear to have a lot in common. Yet, they both promote convenience. The C-store brags about how little time it takes to buy the necessities. The large store says, in effect, "why shop anywhere else for any reason? We're your one stop shop for everything from raisins to raincoats."

The diversification of product lines also demonstrates consumer preference for convenience. It is hard to find a grocery store without a selection of health and beauty aids, a pharmacy, greeting cards, books, hardware items such as household tools and furnace filters, and some auto supplies such as oil. The hypermarket, although novel in proportion, merely takes this full-service trend to its logical conclusion.

Much has been written saying that the hypermarket may be destined to replace the supermarket just as supermarkets replaced many mom and pop grocery stores. Hypermarket success depends on sheer consumer numbers. The greater the concentration of people, the better, because razor-thin profit margins require quantity sales. The format of the store also will determine success. The consumer jury is still out on this verdict—will the shopper respond better to a hypermarket resembling an airplane hanger or to one with smaller sections of modules under one roof? Only time will tell.

The other factor limiting size is convenience. Although it may be nicer to do all one's shopping at one time, the time factor may weigh in against giant parking lots or a feeling of being swallowed up by the store's vastness. It of course is not a choice simply between hypermarkets and C-stores. Specialty "gourmet" Safeways are all the rage in Washington, DC, and other formats are being explored. Still, to the medium-sized store, the squeeze is on between large facilities and competition from convenience stores and restaurants.

Distribution Changing Too

It is important to look at the food distribution industry as well as the retail level. Retail is what people see, but it is simply the tip of the iceberg.

The distribution link in the food chain is frequently overlooked. There are generally two types of food distributors—grocery and foodservice. Grocery is somewhat of a misnomer since distributors also carry paper products, health and beauty aids, and so forth.

The National-American Wholesale Grocers' Association (NAWGA) is a trade association which represents the wholesale grocery and foodservice distribution industry in the United States and Canada. NAWGA member firms account for more than $65 billion worth of annual sales. Foodservice distributors bring food to restaurants, to institutions, and in some cases to educational systems for school lunch programs. The trend toward eating out has encouraged the growth of foodservice in the United States. Wholesale grocers distribute to almost 50 percent of the stores in the United States—the independent (nonchain) retailers.

As with retail, the wholesale side is undergoing rapid change because of the changing nature of the retail store. Wholesalers must adapt to meet retail needs just as retailers and manufacturers need to respond to consumer preferences.

Change in consumer demand forces every other part of the food industry to change. If consumer demand for fresh seafood doubles by the year 2000, as some project, fish harvesting will change, as will packaging. Speedy transportation will be of the utmost importance, and food distributors will have to radically reshape their physical plants to allow for seafood (in some cases, the distributor specializes in seafood). This means special trucks, coolers, and specific training for staff.

Competition Intense

Convenience is not the only common denominator in the food industry. Competition is the other. Consumers will switch allegiances for many reasons, and stores continually battle for the hearts and pocketbooks of the food buyer. Retailers can switch wholesalers too, so wholesalers must also be responsive.

The grocery industry is far from static. Although net profit for supermarket sales is only 1.12 percent, there is considerable movement in the industry. The Food Marketing Institute points to leaders in major markets to show these changes. In 1965, for example, the top Chicago firms were National Tea, Kroger, Jewel, A&P, and Certified Grocers. Now, Kroger, A&P, and National Tea have been replaced as leaders by Dominick's and Eagle. The same story is true for Boston and other cities as well. Once dominant Safeway is declining. In this dynamic, consumer-driven industry, jockeying for the food dollar is constant.

Wholesale competition is keen too. Stores will go to the wholesaler who best helps their bottom line. Because of competition, productivity and efficiency are constantly emphasized. The need for economies of scale has made it more and more imperative for wholesalers to obtain capital, to

grow larger or perish. The past 5 years have seen an unprecedented wave of mergers and acquisitions. This trend is driven by efficiency, capital needs, and technology.

Although it may be tempting to predict concentration to a few super wholesalers in just a few years, a more likely scenario sees consolidations continuing but smaller regional wholesalers still playing a vital role because of niche marketing such as ethnic, Hispanic, and imported. In order to prosper, a company will need to use the latest in technology (such as computer inventory controls, computerized truck routing, and Universal Product Code labeling on cases of materials) to have the same level of efficiency and sufficient resources to generate capital formation and attract capable management. Thanks to competition, room still exists for entry of new business people even though the entry threshold has risen significantly.

More Change in Future

The grocery industry has seen formidable changes and the consumer receives the big benefits—quality food, an incredible variety of products from which to choose, and a reasonable price. This change is by no means over. It is escalating, and no one can really predict what destination the industry will reach. The consumer's desire for convenience is not likely to end soon and competition will continue to intensify, leading to changing structures in marketing and food distribution as well.

Electronic Marketing Energizes Agricultural Trading

Wayne D. Purcell, professor, and James B. Bell, extension economist, agricultural economics, Virginia Tech, Blacksburg, VA

In his article on electronic technology in the 1986 Yearbook of Agriculture, David Dik said, "Electronic technologies are swiftly becoming pervasive. The United States is only 3 or 4 years away from having the major social and economic forces shift from mass society and the industrial age to the information age." In agriculture, electronic marketing is becoming an important application of electronic technology as we see Dik's prediction come true.

Background on Electronic Marketing

Electronic marketing involves the use of advanced communication networks to create a centralized trading arena. Trading takes place based on product descriptions. Physical assembly of the product is not necessary, nor is it necessary for the buyer and seller to come together. Only the price discovery process is centralized.

The emergence of electronic marketing began with the implementation of a teletype network selling slaughter hogs in Ontario, Canada in 1961. Similar teletype systems were developed in Manitoba and Alberta. In 1962, a telephone network was used to sell slaughter hogs in Virginia. Teleauctions have since expanded to feeder pigs, slaughter lambs, feeder cattle, slaughter cattle, and other agricultural commodities.

A new era began in 1975 when computerized communication systems were used to market cotton in Texas. In 1978, USDA's Agricultural Marketing Service supported several development efforts in computerized trading systems. Trading systems for eggs, feeder cattle, slaughter hogs, slaughter lambs, and carcass beef were developed and tested. Across the past decade, a great deal of attention has been paid to electronic marketing systems.

Motivation for Electronic Marketing

The increased interest in electronic markets is due to the need for efficiency and competitiveness of agricultural markets. Many agricultural markets are small and geographically isolated, and have difficulty attracting sufficient volume of product or sufficient buyers to have a competitive sale. Such markets can be called "thin markets," markets in which a small number of buyers or sellers can exert a significant influence on price or other terms of trade.

Thin markets are not limited to the small and remote markets, however. With products such as eggs, cattle, and hogs, where direct sales are prevalent and formula pricing is widely used, industry leaders have charged that prices are influenced by actions of one or a few buyers. As the volume handled and the number of buyers and sellers participating declines, the effectiveness of some of the traditionally larger and competitive markets has been questioned.

In the information age, an electronic marketing system that centralizes the price discovery process, cuts the costs of marketing, and increases the availability of information has the potential to alleviate many problems.

Types of Electronic Marketing Systems

There are four types of electronic marketing systems (some systems, such as video systems and the telephone auction, can be used in combination):

1. **Computerized Marketing Systems.** Computers are programmed to conduct trading between buyers and sellers using an accepted industry negotiating procedure (for example, auctions, bids and offers, sealed bids, firm offer). Computers receive, store, process, and send information.

Several types of hardware, software, and communication systems may be used. The hardware includes a central site computer to exchange and process the information entered by the potential traders. The host computer and the remote terminals or computers are tied together by dial-up telephone, special telephone lines, or satellite communication systems. The selection of the appropriate technology depends on system requirements.

The software determines how the system hardware will function and how each participant (buyer, seller, observer, and system controller) will interact within the system. The software is programmed to control access to information and to define trading options. Examples of computerized marketing systems currently in operation in the United States are TELE-COT, which markets cotton; the National Electronic Marketing Association (NEMA), which sells livestock; and the Computerized Assisted Marketing Program (CAMP), which markets fruits and vegetables.

2. **Video Auctions.** Buyers view videotapes of the product, often livestock, offered for sale. Verbal descriptions of the livestock also are provided, and the seller or selling agent explains delivery options and other terms of trade. The videotapes are distributed to each sale site or are dis-

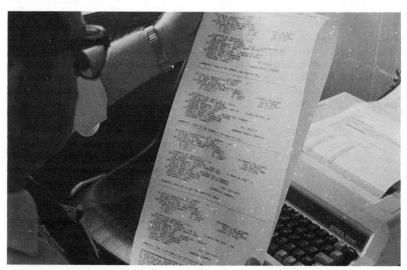

Computerized electronic marketing systems use computers to receive, store, process, and send information. These computers have the capacity to handle large volumes of market information quickly. (Virginia Polytechnic Institute)

tributed electronically using a satellite system.

Using a conference telephone network, the auctioneer starts the auction and sells the livestock to the highest bidder. The livestock, after being graded, are shipped directly from the seller to the buyer. Video auctions have been used commercially in eight States and have been tried experimentally in several others to sell feeder cattle, slaughter cattle, feeder lambs, breeding sheep, and breeding cattle.

3. **Teleauctions.** These are auctions conducted over a conference telephone network. Descriptions of the products are assembled from sellers before the auction. The auctioneer describes the livestock (or other product) to all buyers on the telephone hookup, and the livestock are sold to the highest bidder. The livestock are shipped directly from the farm or sale site to the buyer. Teleauctions are widely used in the United States to sell feeder pigs, feeder cattle, slaughter cattle, and market lambs.

4. **Teletype Auctions.** Consignments are obtained from potential sellers, and the offers are transmitted to teletype printers located in buyers' offices. Buyers bid during the auction by using a special button attached to their teletype machine. This method is generally faster than the teleauction, has the capacity to handle more participants, and produces a written record of the transactions. When the teletype auction was introduced, it represented state-of-the-art technology, but many of its technological advantages have now been eclipsed by computerized systems.

Benefits of Electronic Marketing

The importance of the benefits varies depending on the type of electronic marketing system used, the product marketed, the market structure of the industry, geographic location, and other factors. Nevertheless, studies show six somewhat related benefits are almost always found to exist.

1. **Improved Market Information.** Accurate, complete, and timely market information is necessary for an efficient price discovery process. Buyers and sellers must have access to adequate market information if their bids and offers are to reflect accurately supply and demand conditions.

One of the more obvious characteristics of electronic markets is the ability to process and transmit information rapidly. Since trading is based on product descriptions, information is readily available to large numbers of potential traders and to market observers. In the NEMA computerized lamb sales, for example, market information is not only used internally in the system, but is also available to market reporters for public market reports. As computerized marketing systems become more widespread, they have the potential to greatly improve the generation, distribution, and availability of market information.

2. **Increased Market Efficiency.** The costs of searching for trading partners, successfully negotiating and completing transactions, and physically moving products from sellers to buyers are activities in which electronic marketing can improve market efficiency. Electronic markets enable buyers to quickly search for all eligible sellers, and sellers can access more potential buyers.

Physical movement of products typically is less costly in electronic markets than in conventional markets, particularly auction markets where products and buyers must assemble in one location and the product must then be redistributed after the sale.

3. **Improved Pricing Accuracy.** Pricing accuracy is concerned with

how quickly and accurately prices reflect the true market values for specific products or grades. Under an efficient pricing system, price differentials should not vary significantly from the cost of moving products from one place to another, the cost of storage, or the cost of substituting one product quality for another. Studies of electronic markets for hogs and eggs provide evidence that pricing efficiency in electronic markets is greater than in conventional markets.

4. **Increased Competition.** Most trade in agricultural products occurs by some type of direct private transaction between buyers and sellers. A producer seldom has bids from more than two or three buyers, often only one. It is not economically feasible for numerous buyers to locate in or frequently travel to the dispersed areas where agricultural products are produced. Electronic markets can increase competition by enabling distant buyers to participate in small dispersed markets. In addition, electronic markets may create trading procedures which encourage competitive interaction among buyers. A Virginia study found that because bidders remained anonymous on the NEMA computerized lamb sales, active bidding time was extended and prices were enhanced.

5. **Higher Prices.** Perhaps the most consistent advantage of electronic markets is their tendency to increase market prices. Higher prices result from lower buyer acquisition costs, increased competition from new buyers, and a more competitive pricing structure. A Virginia study documented that the electronic market for lambs returned significantly higher prices to producers than did conventional markets. Studies on other commodities have produced similar results.

6. **Improved Market Access.** Electronic markets offer improved access to both buyers and sellers. Sellers benefit from the exposure of product offerings to a larger number of potential buyers, while buyers have access to a broader array of sellers. Both the large number of market participants and the competition-enhancing dimension of electronic markets permit buyers and sellers to participate regardless of their size, location, or status.

More Electronic Marketing by 1990's

The trend toward electronic marketing will accelerate in the 1990's. Cost-effective communication technology and increased awareness of the economic benefits of electronic systems will force adjustments and change. Changes in industry structure and increased concern over the adequacy of publicly available prices and market information will accentuate the need for new and more progressive ways of marketing. What we have learned in the 1980's will provide the foundation on which we can build.

Perhaps the most important message of the 1980's is that electronic markets work best in situations where marketing problems and inefficiencies exist, an organization of producers or other participants wants to see change, and the electronic system can be introduced with only incremental changes in the trading procedures used by buyers and sellers.

Potential participants will always resist change because of the uncertainty that comes with it, and this should be kept in mind when designing electronic marketing systems. If systems are designed that do not require revolutionary changes in procedures, then the 1990's will witness a major move to electronic technology in our agricultural markets as users move to take advantage of the technical and economic benefits that have been identified.

Scanning the Future

Harold S. Ricker, acting director, Market Research and Development Division, Agricultural Marketing Service, and Oral Capps, Jr., associate professor, Agricultural Economics Department, Texas A.&M. University, College Station, TX

Chances are 50-50 that your last food purchase at a supermarket was scanned to determine the price. You also received a detailed item description of your purchase and possibly coupons for future repeat or complementary purchases.

At the same time, your purchase was providing valuable information to the supermarket. The manager can periodically check to see what items are selling, if a sales promotion is effective, which checker is busy, and for how long, and use other information that helps manage the store.

The Universal Product Codes (UPC's) are perhaps the most important innovation for the retailing industry since shopping carts or computers. Retail food stores are now shifting from conventional checkout systems to scanning checkout systems. Since the Kroger Company first installed a scanning checkout system in a retail store in July 1972, over 15,000 food stores have added scanning at the point of sale.

And scanning is gaining popularity worldwide. Just about all packaged retail merchandise has UPC markings. Apparel and footwear companies have developed programs for scanning, either using bar codes or scannable numbers that can be placed on items or on merchandise tickets. J.C. Penney pioneered the adoption among department stores. Mass retail, specialty, and department stores as well as smaller supermarkets are using scanning systems.

The Universal Product Codes (UPC's) are one of the most important innovations for the retail industry since computers. (William E. Carnahan)

Background of UPC

A system to speed up the checkout operation and eliminate the need to enter prices had long been a dream. The development of computers and scanning technology in the 1950's and 1960's brought the dream closer to reality. Retailing researchers at USDA's Transportation and Facilities Research Division had studied manual checkout systems in the early 1950's and developed standards and recommendations for improvements. In the mid-1960's they developed specifications for what an optical scanning checkout system would have to do to be successfully implemented. Industry, notably Radio Corporation of America (RCA) and Charecogn, Inc., picked up the challenge.

In 1970 a prototype developed by Charecogn, Inc., was delivered to USDA for technical evaluation. At the same time RCA and Kroger Company were testing a system. Charecogn, Inc. used a wagon-wheel-shaped code symbol and RCA used a target symbol. The RCA/Kroger work was proprietary; the USDA findings were made public in 1971. The latter showed that the system would work and would produce hard savings (improved productivity with faster checkouts, reduced errors, etc.) of 1.2 to 1.5 percent of sales, and soft savings (information for management decisionmaking) of more than twice the hard savings. These savings caught the interest of a retailing industry that was only realizing net earnings after taxes of 0.92 percent at the time.

Noting the symbol variation in the two tests and the prospects of other scanners that might require different symbols, food manufacturers became alarmed about the prospect of having to put a number of symbols on their product packages. A joint manufacturer, retailer, wholesaler committee was formed and in 1973 recommended the familiar bar code seen on most products today.

Two methods of scanning merchandise were originally developed, one using a hand-held scanning device and the other featuring a fixed mounted scanner. The latter was better adapted to the high volume food industry, while the former was adopted by many department stores and nonfood retailers. Both types of retailers could monitor sales almost instantaneously.

The retail food industry had been using mainframe computers to handle the large number of accounting functions associated with buying and selling 10,000 items per store and payrolls for the 50 or more employees common to stores in the early 1970's. Because scanners with the UPC codes could make data available in computer-ready form, there was a quantum leap in the data available for managements to assess their business operations and improve their markets and marketing skills.

In fact, data availability has become a real problem for food retailers. When you realize that today each shopper may buy from 10 to 80 or more items, each of which represents a piece of data, you can begin to understand the volume of data accumulated at a single store, let alone a large chain. Converting this mass of data to easily usable reports for different levels of management is the current challenge for the food industry.

Use of Scanning Systems

In 1983 a study of the benefits of scanning was made available to the industry by the National Grocers Association (NGA). Benefits are of two types: hard (tangible) and soft (intangible).

Hard Benefits

These are savings from improvements in speed or accuracy as a result of shifting from conventional checkout systems. Examples are:

- Improvements in checkout productivity (either items checked per labor hour expended, customers handled per hour, or labor cost per item).
- Reductions in shrinkage (product theft or loss).
- Reductions in store bookkeeping (balancing of cash registers, accumulation of total sales, sales by department, and sales tax collected).
- Reductions in labor for item marking and for item price changes.
- Improvements in produce margins from more accurate weighing.

Soft Benefits

These relate to savings from improvements in managerial decisionmaking because of the marketing and management information that scanning systems provide; they are more difficult to measure than hard benefits. Examples are:

- Improvements in shelf space allocation since sales volume and gross margin per item can be compared with the amount of shelf space allocated.
- Improvements in labor scheduling (predominantly cashier and bagger scheduling). Accurate sales data and customer counts by register, store, time of day, and day of the week over a period of time help in labor scheduling, by identifying peak shopping periods.

- Improvements in new item evaluation, which allow manufacturers and retailers to obtain a quick, accurate assessment of new item performance.
- Reduction in out-of-stock position. Improved product inventory and accurate product movement measures help reduce out-of-stocks.
- Improvements in advertising and promotion results. The impact of advertisements, coupons, and special displays is evaluated immediately and more accurately.
- Improvements in pricing decisions. The impact of a price change is readily available.

In addition, the most important benefit could well be the development of an information system designed to meet the special needs of a store. Typically a multistore retailer will initially use scanner data in support of headquarters-level merchandising decisions. At the store level, scanner data are typically used to improve the product assortment and shelf spacing to match consumer demand.

Coupons

Another major application of optical scanners is in various coupon systems. Coupons have long been used by manufacturers and retailers alike as promotional tools. A small portion of all coupons printed are redeemed, but that still means hundreds of redemptions per store each week. The retailer collects a handling charge from the manufacturer, who hopes the retailer has actually sold the right items for each coupon redeemed. With the UPC code on the coupon, it can be read by the scanner, after the consumer's order has been scanned to determine whether a corresponding item has been purchased or not. If not, the coupon amount is not deducted from the consumer's bill. This system also provides the retailer with knowledge of whose coupons were redeemed and in what quantity.

Other approaches connect coupon-producing machines with the register. As the shopper's order is being processed, the coupon dispenser determines if there are related or competing items in the system and prints out corresponding coupons that could be redeemed on the next shopping trip. The manufacturers pay a fee to have their coupons in the system. Coupon redemption with this system is reported to be twice the normal rate, and the coupons specify they are to be redeemed at the issuing retailer's store.

In some stores customers fill out an application form to obtain a scannable ID card for special coupon benefits. The card is presented to the checker at the checkout counter, the order is scanned, and the customer is automatically credited with the coupon value for any items purchased if there is a coupon in the system. The manufacturer pays to have the coupons registered in the computer. The shoppers get the savings, without having to bring in coupons, and retailers and manufacturers get information about the types of people buying their products. This information helps them to target their marketing, especially advertising and promotion efforts.

Research Application

Translating scanning data into information for management decisions is a promising area of research. One approach is a management information system to identify key performance areas and indicators required for various managerial positions. This identification allows for a management by objectives orientation. The critical element of this system is a central data bank from which key reports are generated. The software must have the capacity for database management, analysis, graphics, flexible reporting, and modeling, all in a user friendly environment.

Management of scanner data has traditionally been considered a mainframe application regulated by highly specialized technicians. However, now retail firms may use personal computers to evaluate product performance and sales trends, and to track certain items.

Across the country thousands of households are knowingly participating in advertising tests in return for certain promotional premiums. Their TV viewing habits are monitored and they see selected commercials mixed in with regular commercials, while a demographically matched set of households do not see the same ones but see others. When they shop for

food, they both present their ID's to the checker and their orders are processed. This system is like one of the coupon systems except that this time the manufacturers get response information about their advertisements—providing quicker information about a campaign than traditional methods.

Consumer Resistance

Gone are the days when every item had its own price stamped on it, which is probably the one thing that consumers dislike about scanning systems. Retailers try to offset this issue by vigorously monitoring shelf tags and product spacing to be sure the right price is associated with the right merchandise. These shelf tags also provide unit price information which aids in comparison shopping. Some retailers still put the price on each item 1) as a promotional merchandising effort, 2) because it is required by law in their State, or 3) because they are not yet scanning. On balance, consumers benefit from faster, more accurate checkouts, and more product and price information than they used to receive.

The Future

A tremendous potential still remains for realizing the intangible benefits of scanning.

Decisonmaking

A few firms are using some scanner-derived information in decisionmaking, but a major barrier has been building software to process the data into useful forms. Most retailers still lack the resources and expertise needed to organize and analyze the scanner data. Because of some problems in obtaining accurate data as well as obtaining too much that cannot be presently used, some retailers doubt the value of scanner data in decisionmaking. Changes in item's

UPC, size, number in a case, and description require computer file maintenance procedures. Also, the data base should include information on factors which may influence item performance: out of stocks/no distribution, shelf inventory levels, type of merchandising activity, pricing errors, and allowances from manufacturers. It will be 3-5 years before most retailers can use this information.

Shopping from Home

Now that nearly every item in the food store has a unique product identification number and scannable code, the time is not far away when consumers will be able to order food at home, be assured of specific product quality, and have it delivered. This concept may take the form of scannable codes in a catalog to be scanned on a home scanner. Or, a home computer may be used with a modem and phone to dial up a catalog, and an order may be placed by using a keyboard or mouse for data entry.

Economic Research

The availability of daily sales volume and pricing information collected by scanning checkout systems has almost unlimited potential application in economic research and management decisionmaking. Because scanner data has been generated with enough reliability and consistency for economic research only since 1979, there has been limited use of scanner data as a basis for demand analyses.

Nutrition Information

As a result of diet and health concerns of consumers, nutrition information may be readily available by code in the near future and may supplement the information collected by officials from the Department of Health and Human Services and USDA.

Yes indeed, the future is scannable!

Farmers' Marketing Businesses Will Surprise You

Randall E. Torgerson, administrator, and Gene Ingalsbe, director, Information and Education Staff, Agricultural Cooperative Service

What's your image of a farmer? More than likely it is a family operating trucks, tractors, and other farm equipment. They're feeding livestock, or cultivating and harvesting crops. Summed up, they're on the farm producing food and fiber products.

Now, picture this: Blue Diamond, Land O'Lakes, Ocean Spray, Sunkist, Welch's, and a textile mill manufacturing denim. All of these are farmer-owned cooperatives, and they illustrate the marketing side of the farmer's business. These widely known brand names indicate these businesses are among the most effective marketers of branded food products in the United States. The cooperatives owning these brands are among more than 100 cooperatives owning more than 350 brands.

In 1986, farmer cooperatives had total sales of $58.4 billion, and $41.5 billion of that amount was for marketing farm products. Farmers use marketing cooperatives for research, manufacturing, processing, and brand merchandising. In some commodities, they are major food exporters.

Most commercial farmers (annual sales in excess of $40,000) use cooperatives. A survey revealed in 1986 that 78 percent of such farmers were either members or used cooperatives to buy farm supplies or market products. At the first stage of marketing beyond the farm, cooperatives handle 28 percent of all farm products, though in several commodities the percentage is much higher. These cooperatives range in size from small local elevators, cotton gins, and packing cooperatives to large multibillion dollar regional cooperatives that market nationally and internationally.

Marketing Major Activity

Historically, about three-fourths of farmers' total activity through cooperatives they own has been devoted to marketing. In fact, the earliest known agricultural cooperatives in the United States were formed in 1810 as dairy manufacturing and marketing cooperatives. The total number of cooperatives operating in 1986 was 5,369, and of this number 4,589 were involved in the marketing of farm products. These long-time efforts have resulted in a sizable investment and some sophisticated marketing organizations.

- Blue Diamond Growers, Inc. (see *A Jewel of a Market for Blue Diamond* by Walt Payne) is the world's largest almond processor and marketer. Sioux Honey Association is the world's largest honey marketer; Riceland Foods, the world's largest rice milling and marketer; and Tree Top, the largest U.S. processor and marketer of apple products.
- Cooperatives are leaders in innovative product combinations, processing equipment, and packaging. Dairymen, Inc., was the first U.S. processor of Ultra High Temperature (UHT) treated milk. Ocean Spray (see *New Product Development: The Ocean Spray*

*This is one of more than 5,000 cooperatives that were operating in
1986. In that year, total sales through farmer cooperatives amounted to
$58.4 billion. Of this, $41.5 billion came from marketing farm products.
(William E. Carnahan)*

Way by Tom Bullock) and
Welch's have been industry leaders in developing product combinations and innovative packaging
such as aseptic cartons and
squeezable plastic containers for
jams and jellies. Sunkist
employees hold more than 200
patents on citrus equipment, products, and processes.

In 1986, farmers' total assets in
marketing and purchasing cooperatives was $26.5 billion. Fifteen of their
cooperatives are among the Nation's
500 largest industrial corporations.

Development of Cooperatives

Agricultural producers chose group
action approaches to marketing from
the earliest days when farming progressed beyond supplying food just
for the family. Early barn raisings and
corn husking bees as group activities
moved to more formalized livestock
assembly, cheesemaking, tobacco
marketing, and cotton ginning.

Farm operators undertook cooperative action for one of three reasons:
1) Their relatively small size and
large numbers compared to buyers
meant a disparity in market power
that had to be counterbalanced, 2)
Services were not available to them in
their rural communities, or 3) Marketing services were not available at
reasonable costs.

As commercial production developed, producers looked for ways to
convert milk into a variety of dairy

products, store grain and other crops, process fruits and vegetables, and move livestock and meat products to distant locations.

Cooperatives to carry out these marketing tasks were strongly promoted by farm organizations from 1880 through the 1920's as the best means to overcome depressed price conditions. Organizations like the Patrons of Husbandry (Grange), National Farmers Union, and the American Farm Bureau Federation each were major promoters and catalysts for development of cooperatives. USDA and Federal and State Extension Services likewise fostered the development of marketing and purchasing cooperatives as a way to enhance farm income and to bring electricity, credit, and telephone services to rural America.

In the Midwest, large numbers of locally owned cooperatives emerged and dotted the countryside. Typically, many of these then affiliated with each other to form regional organizations that could consolidate products in large volumes and move them to distant markets. This pattern led to the growth of such organizations as Land O'Lakes, Inc., Mid-America Dairymen, Inc., and Associated Milk Producers, Inc., in dairy; Farmers Union Grain Terminal Association (now Harvest States Cooperatives) and GROWMARK, Inc. in grain; and Farmland Industries, Inc. in the manufacture and distribution of farm supplies such as petroleum, fertilizers, farm chemicals, feed, and seeds.

Similar regional organizations developed on the East Coast, such as Agway, Inc., Southern States Cooperative, Inc., and Gold Kist Inc.

West Coast cooperatives organized differently. A large number of marketing cooperatives were organized by commodity, not community. As a result, relatively large direct membership organizations were formed in raisins and other fruits and vegetables, nuts, cotton, rice, dairy, and livestock. Like their regional counterparts in other areas of the country, these centralized cooperatives were early promoters of State and Federal grades and standards. They also developed quality programs and many of the brand names that are widely recognized today.

Cooperative distribution networks have become national and international in scope. Direct exports by cooperatives, valued at nearly $4 billion annually, go to more than 100 countries. Cooperatives account for 41 percent of U.S. exports of nuts and 32 percent of fruit exports. One-fourth of all U.S. cotton exports originate with cooperatives.

Research Activities

Historically, farmers and their cooperatives have relied heavily on public institutions such as the land-grant universities and USDA for research, primarily associated with agricultural production. However, they also have carried out market research, investing heavily in projects undertaken in the laboratory, in test farms, and in test kitchens.

Research activity is carried out under several organizational arrangements. It may be the principal activity of a cooperative, such as NC+ Plus Hybrids, a regional seed cooperative for field crops. It may take the form of Land O'Lakes' test kitchen, which turned out an industry-first new product, a butter/margarine blend, out of two fiercely competitive products. Several of the large regional cooperatives operate their own research and demonstration farms.

Additionally, they've combined efforts by forming interregional organizations. FFR Cooperative, owned be seven U.S. cooperatives and one each from Canada and Japan,

Business profile of farmer-owned cooperatives, 1986[1]

Commodity	Cooperatives handling	Net volume
	Number	1,000 dollars
Products marketed:		
Beans and peas (dry edible)	49	146,958
Cotton	435	1,444,158
Dairy	354	14,821,044
Fruits and vegetables	371	5,106,099
Grain, soybeans, and soybean meal and oil	1,995	11,605,175
Livestock	361	2,976,430
Nuts	34	1,132,721
Poultry	56	916,795
Rice	56	827,641
Sugar	46	1,482,512
Tobacco	33	181,556
Wool and mohair	168	19,766
Miscellaneous	101	879,305
Total farm products	3,719[2]	41,540,160
Supplies purchased:		
Building materials	1,746	371,460
Containers	486	139,211
Farm chemicals	3,102	1,358,335
Farm machinery and equipment	1,564	342,508
Feed	3,000	2,883,316
Fertilizer	3,134	2,915,354
Meats and groceries	408	113,406
Petroleum	2,497	4,998,039
Seed	3,020	513,896
Other supplies	3,570	1,459,540
Total farm supplies	4,151[2]	15,095,065
Receipts for services:		
Trucking, cotton ginning, storage grinding, locker plants, miscellaneous	3,621[2]	1,760,246[3]
Total business	5,369[2]	58,395,471

[1]Totals may not add due to rounding.
[2]Adjusted for duplication arising from multiple activities performed by many cooperatives.
[3]Charges for services related to marketing or purchasing but not included in the volume reported for these activities.

specializes in developing original seed products for corn, soybeans, and forages. Cooperative Research Farms, another interregional organization owned by 13 regional cooperatives and the world's largest of its kind, operates five livestock and poultry research centers in North America. This range of research activity has helped farmers stay on the cutting edge of new technology from plant and animal breeding to consumer tastes and preferences.

New Marketing Efforts

Farmers and other rural residents continue to find new ways to use cooperatives to increase their income. Recent organizing efforts have applied cooperative marketing to new crops and to new forms of old crops.

A declining market for tobacco spurred growers around Monticello, KY, to look for alternative crops. They decided to raise and market fresh vegetables. Cumberland Farm Products, Inc., owned by 300 growers, was formed in 1975 to market their new crops. Growth required them to add a new packing shed in 1986.

USDA's boll weevil program resulted in cotton production again becoming a viable income source in agricultural areas around Edenton, NC. Cotton gins from earlier production days were long gone. So cotton producers formed Albemarle Cotton Cooperative in 1980 and then doubled its capacity in 1985.

In Virginia, peanut farmers decided to take on additional stages in marketing to enhance returns. In 1985, Virginia-Carolina Peanut Farmers Cooperative, Franklin, VA, organized by 150 growers, began operating a $3-million shelling plant. The growers are adding to their income by marketing both shelled and inshell peanuts to domestic and export markets.

The largest new cooperative venture began right in the middle of the downturn in agriculture in the early 1980's. About 1,100 corn producers in southwest Minnesota invested the price of a pickup truck for membership in Minnesota Corn Processors, Inc., at Marshall. Their corn wet-milling plant to convert corn into starch and syrup began operating in 1983. MCP is now adding an ethanol production unit.

Smaller cooperative marketing efforts in recent years have involved a wide range of agricultural products, including fresh vegetables, shiitake mushrooms, wild rice, blueberries, wine, goats, catfish, retail beef, hydroponic production, horticultural products, Christmas trees, and handcrafts.

Research To Make U.S. Products More Competitive

Gordon Rasmussen, research leader, European Marketing Research Center, Agricultural Research Service, Rotterdam, the Netherlands, and R. Tom Hinsch, agricultural marketing specialist, Horticultural Crops Research Laboratory, Agricultural Research Service, Fresno, CA

Long-term, stable export growth is crucial to the agricultural economy and economic growth of the United States. But, during the 1960's and 1970's, U.S. growers, shippers, and exporters of fresh fruits and vegetables became increasingly unable to exploit the growing European market for their products.

Some of the reasons for their inability to compete with exporters from other countries were long transit time, inadequate transport equipment, costly packaging, and lack of inexpensive handling systems and techniques for getting their products to European consumers in good condition. Experiences in shipping by refrigerated van containers to European markets were disappointing, and, in many instances, financially disastrous. Many shipments arrived in Europe with excessive physical damage and deterioration, which made them unacceptable to buyers.

Shippers were more deeply concerned with the long-term effect of a poor reputation being created for U.S. products in European markets. The situation became so critical that some shippers were not participating in the growing European market and were in danger of losing the modest gains made in the 1960's. Also, foreign competitors were upgrading the quality of their products, which forced U.S. shippers to continually seek ways to remain in the marketplace.

The European Marketing Research Center, one of five overseas laboratories of USDA's Agricultural Research Service (ARS), was founded in 1969 in response to requests by U.S. growers, shippers, and associations for assistance in exporting their products. It is in Rotterdam, the Netherlands, because it is the world's largest port, the gateway to Western Europe. Research at the Center is aimed at maintaining the quality of agricultural products, reducing losses from product decay and disease, developing resistance to fungicides, and lowering the costs of handling, packaging, and transportation. Scientists there have access to a wide cross-section of U.S. farm products destined for markets in all of Europe, as well as a wide variety of items offered by U.S. competitors.

With the cooperation of the Foreign Agricultural Service, Agricultural Trade Offices, and State Departments of Agriculture, these researchers are constantly looking for new agricultural products for export or products that can be accommodated in the European market, developing and supplying the technology so that these new products can be available to consumers.

Personnel at the Center collect and evaluate data from test cargoes of products to identify and solve problems. The data may include the quality of product at destination; analyses of packaging, handling, and transportation methods; shipping and han-

Gordon Rasmussen inspects produce at the European Marketing Research Center at Rotterdam in the Netherlands. (Dana Downey)

dling costs; and overall efficiency of the postharvest handling system. Many times refinements of procedures are necessary, such as improved cooling methods of commodities carried in large ships, film wrapping of fresh fruit and vegetables, proper and appealing packaging, pesticide treatments, and temperature and humidity control, as well as the selection of quality products for export. Quality, however, cannot be improved, only maintained as nearly as possible, during handling and shipment. Research to improve the handling and shipping of products is a continuing process in ARS laborato-

ries in the United States, but the procedures need to be tested under commercial conditions to determine whether they are physically and economically feasible.

The Center has helped increase exports of some U.S. products as the following examples show:

1. Kiwifruit exports from California have continued to increase during the past several years (even though more of these fruits also are being produced in Southern Europe) as a result of improved selection of quality fruit packaging, ethylene removal, temperature and humidity control, and palletization.

2. New loading patterns, packaging, and better temperature control during transit have helped to reduce the loss of leatherleaf fern (an ornamental plant) from 40 to 2 percent during shipment. Sales of this Florida product increased from $1 million to $9.2 million a year before the drop in the value of the dollar.

3. About 35,000 tons of grapefruit from the United States are sold in Europe each year. The amount of decay and physical damage has decreased while better selection of fruit for export has resulted from numerous test shipments. Also, heat-shrinkable film applied to each fruit can be used to extend the shelf life or possibly allow for nonrefrigerated transport in sea containers most of the season, reducing delivery costs. Fungicides also can be incorporated into the film or applied to the fruit before wrapping so that decay and disease are reduced or eliminated. Other high-value horticultural crops also have an extended shelf life when wrapped with heat-shrinkable film.

4. Subtropical ornamental trees are now appearing in new shopping malls, banks, and office building lobbies in Western Europe. Interior architectural landscaping is an important part of new building design, so that the demand for ornamental plants is increasing. The value of these U.S. exports to Europe has increased from $547,000 in the 1970's to over $2.9 million in 1985. Some species of these trees can be shipped without soil, so more trees can be loaded in a van container, which will reduce shipping costs. The trees are then repotted and conditioned in the European importers' greenhouses before being offered for sale.

5. Dried fruit is occasionally infested with insects when offered for final sale in Europe. We found that California raisins shipped by sea containers were free of insects on arrival in Europe, and that contamination took place in warehouses where fruit from other countries was stored. Thereafter, some of the storerooms were refrigerated to prevent insects from migrating from infested fruit to clean fruit.

6. Design of new packages and development of modified atmospheres may make it possible to ship blueberries in sea containers. Tests have shown that new varieties arrive in better condition than older varieties and that consumers desire small packages.

Comparison of U.S. Products with Others

Researchers in the United States, Foreign Agricultural Service personnel, the marketing industry, and exporters rely on the technical information and assistance given by the Center personnel on European standards for quality, packaging, refrigeration, and transportation methods for acceptance of U.S. products. Information from several studies comparing the condition and quality of U.S. products with those from competing countries has been published in scientific journals and also given to exporters in the United States so that they will know about their competition.

One study shows that certain quality factors of U.S. grapefruit are higher than those of fruit from competitors during the main season for marketing our fruit. Comparative presentations of red and white grapefruit have increased consumer awareness of the red fruit and resulted in increases in sales and value.

A recently completed study of raisins—comparing color, sugars, moisture content, mold contamination, damaged berries, and residues of raisins grown in California with those grown in competing countries—indicates that the quality and uniformity of U.S. raisins is superior to those of our competitors, which is important to the baking industry.

Currently, laboratory personnel are sampling soybeans from the United States and various South American countries to compare their quality and condition on arrival in Europe. This study, conducted in cooperation with the ARS Northern Regional Research Laboratory, Peoria, IL, and the Federal Grain Inspection Service, Kansas City, MO, started because of concern about U.S. soybean quality and how it compares to our competitors' crops. Soybeans are the number one U.S. agricultural export crop, and to increase or hold our share of the ever more competitive market we need to know how our crops compare with those of other major exporting countries. The American Soybean Association and several soybean crushers in Europe are cooperating to make these studies possible.

Approximately 55 percent of the peanuts sold in Western Europe come from the United States. To help maintain this market, peanut samples from the major exporting countries are collected and sent through the Animal and Plant Health Inspection Service to the ARS Southern Regional Research Laboratory in New Orleans for flavor and composition analyses.

Technical Information Provided

The Center provides advice to Agricultural Counselors and Trade Officers throughout Europe about the technical requirements of exporting new products. Information on quality, environmental conditions, transport methods, and packaging is provided to assure good arrival condition of U.S. products at the lowest cost possible.

Small watermelons are popular in Europe and until recently most came from Southern European countries in mid-to-late summer. New varieties have been developed in the United States and, because of an earlier harvest in southern States, a market window exists for these melons in May and June. Several importers in Europe saw samples of these melons in 1987 and their response was favorable. These melons have a longer shelf life and better quality than others in the market. From preliminary results, it may be possible to ship them in sea containers without costly refrigeration beginning in 1988. Laboratory personnel will monitor the shipments and report the results. The Center also maintains a close working relationship with professional surveyors, who monitor the quality of the commodities shipped, and helps to identify problems with them, even though the problem may not involve a U.S. product. The information received from these discussions and observations may be valuable later to help solve problems related to U.S. agriculture.

Emphasis in the 1960's and 1970's was on problems associated with the export of fresh fruits and vegetables. However, more emphasis is now being placed on value-added and high value products, such as canned and frozen products. Interest in partially processed foods is growing in Europe as well as in the United States, but at a slower rate. The laboratory will help develop new technologies for these products to extend shelf life, maintain quality, and make them more suitable for European consumers.

Export Growth Essential

Although our share of the market increased in 1987 because of the lower value of the dollar, we must continue to develop better shipping procedures that maintain the quality of the best U.S. products for export so that we remain competitive in the important European market.

Technologies for Maintaining Food Quality

Robert Davis, director, Stored-Product Insects Research and Development Laboratory, Agricultural Research Service, Savannah, GA

Food is vulnerable as it grows in the field, but its susceptibility to insects, micro-organisms, and other factors does not end there. Each year an estimated $30 billion is lost as food moves through marketing and distribution from the farm to consumers in the United States and overseas. These losses occur not only from insects and micro-organisms, but also from handling and the normal aging of the commodity. The quality of our food and its marketability depend largely on how well these problems are handled.

Managing insect pests is a major problem that agricultural research is helping to overcome. Federal and State Governments have established defect action levels (DALs), and the food storage and processing industries have, in many instances, established Good Manufacturing Practice Statements. These DALs and good practices, however, are based on labor-intensive inspection procedures that are often inadequate.

The importance of properly identifying pests cannot be overemphasized in establishing an effective pest management procedure. To include the newer management techniques, such as pheromones, insect growth regulators, biological control agents, modified atmospheres, and specific chemicals into an integrated program, one must know the pest and its biology. Federal and State labeling requirements for most pest control substances usually require that the

application methodology and application sites be stated for the management of pests and pest groups. The USDA Cooperative Extension Service located throughout the States and at each land-grant university can usually provide or assist in securing an authoritative identification.

Chemical Pest Management

The mainstay of pest control is still chemical pesticides. The use of these pesticides in the United States, however, requires that they be applied in strict accord with their approved manufacturer's or formulator's label and labeling materials. Some pesticides may be designated as restricted-use pesticides and carry the additional requirement that they be applied by or under the supervision of a certified individual. This certification program is vested in the States by the Environmental Protection Agency (EPA) and those interested should direct their inquiries to their State Department of Agriculture or comparable agency.

Preventing insect infestation usually involves one or more of the following:
- Spraying a residual-type pesticide onto the walls and floor of the storage facility before it is filled,
- Spraying or dusting a residual-type pesticide onto the grain or oilseed as it is placed in storage,
- Dispensing a pesticide vapor or aerosol into the headspace over

the grain or oilseed during storage or into a warehouse or food processing facility,

- Spraying or dusting a residual-type pesticide onto a surface during storage or undertaking a spot or crack and crevice treatment in food storage, transportation, or processing facilities.

To assure that a commodity is free of live insects, chemical fumigants are often the only practical approach. Fumigants, when properly handled and applied, are a safe, efficient, and effective means of eliminating infestations. But in the hands of an inexperienced person, they can be hazardous and often ineffective. Efficacy will depend upon achieving gas distribution throughout the food mass or structure for the proper time interval.

The legality of using a particular fumigant is entirely within the province of Federal, State, and local regulatory agencies. The EPA's approved label and labeling materials will provide information on all Federal requirements and restrictions. It is always a good practice, however, to inform all parties involved with the commodity, even those with a remote interest, that it is to be or has been fumigated.

Pest resistance is often the major cause of pest management failure. In fact, the level of pest resistance to many of our pesticides is beginning to cause concern and may soon complicate the marketing and export of both our raw and processed food and fiber.

Nonchemical Pest Management

Many new areas of nonconventional chemicals and nonchemical methods of pest management have recently received more attention and offer exciting potential. Not all these methods are new. Some are being reexamined again after years of dependence on conventional pesticides. Nor do these new practices offer the opportunity to entirely escape the more traditional use of chemical pesticides. But they may be effective supplements and help minimize chemical pesticides' use, possibly eliminating their use altogether in certain cases. Integrated pest management (IPM) plans have encouraged and stimulated continued research on these pest management approaches.

Irradiation

A great deal of information has been accumulated on using irradiation to control pests, particularly in grain and grain products. Irradiation or ionizing radiation may be used in two ways (direct treatment and genetic control) to manage pest populations. Both types of treatment of infested commodities to control pests provide a residue-free process. Genetic control involves releasing insects that have been sterilized by radiation. The sterile insects then compete with normal ones. Subsequent generations undergo population declines as a result of sterile progeny or infertile eggs.

The effects of irradiation have been evaluated for two sources of ionizing energy, that is, gamma radiations produced by nuclear disintegration of radioisotopes (cobalt-60 and cesium-137) and high speed or accelerated electrons emitted from a heated cathode. Gamma radiations have much greater penetration than do accelerated electrons and have received the most research attention, particularly on bulk raw commodities. However, the use of accelerators is now beginning to receive attention, and a grain elevator in the Soviet Union has been equipped with an electron accelerator.

The use of ionizing radiation has both promise and limitations. The method is effective and can be inexpensive over the long run. However, the initial cost is high, and the cost of transporting sufficient commodity to the irradiator for maximum utilization may be prohibitive. Nevertheless, even with these economic considerations, we can expect to see irradiation used in the future for disinfestation of high-value commodities such as fresh fruits, nuts, dried fruits, seafood, and some meats.

Controlled Temperatures

Both high and low temperatures have been used in selected situations and offer promise as control interventions. Insects are coldblooded, so their body temperatures closely follow that of their environment. When temperatures are lowered, insect activity decreases until all activity stops. Further decreases in temperature can result in death. When temperature increases, activity increases to a point where some vital process is inhibited and activity then ceases. Continued exposure or further increase in temperature results in death.

Protective Packaging

Food-processing and-distributing industries ship and store foods susceptible to infestation. Protecting these foods is a prime concern of the package industry and the packager. Neither can maintain control over the handling and storage environments throughout marketing and distribution channels after a commodity leaves their facilities. Good package construction, which offers few avenues of access to the packed commodity, should be a prime concern of management.

Biological Control

The increased use of biological control agents—parasites, predators, and pathogens—offers promise. Great advances were made in understanding the use of parasites and predators during the first half of this century. Then the era of organic pesticides virtually halted this research, and we waited until the mid-1960's and the 1970's for its continuation. There are many possible applications for the use of parasites and predators in protecting postharvest agricultural commodities, particularly the raw commodities.

Pathogens seem to have the greatest potential. Parasitic protozoa have been used successfully in conjunction with a pheromone lure and a bait station. The bacteria *Bacillus thuringiensis* and various granulosis viruses offer promise for the control of the Indianmeal moth, the almond moth, and the Angoumois grain moth. Considerable research still needs to be done in this area when one considers the myriad of viruses, rickettsia, bacteria, fungi, and protozoa that exist in varying associations with insects.

Modified Atmospheres

Using modified atmospheres is an adaptation of the ancient practice of hermetic storage. Hermetic storage seals raw agricultural commodities such as grain, beans, or oilseeds, generally in underground pits, and allows the respiration of the commodity to deplete the oxygen to a level that asphyxiates the pests. Hermetic storage in preindustrial times was probably the only means of keeping large quantities of grain free from insect attack between harvests in areas with mild winters.

The use of modified atmospheres offers a more practical method of pest management in stored foods. It controls insect pests much quicker than hermetic storage, and, like hermetic storage, does not leave chemical residues. The method simply changes the existing atmosphere in the storage structure to one lethal to insects by purging with carbon dioxide

(CO_2), nitrogen (N_2), or the combustion gas products from a modified ("inert") atmosphere generator. EPA has granted these gases exemptions from the requirement of tolerances for raw and processed agricultural products.

Pheromones

The use of various signal chemicals has stirred excitement among everyone from the less informed among the general public to the most knowledgeable scientists. Use of this potential management tool allowed some early successes in reducing numbers of agricultural pests in cropping situations. The use of sex pheromones in conjunction with traps has increased collections and reduced the occurrence of mating by confusing the males as to the presence of females.

Research has shown that, while pheromones may not necessarily lead to a control or management technique by themselves, they can be used as effective tools for monitoring infestations and therefore should be considered for integration into overall management programs. A recent innovation uses pheromones as lures for the inoculation of pathogens into pest populations.

Acceptance of such survey tools as pheromone traps may be slow, especially by those in the processing and distribution of foods. To many, the presence of a trap with insects will be an indictment that a facility has a pest problem. Also, an empty trap may imply that management has just had or suspects a pest problem. This philosophy also extends to other attractant or repellent devices.

Product Modification

This pest management tool can take one of a number of approaches. Host plant resistance to postharvest pests is being researched. Scientists also are investigating the possible use of

chemical compounds found in plants such as citrus and various spices as natural product pesticides. One product modification that helps suppress pest populations is the use of mineral supplements. For example, tricalcium phosphate, a nutritional source of both calcium and phosphorus for humans when added to blended cereal foods (CSM, a mixture of cornmeal, soya flour, and dry milk), will suppress the development of insects in the commodity.

Future Research

The newest tool that stands ready to assist us with some of our most pressing problems is the computer. Its use is now beginning to be felt in the area of managing the business aspects of pest management firms. The sanitarian and postharvest pest managers need to emulate the modest degree of success that the agricultural pest management consultants are beginning to sustain.

The development of predictive models of pest populations in storage, marketing, and distributing are needed. Such models will provide greater assurance that our pest management treatments are applied with proper timing.

Simple, reliable, fast, and nondestructive insect detection tools and techniques are needed. Such devices should be available not only for detecting pests inside foods such as grains, nutmeats, dried fruit, etc. and their packaging, but also for detecting the presence of the more exposed pest populations.

It is quite obvious that we will require the use of conventional chemical pesticides for some years into the future. This continued use will depend upon using these materials in the right place and at the right time. Research into application technology to maximize control and minimize pesticide residues and resistance is urgently needed.

Part VI

Promoting Agricultural Products

Marketing Products to Foreign Customers

William L. Davis, assistant administrator for commodity and marketing programs, Foreign Agricultural Service

Successful sales abroad involve more than getting a product from here to there. As the importance of agricultural exporting has grown and as competition has increased, U.S. exporters have learned to hone their marketing skills on everything from french fries to french dressing, from denim to duck.

Through market analysis, trade leads, and all the sophisticated tricks electronic technology can provide, exporters are better informed than ever before on where the markets are. But successful export strategies only begin with trade data. Keen attention to quality, competitive prices, and reliable service also is essential.

In addition, U.S. exporters face a unique mix of cultures, taste preferences, and trade practices in dealing with overseas customers. One of the most important tasks in exporting is determining what foreign consumers want and how to market that product to them. Making that determination accurately can spell the difference between success or failure of an exporter's marketing efforts.

Florida Citrus Campaign

Any good marketing campaign must take into account consumers' likes and dislikes. One good example of this is the Florida Department of Citrus' wide-ranging advertising and promotional campaign for fresh Florida grapefruit. (See Behr's article, *Florida Citrus Industry Sets High Standards* for more information.) The campaign is geared to the fact that although some people prefer white grapefruit, others are accustomed to buying the pink or red variety.

In Japan—the biggest market for Florida grapefruit—the Citrus Department is sponsoring television commercials and sales promotions designed to raise consumer awareness of Florida grapefruit, specifically the white grapefruit, which is popular there. However, consumers in France, Italy, the Netherlands, the United Kingdom, and West Germany prefer pink or red grapefruit, so supermarket demonstrations, point-of-purchase materials, taste tests, and television, radio, and print advertising capitalize on European consumers' preference by promoting the pink variety.

The Florida Sunshine Tree also is starring in television commercials in Tokyo and Paris, in "All American Breakfast" promotions in Taipei, and in women's magazine ads in Rome. And sales are up in all markets as a result. The targeting of marketing efforts to meet customers' preferences illustrates why Florida citrus marketers have been so successful in promoting grapefruit.

Changing Food Perceptions

Sometimes overseas marketing of U.S. products requires changing consumers' perceptions of traditional food items.

Lentils in Spain
In Spain, for example, lentils had an unfavorable image. Consumers

thought of them as a filling, fattening food. That impression is beginning to fade, thanks to U.S. marketing efforts. Like many people around the world, Spaniards are becoming more health conscious. In addition, more women in Spain are joining the work force and need food products that take less time to prepare. The U.S. lentil industry capitalized on those trends and began a campaign to promote the nutritional benefits of lentils, as well as the fact that U.S. lentils cook in about half the time as lentils from other countries.

The campaign, which included print and television advertising, in-store promotions, and a contest to develop Spanish recipes using U.S. lentils, has resulted in a significant increase in Spanish consumer awareness of U.S. lentils. Spanish purchases of U.S.-origin lentils increased markedly after in-store promotions were conducted. Future efforts will focus on the food service sectors and joint activities with key lentil importers and packers.

Prunes in the United Kingdom
Similar efforts, this time on behalf of California prunes in the United Kingdom, also have been successful. Through a promotional program ranging from advertisements to in-store promotions, the California Prune Board is trying to convince the British that California prunes are sweet nuggets of nutritional goodness on their morning cereal, in their lunchtime yogurt, and with their evening salad. The Board is also touting prunes for snacking.

With increased awareness of the benefits of healthy eating, the British are increasing their consumption of fresh and dried fruits. Many consumers are willing to pay a little more for them. Through slogans such as "Prunes—The High Fiber Fruit," the

California prune industry is convincing the British that their product fits perfectly into today's healthy food trends.

Introducing New Products

While changing the image of traditional foods presents a challenge, introducing new products calls for even more innovative efforts. There are a number of ways to introduce new foods to foreign consumers, including in-store displays, advertising, and trade exhibits.

French Fries
The fast food industry has been the major vehicle for introducing this product as a side dish to overseas customers. Nowhere has this been more successful than in Japan, where popular U.S. fast food franchises have acquainted the Japanese consumer with U.S.-style french fries.

As Japanese consumers became acquainted with french fries at restaurants, leading U.S. frozen potato producers, including Ore-Ida, turned their attention to food shoppers. But the U.S. industry realized that the product would have to be adapted for the home market. Most Japanese consumers, for example, own toaster ovens, but not deep fryers. So the product was prefried and adapted for cooking in the toaster oven.

U.S. producers packaged the potatoes in small (300-gram) packs because Japanese consumers prefer to buy food each day, making large packages of frozen potatoes inappropriate. However, as more and more Japanese women began working outside the home, they discovered that larger packs would be more convenient, so frozen potato producers developed the 500-gram pack.

As Japanese supermarkets expand freezer display and storage space, U.S. producers have been ready with a

The fast food industry has been the major vehicle for introducing to Japan french fries being enjoyed here by these Japanese children. (The Potato Board)

wider variety of frozen potato products such as hash brown patties and tator tots. To boost consumer familiarity with new potato products, U.S. potato producers have given away free bags of fries and other potato items in stores. These marketing efforts are expected to keep Japan the No. 1 export market for U.S. frozen potatoes.

Crawfish

That extra effort to adapt products to satisfy customer needs can have big payoffs. For example, over the past few years, U.S. crawfish processors have worked with three major Swedish importers to provide the type of crawfish Swedes prefer—cooked in brine with dill and with a softer shell than the way they are eaten in the United States. These extra efforts were rewarded when Louisiana became the principal source of Sweden's crawfish in 1987, netting the industry in Louisiana nearly $8 million worth of sales.

Wood Products

One of the biggest challenges, which dwarfs the above efforts by comparison, is changing the way an entire country feels about a product. Japan's attitude about processed wood products is a prime example. Although Japan is the largest market for U.S. forest product exports, most sales are of raw materials, such as logs and chips. The U.S. forest products industry wanted greater access to Japan's construction industry for a wide range of processed wood products.

Although the Japanese have a long tradition of living in wood houses, cement and steel structures are more popular today. The first step in expanding the market was to convince Japan to reduce its tariffs on wood products. After that was accomplished through a year of intensive trade negotiations, the U.S. wood industry needed to demonstrate that modern wood building systems not only meet the performance characteristics of steel and masonry construction, but also perform better.

To demonstrate the advantages of energy-efficient and economical wood buildings, the U.S. wood industry built a model wood house in Tokyo. The three-story house showcased the latest in U.S. timber framing and structural wood panel technology.

The demonstration house, a multipurpose building combining office and living accommodations, has revitalized Japanese interest in wood construction in general. Although multistory wood houses previously had been prohibited, the model house was granted a special permit by Japan's Ministry of Construction. Since then, Japan's building code has been revised to allow three-story residential units—a breakthrough for the U.S. wood industry.

Marketing Efforts Pay Off

Over the past few competition-intensive years, U.S. exporters have learned to wear many hats—analyst, marketer, and master of cultural differences. To be successful in all those roles, they have had to adapt their products, their selling approaches, and even themselves. Exporters have turned the old marketing adage "The customer is always right" into "The *foreign* customer is always right." And the efforts have paid off. U.S. agricultural exports are on the rebound, as consumers worldwide find themselves surrounded by U.S. products that have been adapted to their tastes and needs.

Building Foreign Markets in a Competitive Environment

Kevin Rackstraw, U.S. Feed Grains Council, Washington, DC

During the 1980's, the U.S. feed grains industry saw a remarkable turn of events on the trade front. U.S. feed grains exports declined from a peak of 2.8 billion bushels in 1979/80 to a bottom of 1.55 billion bushels in 1985/86. The last few years have been spent in rebuilding U.S. competitiveness in feed grains and in many other products as well, since the loss of overseas markets was felt throughout U.S. agriculture. Now that annual feed grains exports have recovered to the 2-billion-bushel level again, the U.S feed grains industry looks to the future with renewed confidence.

The lesson learned from the past few lean years is that the United States must make a continuous effort to remain competitive in the world grain market. When we investigate what constitutes competitiveness, the easy answer focuses on price. But this focus masks the complicated nature of competitiveness and simplifies the real process of market development. Price is only one component of competitiveness; proper market development and promotion of the product are also important in determining sales.

Traditional farming practices often exist side-by-side with modern equipment in countries like Egypt, where this dairy farm is located. The Feed Grains Council helps these countries adopt nutrition and health management practices that make them more efficient users of feed grains, thereby increasing demand for U.S. exports. (U.S. Feeds Grains Council)

Responding to Change

The U.S. Feed Grains Council (USFGC), in its 28th year of promoting U.S. feed grains and their coproducts overseas (e.g., corn gluten, cornmeal, barley malt), has seen tremendous change in the overseas markets for U.S. feed grains. Japan, for instance, has leapt from being a struggling, developing economy to an economic powerhouse among industrialized nations, as well as the best customer for U.S. feed grains. Consumption patterns and tastes in Japan have changed dramatically and now call for dramatically different kinds of promotion programs. USFGC has responded by pursuing a wide variety of flexible approaches targeted toward the various growth sectors, both traditional and nontraditional, within Japanese agriculture. (Some examples are industrial corn, barley malt for beer, and livestock feeding sectors.) This flexibility and responsiveness are characteristic of USFGC's programs in more than 50 countries.

Enhancing Traditional Market Development

The cornerstone of USFGC's programs has been helping prospective importers develop their capacity to handle, use, and import feed grains. This approach is still the underpinning of USFGC's worldwide market development effort, but the organization has also developed innovative projects that build on more traditional market development programs, such as providing technical assistance on health and nutrition to livestock and dairy industries in the various target countries.

Influencing Trade Policy Vital to Market Development

In a world trading environment increasingly dominated by governments, it is impossible for any market development group to ignore trade policy. In the past 2 years USFGC has become a major voice in the world trade arena on disputes about feed grains. In one instance, it coordinated the action of U.S. producers in successfully putting pressure on the European Economic Community (EEC) to come to terms over a dispute with Spain, a major market for U.S. feed grains until it joined the EEC. The resulting agreement allows U.S. feed grains exporters to sell 2.3 million metric tons of corn and sorghum to Spain each year through 1990. This example illustrates how trade policy can directly affect the pocketbooks of U.S. farmers and agribusiness.

Government Programs Aid Private Sector

USFGC has developed short-, medium-, and long-term programs that work together to generate continuous payoffs for U.S. feed grains exports. These programs are a vigorous combination of private sector efforts and U.S. Government programs, which meld these two forces into a comprehensive market development effort. Making the best and most immediate use of the various Government programs that can promote U.S. feed grains is crucial, because of the temporary nature of Government programs and funding.

Promoting for Immediate Gains

Historically, the U.S. barley industry has been a residual supplier to a world market dominated by subsidized barley from the EEC. U.S. barley sales had been in a slump until USFGC found and built a new market in Saudi Arabia using USDA's Export Enhancement Program (EEP). The Council's overseas staff discovered that the Saudi Arabian Government

U.S. farmers involved in Feed Grains Council programs find that their advice to foreign producers can help build demand for U.S. feed grains overseas. Jim Christianson, second from right, a Montana barley grower, shares his expertise with producers on a Taiwanese duck farm. (U.S. Feed Grains Council)

wanted to import large amounts of barley to supply the country's Bedouin sheep and livestock producers. Because the Saudis had been receiving highly subsidized barley from the EEC, Saudi Arabia became an ideal target for EEP, which helps to combat unfair trade practices.

Not only did the staff identify the market, it also identified new-to-market Saudi importers using the program, and it served as an intermediary among the Saudis, the U.S. Government, and U.S. exporters. As a result, U.S. barley exports increased from 22 million bushels in 1985/86 to more than 150 million in 1986/87.

Familiarizing Foreign Buyers with the U.S. Grain Marketing System

One of USFGC's most promising programs is made possible through the U.S. Government's Targeted Export Assistance (TEA) Program. Many countries are privatizing their grain purchasing systems, which brings to the fore a new group of inexperienced buyers unfamiliar with the U.S. free market system. To many of these buyers, the U.S. system seems vast and complex, which sometimes discourages them from buying from the United States. USFGC's efforts under the TEA Program teach foreign buyers the advantages of purchasing from the United States and how they can make the most effective use of that system.

Promoting Alternative Uses of Feed Grains

Developing a large number of customer countries is one way to broaden markets for U.S. products, but another way, no less important, is to develop markets for alternative product uses. USFGC maximized its use of the TEA

Program in promoting industrial and food uses of feed grains. Through the "samples" programs, it introduces U.S. feed grains into markets that are unfamiliar with these products by offsetting the cost of shipping milling- or brewing-sized samples to interested buyers. The resulting shipments are used by brewers, feed manufacturers, and industrial users to compare U.S. grains with the grains they are currently using. In most of these cases, the buyers are convinced that the extra yield or quality they get makes the U.S. varieties, including waxy, high amylase, and hard endosperm corn, a better value.

The samples program has allowed shipments of high-starch U.S. hybrids to wet millers, for instance, in the United Kingdom, which is already a strong market for U.S. industrial corn. These wet millers have been aware of U.S. quality, but the bidding process they use has usually yielded a lower price and, consequently, lower quality grain. The cost of shipping a test-sized sample (about 120,000 bushels) has dissuaded them from trying higher grade U.S. corn. This project has shown them they can get more and better starch from U.S. hybrids than from the Italian or French varieties they now use.

Market Development: One Key to Competitiveness

The successful promotion of a product can make the difference between potential sales of a product and actual sales. Successful market development is a function of knowing the markets and being in the right place at the right time. USFGC can do this by maintaining permanent offices in the major growth markets for feed grains and by hiring foreign nationals of those countries to provide market intelligence and implement programs. The United States can no longer afford to rely on buyers' own initiatives to make sales happen. USFGC has recognized the value of actively promoting U.S. feed grains for more than a quarter of a century and looks forward to staying in the forefront of U.S. market development abroad well into the next century.

Opening New Markets for U.S. Soybeans

Wayne Bennett, president, American Soybean Association, St. Louis, MO

To create growth in the soybean marketplace, farmers who saw a bright future for a new commodity in the United States established in 1920 the American Soybean Association (ASA). After 68 years, ASA continues to find new markets for U.S.-grown soybeans through 11 offices worldwide and 26 State associations.

Currently, the United States produces about 2 billion bushels of soybeans each year, half of which is exported. Overseas market development has worked well for the U.S. soybean farmer.

Japan: Oldest Market

Japan represents not only the oldest but also the largest single market for U.S. soybean farmers. When ASA opened its first overseas office in Tokyo in 1956, Japan imported only 26 million bushels of U.S. soybeans.

ASA's initial task was to establish a reputation for soybean meal with the feed and livestock industry that equaled the good name of many traditional soy-based foods for human consumption. In 1957, ASA launched a consulting program to help build the Japanese hog industry, which uses soybean meal as a primary feed ingredient. The office also promoted the benefits of using soybean cooking oil to the Japanese public.

Today Japan imports 162 million bushels of soybeans from the United States. ASA actively works with livestock producers, employs two full-time animal nutritionists in Japan, and continues promotion efforts to increase consumer use of soybean oil.

New Undeveloped Markets Offer Potential

Market development in Southeast and East Asia has been stimulated by the gradual opening of the Chinese market and new aquaculture techniques.

Chinese Market

"When you're dealing with more than a billion people, it's almost impossible not to see potential markets," said Don Bushman, the American Soybean Association's director for the People's Republic of China, who works in Beijing. "When you start thinking about the nine zeros in one billion and that it means four times the U.S. population, you quickly realize the resources China has to work with."

Feeding trials and seminars in China have demonstrated to dairy, poultry, and swine producers how to build their industries. To support a rapidly growing livestock demand, China plans to build 200 to 400 feed mills in the next 15 years.

Projections show China will need 100 million tons of feed annually by the year 2000. If 10 percent soybean meal is used in the feed, China will need 10 million metric tons of soybean meal—an equivalent of 440 million bushels of soybeans—to fulfill its goals.

As recently as 1985, China did not import any U.S. soybeans. In 1987, China imported 10 million bushels and is expected to quadruple that amount within the next 3 years.

Aquaculture in Southeast Asia
Shrimp culture in the region is booming, according to Dr. Dean Akiyama, technical director of ASA's aquaculture program in Singapore. By mixing soymeal with fish meal, the feeding costs of raising shrimp and other fish can be cut by 45 percent.

Aquaculture research at Texas A&M University shows that dry feeds for saltwater shrimp can contain up to 45 percent soybean meal without significantly reducing shrimp survival and growth rates.

That means countries can raise enough food to feed their entire

The United States produces about 2 billion bushels of soybeans annually. Half of that total is exported, with Japan representing the oldest and largest single market. (William E. Carnahan)

populations and start booming export industries.

Soybean meal in shrimp feed is at 10 percent currently, but with continued promotion, use of soybean meal in shrimp and fish feeds in Southeast Asia could reach 30 percent. That rate of growth translates into a new soymeal market equal to 10 million bushels of soybeans by 1994.

Opening the Soviet Market

ASA's marketing program is working with the U.S.S.R. to improve its livestock industry. ASA and GOSAGROPROM, the Soviet Ministry of Agriculture, are cosponsoring a swine feeding trial that started in January 1988. A successful trial could mean opening up a market for 300 to 450 million bushels of soybeans in the U.S.S.R.

Soviet officials have said recently that they want to add soy protein to animal feeds. That could mean importing up to 450 million bushels of soybeans every year—equal to the entire soybean crops of Ohio and Illinois.

The U.S.S.R.'s purchases of soybeans and meal were more than 90 million bushels by early 1988. Soviet breeding specialists have visited swine research feeding stations in Great Britain which already use corn cob mix and soybean meal for feeding trials.

Expanding Sales in Great Britain

ASA has had great success in coming up with specialized solutions to marketing problems in particular countries, using funds from the Targeted Export Assistance Program (TEA).

The TEA Program funds promotional campaigns in other countries for U.S. agricultural products and helps fight unfair trade practices.

In Great Britain, for example, consumer awareness of soybean oil was low and sales were slumping. TEA and ASA together funded a television and print campaign to help increase the sales of soybean oil. The success of the campaign has been phenomenal, with soybean oil consumption up 21 percent in Great Britain. That's a new market of 7.7 million bushels for U.S. soybean farmers.

Similar TEA promotions are currently underway in Belgium, Denmark, France, Greece, Italy, the Netherlands, Portugal, Spain and West Germany.

Foreign Agricultural Service (FAS) Teams Up With ASA

West Germany purchases about 80 percent of the soybeans and soybean meal sold in northern Europe. But that wasn't the case 25 years ago when their law prohibited the use of soybean meal in animal feeds. In 1960 ASA and FAS banded with the German Oil Millers Association to convince the German Government to change the law. They succeeded, and soybean meal today is a leading protein in animal rations in West Germany.

In large part because of this major breakthrough, the United States has dominated this market for soybeans. In the last 25 years, U.S. soybean farmers have accumulated an overall 75 percent market share amounting to 2.5 billion bushels of soybeans valued at $14 billion.

Farmer Involvement Key to Success

Few of ASA's activities overseas would be possible without U.S. soybean farmers investing time and money in international market development. More than 440,000 farmers invest from a half-cent to three cents a bushel, matched by FAS, to help fund ASA activities and state association programs.

Farmer funding also is coupled with money from agribusinesses, which work with ASA on programs that benefit U.S. soybean farmers.

Farmers also travel on international trade missions to further the effort of creating marketing ties overseas. In 1988, ASA farmer leaders traveled to Latin America, the Soviet Union, Asia, and Europe.

New Ways To Use Soybeans

The success of U.S. soybeans in the international marketplace has hinged on the versatility of the commodity. Research keeps finding new ways to use soybeans, and that increases their value in overseas trade.

The more ways products can be used, the more marketable they become. Research helps ASA prove that new ideas work in this country, which helps to open up new markets overseas.

Newspapers Use Soybean Oil Inks

U.S. and Canadian newspapers are giving soybean oil inks a try, and more and more are switching from petroleum-based inks for better reproduction.

These inks are environmentally safe and produce bolder and brighter colors. They also stick to the paper and do not rub off as easily as traditional inks.

U.S. newspapers use more than 500 million pounds of ink each year. About 70 percent of that is the petroleum carrier which soy oil could replace. Soy oil ink holds promise as a market for 61.5 million bushels of soybeans.

The American Newspaper Publishers Association (ANPA) developed soy oil ink in response to problems with quality, rub-off, and the high cost ($300 a barrel) of disposing of petroleum-based inks. Soy oil ink is biodegradable and is made from soybean oil readily available in the United States.

By 1989, soy oil ink may take the newspaper industry by storm and become much more widely available. ANPA has licensed its soy oil ink formula to all major ink companies.

ASA is assisting in these efforts as well as in a marketing plan to get the word out about soy oil ink to the printing industry.

ASA's Total Marketing Concept

ASA is a service organization and its major assets are people. Educators, technicians, communicators, and marketing representatives make contacts and help build soybean markets. No market is too small for U.S. soybean farmers.

The cooperative partnership between FAS and the U.S. soybean farmer continues to be critical to the success of ASA's market development initiative.

ASA's total marketing philosophy means going out to find every avenue possible to market U.S. soybeans and to maintain a good balance of research and promotion to find new ways to use soybeans as well as to improve traditional uses.

Promoting High Quality U.S. Foods Through Regional Trade Associations

James Youde, executive director, Western U.S. Agricultural Trade Association, Vancouver, WA

Four regional marketing associations form vital market development and promotion links among State Departments of Agriculture, food companies in their member States, USDA's Foreign Agricultural Service (FAS), and overseas buyers. These four nonprofit groups are:
- Eastern U.S. Agricultural and Food Export Council, Inc. (EUSAFEC)
- Mid-America International Agri-Trade Council (MIATCO)
- Southern U.S. Trade Association (SUSTA)
- Western U.S. Agricultural Trade Association (WUSATA)

The activities and accomplishments of WUSATA provide examples of the important marketing functions carried out by these regional trade associations.

The Western United States produces a vast agricultural bounty that offers overseas importers an unlimited supply of the finest foods in the world—juicy California citrus, sweet Pacific Northwest berries, flavorful nuts, hearty potatoes, tender beef, delicate Pacific salmon, and a variety of specialty foods.

Western U.S. agriculture, with its wide diversity of climatic conditions, produces over 200 different crop and livestock commodities. Thousands of consumer items are derived from these commodities.

While bulk commodity exports are important to the West, this region also produces a wider range of specialty, high-value foods and beverages than any other region in the world.

Expanded efforts are needed to sell more of these high-value U.S. foods in export markets. The WUSATA region is strategically located to respond to fast-growing consumer demands for specialty foods in Pacific Rim markets, including Japan, Korea, Hong Kong, Singapore, Taiwan, and Malaysia. WUSATA also carries out market development programs in Europe, the Middle East, and Latin America.

A Working Partnership

Formed in 1980, WUSATA is a nonprofit organization dedicated to promoting the West's high quality agricultural products. WUSATA acts as a vital link between international food buyers, Western U.S. suppliers, State agricultural agencies, and FAS.

The 11 State Departments of Agriculture that form WUSATA's core membership are Alaska, California, Colorado, Hawaii, Idaho, Montana, New Mexico, Oregon, Utah, Washington, and Wyoming.

These States are in their ninth year of jointly promoting exports of food and agricultural products. Their directors of agriculture guide WUSATA as its board of directors. The States' marketing officials work closely with the WUSATA staff to design and carry out marketing programs. This region harvests more than one-fifth of all U.S. farm products and more than half of most specialty crops.

As a cooperator of FAS, WUSATA coordinates its activities with the

The Western U.S. Agricultural Trade Association is a nonprofit organization dedicated to promoting the West's high quality agricultural products like the California wines being sampled here at a shop in Japan.

agency's High Value Products Division, commodity divisions, and foreign-post personnel in markets around the world. FAS contributes market development funds to support WUSATA's export activities.

Western food producers and marketing firms with products to sell and a commitment to market development are also part of the partnership. They participate in a variety of WUSATA activities, including food show exhibits, menu and retail store promotions, development of promotional materials, and trade missions.

WUSATA continually forwards trade leads from importers to suppliers throughout the region, monitors changing market conditions, and apprises new and established firms of export opportunities. The association also helps smooth the logistics of product shipments for new-to-export firms.

Overseas Linkages

Foreign food importers, distributors, retailers, foodservice operators, and consumers benefit from WUSATA activities. The association puts importers in direct contact with U.S. producers and suppliers. The West's food industry grows, processes, and sells a wide range of products—from fresh produce to packaged specialty foods—all available for export. WUSATA's vital role is to assist in bringing buyers and sellers together. All the partners share a common goal: expansion of international food product trade.

WUSATA's export market development programs fall into two categories: generic or "umbrella" activities, and company-branded product programs.

Generic Activities

WUSATA carries out a wide variety of programs to benefit a broad range of companies and products. These overseas activities include market research, product presentations, in-store promotions of U.S. foods, media advertising, development of new packaging concepts, and testing of new distribution channels for U.S. food products. Some recent generic activities have included:

Frozen Berries to Japan

U.S. raspberries, blackberries, and boysenberries were virtually unknown in Japan. WUSATA worked with Northwest producer groups to sponsor baking seminars and to develop recipes and technical information on baking with U.S. berries. The seminars were held jointly with U.S. cling peach and prune industry groups. As a result, a Japanese importer/distributor made its first purchase of these berries, and plans to buy about 100 metric tons during 1988.

In-Store Promotions

WUSATA has cosponsored U.S. food promotions with supermarket chains in Malaysia, Singapore, and Japan. One chain that had never before held such an event purchased $2.2 million of U.S. foods for the promotion. After the 2-week event, the chain repurchased more than 40 new-to-market items for permanent sale in its stores.

Umbrella Promotions

WUSATA has worked with other U.S. market development cooperators—including commodity groups and regional associations—to jointly organize and sponsor promotions for a wide range of U.S. food products. This umbrella approach has increased the market awareness of all U.S. foods and has resulted in the cost-effective sharing of promotional expenses. In one such promotion, a Japanese supermarket chain purchased more than $15 million worth of U.S. food products.

Market Research

Determining the market acceptability and required changes for products is an important step in a total marketing program. WUSATA has supported research projects on the acceptability of U.S. food gift packs in Korea, and Rocky Mountain food products in West Germany, England, and Japan. The information developed is increasing the prospects for successful market introduction of many U.S. products.

Product Presentations

New-to-market items must be introduced to the trade in attractive settings. WUSATA has sponsored displays of Western wines, seafoods, snacks, and beverages at new-product tastings in Japan, Korea, Singapore, Thailand, England, France, and West Germany. Many Western companies have successfully introduced their product through these events. For example, six Washington wineries established distribution partners in Japan during the first year of WUSATA-sponsored tastings, literature development, and media events.

New Distribution Channels

In some markets, the unique nature of American specialty foods calls for nontraditional marketing approaches. WUSATA has organized an experimental program to test the feasibility of selling Western U.S. gourmet foods directly to Japanese consumers through mail-order catalogs. New methods for marketing gift packs also have been test marketed in Korea.

Branded Product Programs

WUSATA works with Western food companies through USDA's Targeted Export Assistance (TEA) Program to promote and market branded products in specific overseas markets. Under the TEA/VAPP (Value Added Products Promotion) Program, a company carries out a marketing plan agreed upon with WUSATA for their branded food and beverage products. Federal funds are used to reimburse the company for one-half of eligible promotional expenditures, creating incentives for expanded private-sector market development activities. Many marketing successes have been realized by TEA/VAPP participants.

Garlic Sales Gains in Southeast Asia

Carefully planned promotions and a high quality product (in this case, California garlic) are proving to be a winning combination in Southeast Asian and Australian markets. A major garlic grower/processor is marketing garlic in fresh and processed forms by taking its products directly to the consumer with in-store product sampling, and by offering retailers vital promotional support during product introduction.

The firm has been participating with WUSATA in activities in this area of the world. In April 1987, this garlic firm joined WUSATA at the Jaya Stores American Food Fair in Malaysia. They also participated in the Perth Hilton menu promotion which featured all U.S. products during the America's Cup races. Sales results from these efforts have been impressive. More recently the company has teamed up with another firm to produce garlic capsules, which show great promise in the health food markets of Southeast Asia.

Washington Winery Product Launched in Japan and Taiwan

A Washington winery is making impressive sales in Japan following trade leads offered by WUSATA and using its TEA/VAPP Program. The winery began its targeted marketing in Japan in January 1987. Initial business discussions were held with a small restaurant chain located in Tokyo. Then the winery joined WUSATA at the FOODEX Show in Tokyo during March 1987. Contacts were made with many firms, including the importer for a major retail department store chain in Japan. U.S. military food and beverage buyers also were contacted.

Results during the first half of 1987 were impressive for this new-to-export company. Over 1,000 cases of wine, with free on board (f.o.b.) value of more than $80,000, have been sold in Japan and Taiwan to three buyers. Permanent arrangements with importers/distributors and expanded marketing programs should result in substantial export increases during future years.

Asparagus Promotion in Japan

Washington asparagus growers organized a promotion of their products in a Japanese supermarket chain during May 1987, using TEA/VAPP matching funds. As a direct result of this promotion, some 100 tons of asparagus were shipped to and sold in Japan. These sales had an f.o.b. value of $160,000. Sales were continued beyond the promotion by another supermarket chain in Japan, and several other companies have expressed interest in conducting similar promotions during the 1988 season, which should result in further sales.

Pecan Sales in Japan and Europe
The New Mexico pecan industry has been an active participant in marketing activities sponsored by WUSATA. For over 2 years, their efforts in Japan have centered around product development and identifying an appropriate importer/distributor. In 1986, a major pecan producer appointed a prominent Japanese importer to handle their bulk pecan sales in Japan. The results have been immediate. In fiscal year 1987, 400,000 pounds of pecans worth approximately $800,000 were sold.

Equally positive results occurred in Western Europe (Denmark, France, Belgium, the Netherlands, Switzerland, and the United Kingdom). The pecan growers and their marketing organization have developed an extensive set of point-of-sale materials and have provided their importers with significant advertising support. Sales revenues for Europe exceeded $800,000 in fiscal year 1986 and surpassed $1 million in fiscal year 1987.

Hong Kong Retailer Adds U.S. Label Grocery Products
A major Hong Kong company seeking a U.S. private label brand for its new 22-store food chain made its interests known to WUSATA. A large West Coast grocery products wholesaler began discussions with the Hong Kong firm during fall 1986. After several months of shipping samples and business discussions, the U.S. private label brand has been accepted, and two mixed containers of grocery products have been shipped. This appears to be the beginning of a long business arrangement that will expand sales of U.S. grocery products in Hong Kong.

New Snack Foods for Japan and Southeast Asia
A West Coast snack foods company is off to a fast start marketing its potato chips and other snack foods in Japan and Singapore. In the spring of 1987, WUSATA encouraged the firm to display its products at the NASDA (National Association of State Departments of Agriculture) Show in Seattle. At that time WUSATA introduced the firm to Singapore's largest supermarket chain, serious business dicussion began, and initial sales were made. During 1987, sales to Japanese customers exceeded $100,000. The company also is shipping its products to France, Hong Kong, Malaysia, Korea, Tahiti, Taiwan, Iceland, and Bermuda. Future export sales for this TEA/VAPP participant appear bright.

Herbal Tea Exports Expand
A Colorado herbal tea company became a WUSATA TEA/VAPP participant in December 1986. During the first half of 1987, their international sales were nearly 50 percent above the previous year. The TEA/VAPP Program provided an impetus for the company to expand its export sales and marketing plan. As a result, promotional materials have been tailored to the needs of international customers. This company also has initiated TV advertising in the international market.

Restaurant Foods Promoted and Sold in Western Australia
Working closely with the agricultural trade officer in Singapore and the agricultural counselor in Canberra, WUSATA cosponsored a menu promotion at a U.S.-owned hotel in Western Australia during the America's Cup. U.S.-fed beef, wines, garlic,

and other high quality products were purchased and served during this promotion, expanding market awareness and acceptance of these products. As a result of this event, new distribution channels have been established, and the hotel plans to organize future events to promote food products from the Western United States.

Promotion Spurs Sales in Malaysia
A point-of-purchase U.S. food promotion was organized by the U.S. agricultural attaché in Kuala Lumpur at a plaza outside a major supermarket chain. WUSATA was a major participant, with six Western food companies represented. Special promotional features included food preparations, food demonstrations, and special sales. Participating companies experienced brisk sales, and followups have led to additional orders. Management of the supermarket stated that their twofold increase in sales was the most successful promotion of foreign food they have cosponsored. Discussions are underway to hold additional WUSATA promotions with this food chain in the near future.

Fruit Juices to Japan
A major beverage distributor in Japan was seeking a U.S. fruit juice producer/supplier to broaden its product lines and supply sources. WUSATA introduced the Japanese firm to one of its TEA/VAPP participants with the capability to supply its fruit juice requirements. Seven months later, the two companies jointly announced a major product launch in Japan, which will lead to annual exports of several million cases of beverages from the Western United States.

Exporting with Foreign Sales Agents

Bruce J. Reynolds, program leader, International Trade Program, Agricultural Cooperative Service

Foreign sales agents are an overseas link in the marketing chain for high value food exports. Selecting agents and building dedicated working relationships with them are important tasks for exporters (those who are involved with agricultural packing, processing, and shipping, in contrast to export management or trading companies). To make improvements in this overseas marketing link exporters need to understand the nature of foreign sales agents' incentives and of their relationship with an exporter.

There are other ways to export than direct dealing with foreign sales agents. Many exporters use export management companies (EMC's) which perform exporting functions and services, while others establish their own sales offices in foreign countries. A foreign sales agent approach can be viewed as an intermediate level of involvement. It has advantages and disadvantages that exporters must each evaluate in terms of their resources and the market potential for their products.

Foreign sales agents are an overseas link in the marketing chain, and a dedicated agent will help increase exports. (Port Authority of New York and New Jersey)

An Agent's Business

Foreign sales agents operate import businesses and usually do not work on commission. The fact that they trade with exporters in a buy-sell manner raises questions about what distinguishes dealings with agents from any other kind of market transaction.

Agricultural packers and processors who directly supply importers usually have exclusive trading relationships and continuous international communications with them. This relationship requires more coordinated planning than is typical between suppliers and U.S.-based export management companies. Unlike EMC's, importers who function as agents will promote sales. Their export suppliers can be kept informed about distribution and consumer behavior even after transactions are completed.

As an agent, an importer may, for example, make sure that products are sold at prices and in retail outlets appropriate for the image that an exporter wants. In contrast, a U.S. producer's dealings with EMC's often will not involve them with issues of storage and distribution in foreign markets.

There are special contracts that govern principal-agent relationships between export supplier and import distributor. Some countries have explicit policies that impose restrictions on such matters as duration of contract and grounds for termination. However, a wide range of agent activities and services not covered by formal contracts comprise key elements that determine whether these relationships will be successful. For example, formal contracts may not make agents dedicated to promoting sales, seeking new outlets, and providing feedback on modifications of product or packaging.

How to Locate an Agent

Exporters often locate agents through informal channels such as trade shows, or by referral from foreign customers or business contacts. Many importers stay informed about U.S. products and actively seek agent status from producers who export. These informal sources of information are a helpful way to identify prospective agents, particularly when they take the initiative to visit a U.S. exporter. But it is advisable for exporters to take their own initiatives in finding the right agent for their products.

Foreign travel should be an essential part of finding the best agent available. U.S. agricultural attachés maintain a list of importers who offer agent services. An exporter also should work on supplementing these lists by visiting local food retailers, bankers, and other business contacts. Most lists are unlikely to include all available importers because new firms regularly enter while others exit the market. There also can be high caliber agents who have not yet had experience with food products but are interested in marketing them.

Exporters should do independent checking on importers' reputations. They should be familiar with the other products that an importer represents, how they are marketed, and also if they are associated with a certain quality of products. In some countries, a U.S.-branded product might carry slight, if any, recognition by consumers, and some importer reputations might be better than others for building a particular quality image.

Challenge of Mutual Commitment

It is difficult to know the extent of an agent's dedication over the long haul. Importers might agree to provide agent representation for a product without indicating doubts they might have about its sales potential or their apathy toward promoting it. The cost to importers of entering into agent agreements is not significant, but poor selection of an agent can be costly for an exporter. There is no guarantee on agent performance, and exporters have limited opportunities to monitor their work. Foreign sales agents have more incentive to add product lines or new client accounts than to expend increased effort on any one product.

Commitment is a two-way street. Agents may not always want to indiscriminately add product lines or more overseas clients. Although supplying agent services does not usually impose significant business risks, there are opportunity costs in expending effort to promote sales. If a product appears to have limited potential and an exporter exhibits no inclination to tailor it for local tastes or preferences, it is unlikely that an agent will provide ancillary services that help expand its market.

Exporters must be convincing about their products, particularly when they appear to have slight sales potential in a given country or may have had weak sales there in the past. In these cases, an exporter would want to not only offer a product, but also show a willingness to learn about the importer's market and to make adjustments.

Concerns of Agents

An agent can be an excellent resource for monitoring consumer trends and for identifying product or packaging modifications that will expand sales. Many agents offer suggestions, but often exporters do not respond. The typical excuse is that a particular foreign market is too small in relation to domestic sales in the United States to make modifications economical. No doubt an agent may capture more of the relative gains if an exporter were to provide them with a customized product, but these decisions should be made in light of long-term growth potential. Some countries may experience faster growth in consumer spending in the future than the United States.

Some agents also have an interest in customized products as a way to diminish "parallel imports"—the portion of a firm's domestic sales that, independent of its actions, end up in export channels. Foreign sales agents view these imports as not only undermining their exclusive dealings with the U.S. suppliers, but also destroying their incentives to promote and identify consumer trends. Whether exporters would want to take steps to curb parallel imports depends on the situation. Exporters should weigh the value of what they expect to get in return if they were to make special efforts to create an effective monopoly franchise for their agents.

Taking full advantage of opportunities to develop an effective marketing strategy by dedicated work with foreign sales agents is a challenging task.

Export Management Companies

An exporter who does not want to explore agent services for major importing countries or to use an agent's capabilities more completely may consider EMC's.

Many agribusinesses are either not large enough or lack adequate commitment to economically internalize all the functions of a direct exporter. If a firm wants to export for the first time, using an EMC can eliminate the operating expenses of having to create an export division or staff. Furthermore, an EMC will probably offer access to more markets because they generally have an effective global trade network. Increasingly EMC's take title to products rather than operate on commissions.

Some exporters have foreign sales agents in a few of the larger overseas markets and use EMC's for the rest. Usually they will plan to establish agents in more countries once their markets begin to expand. It is worthwhile, however, for an agribusiness to scrutinize its export operations because an EMC would probably provide better service if it were responsible for exports to all markets. The most critical consideration is the quality of an exporter's relationship with its agents. If mutual commitment is lacking for building a marketing program, an exporter might do better by relying on EMC's.

Foreign Sales Offices

When an exporter perceives that an agent relationship will never lead to a more comprehensive marketing program, establishing some type of sales office, subsidiary, or joint venture is another alternative.

Many overseas markets have such a significant long-term growth potential that exporters prefer to establish their own sales offices. A subsidiary or joint venture usually involves overseas packing or processing, and requires enterprise management beyond the scope of what many agents offer. In contrast, a foreign sales office is more comparable in scope to what agents do.

Exporters who want significant control over an overseas marketing program generally prefer having sales offices to agents. Management of

sales promotions is one advantage in having more control. The amount and timing of promotions by agents is usually a positive function of their sales volume. It can be beneficial to do promotions when sales are in a slump, which is precisely when agents have the least financial resources to promote. Although some exporters make special promotion payments to their agents, the risk of improper use of such funds is much higher than if it were managed by an overseas employee.

Selecting the Right Agent

Foreign sales agents can provide an opportunity to develop overseas markets without incurring substantial costs of overseas direct investment. As independent entrepreneurs, agents are highly motivated and experienced dealers in their countries. In fact, the quality of human resources offered by some agents is often difficult for exporters to replicate when hiring their own sales staff.

Substantial uncertainty exists, however, about whether or not using a foreign sales agent will achieve the full potential for market development. Variability of exporter experiences with agents seems to result in part from the difficulty of finding or selecting the best or most appropriate ones available. It can also be more costly to change agents as compared to changing EMC's or foreign sales personnel. Much depends on an exporter's ingenuity in selecting the right person as agent and in developing an effective working relationship.

Bringing Buyer and Seller Together

Lisa Jager, director of communications, U.S. Meat Export Federation, Denver, CO

Internationalization, a buzz word of the 1980's, is affecting all sectors of the U.S. economy, including the meat industry. Many American meat companies are looking beyond the United States for new customers for their products. Selling products overseas, however, presents a new set of responsibilities and tasks for a company, which it may not be able to accomplish because of lack of staff, resources, and market knowledge. But an organization exists with a track record of success in helping U.S. meat companies sell their products overseas—the U.S. Meat Export Federation (MEF).

Getting Started

Since 1976, MEF has helped U.S. meat companies sell beef, pork, and lamb throughout the world. Based in Denver, Colorado, MEF has offices in Tokyo, Singapore, Hamburg, and Caracas. MEF helps U.S. meat packers, processors, and exporters sell more of their product overseas through market development, trade servicing, and market access. It is funded not only by meat packers but also by livestock organizations, grain promotion groups, farm organizations, and agribusiness companies.

Through its trade-servicing function, MEF provides assistance and knowledge to its member companies. For example, a small meat-processing company might hear that the market for U.S. meat products is growing in Japan. Through further discussions with other industry members, the company might discover that companies involved in exporting are MEF members.

A call to MEF in Denver puts the company in contact with the Technical Services Department. This department explains market potential as well as the basic requirements in exporting meat overseas. These requirements include export documentation, shipping procedures, importing country requirements, and labeling. Following additional discussions, the company might decide to join MEF in order to receive full-fledged trade servicing. A representative from the company will then most likely call the MEF overseas director responsible for the country or region in which the company wants to sell its product.

According to its European and Middle East director, Willem Zerk, common questions asked by exporters new to selling to a particular region include these: Who are the end users—retail outlets, restaurants, companies that carry out further processing? What are the preferences for marbling and portion size? What are the requirements for labeling, packaging, and documentation? What is the reliability of the supplier and the potential of the market?

In addition to answering questions, overseas directors can provide a vast amount of research about a country or market. For example, MEF's office in Japan has thoroughly studied the Japanese market for U.S. meat and has produced two research books, detailing every aspect of the Japanese market for both beef and pork. Such research could take years for individual exporters to compile. In addition to research, MEF has a vast network of trade contacts throughout Japan, which it can provide to MEF members.

Lending Credibility

According to vice president of international programs Phil Seng, MEF also lends its reputation and credibility in introducing exporters to potential customers. Unlike their counterparts in the United States, firms in many foreign countries conduct business only after a period of establishing a business relationship. In Japan, it is important to have credibility before business is conducted. MEF/-Tokyo has such credibility and lends credibility to exporters new to a market or buyer when introducing the exporter. "Our job is basically to put buyer and seller together," Seng said. "However we also assist in following up on sales, which is very important."

Conducting business in a foreign country can sometimes be frustrating for U.S. exporters if they are unsure about cultural differences. MEF is always able to assist with one obvious difference—language—by sending along a bilingual staff member to translate. In addition, exporters may not understand cultural differences, from body language to ways in which business transactions are begun and closed. Seng said sometimes a U.S. exporter might return to MEF's office from a meeting with a buyer and be uncertain how to analyze what took place at the meeting. MEF staff can help the exporter understand what the buyer was saying or insinuating. MEF can also advise from a cultural standpoint the next step the exporter should take to carry through a sale.

Keeping Customers Happy

Along with introducing exporters to customers, MEF plays a valuable role in maintaining contacts with importers; the hotel, restaurant, and institutional (HRI) trade; importers; and trade associations. MEF-member Tom Healy of the Excel Corporation said MEF is good with followup or "keeping customers happy." He cited a current situation in which MEF's Hamburg office works with retail outlets in Belgium. In addition to calling on trade members on a regular basis, MEF has helped retailers develop recipe leaflets for U.S. beef tongues. Maintaining these contacts requires MEF overseas directors to travel frequently as they are responsible not only for the country in which the office is located, but also for the surrounding countries or regions as well. Such travel is difficult and expensive for many exporters to do regularly.

For example, Foo Meng Hian is the MEF director responsible for ASEAN—the Association of South East Asian Nations. Its member countries are Brunei, Indonesia, Malaysia, the Philippines, Singapore, and Thailand. During a 12-day swing through the Phillipines and Brunei, Foo met with more than 50 trade members, including hotel food and beverage managers, purchasing managers, chefs, restaurant personnel, importers, and tourist associations. The meetings covered a variety of subjects, typical of discussions any overseas director would have during similar meetings in other countries. In the Philippines, Foo's meetings included a discussion with an importer about a new brand of beef he recently began buying. The importer also was interested in obtaining funds from MEF to conduct promotions of U.S. meat. Meetings with hotel food and beverage managers produced several trade leads and requests for MEF purchasing guides and meat charts.

In Brunei, visits with hotel managers revealed that U.S. beef was being featured and that at one hotel, MEF's place mats and other materials had helped build a steady demand for U.S. beef. In all the countries, many of the trade members Foo met with for the first time said they were glad to know about MEF and would use the organization in the future.

The Latin American/Caribbean region poses a similar situation to MEF representative Jerry Perez, whose office is in Caracas, Venezuela. To help maintain business in the Caribbean, an important market for U.S. meat, Perez travels throughout the islands calling on importers and HRI members. Like other overseas directors, Perez conducts trade seminars to educate trade members about the quality of U.S. meat and how to handle and store frozen meat.

Discovering New Markets

Trade servicing trips and seminars also help MEF uncover new markets or potential markets. MEF then relays this information to its members, who often then find new customers for their products.

North Yemen is an example of such a discovery and resulting sales for MEF members. During the oil boom years, Middle Eastern countries such as Saudi Arabia were an excellent market for U.S. meat. However, as the oil industry declined and many expatriates left these countries, U.S. meat exports to the region declined. MEF monitored the situation in these countries and periodically assessed market potential in nontraditional markets.

During a market survey trip to North Yemen in 1986, European and Middle East director Zerk found the country's buying power was increasing because of the recent discovery of oil. He relayed market potential information to MEF members, who were somewhat reluctant to respond because of their lack of knowledge about the region. However, Zerk persisted and today, several MEF-member companies are supplying variety meats to the region.

Through a market survey trip to the Canary Islands, Zerk discovered a large potential for beef liver sales. Zerk once again relayed this information to members. One member visited importers and end users, investigated the market, made changes in its packaging, and began selling large quantities of beef livers. Zerk said this business had a spillover effect, and the company also began selling high quality beef.

The sale of beef livers to the Canary Islands is an example of how MEF's market development efforts—particularly promotion and education—tie in with an individual company's sales efforts. Given the large potential for beef liver sales in the islands, MEF developed a leaflet to educate the HRI trade and consumers about the advantages of U.S. beef livers. MEF worked with companies selling the product in the region, importers, and end users to develop recipes and other information for the leaflet that would appeal to Spanish consumers' tastes.

Selling More Meat

The advantage of MEF's market development efforts to U.S. meat packers was no better experienced than in Japan in 1987 under the Targeted Export Assistance (TEA) Program. The $6.5 million MEF received in TEA funding was used for television and print advertising, restaurant and retail promotions, consumer seminars, and educational publications. Trade seminars allowed individual U.S. companies to present their

Japan's first meat month, staged by MEF, provided many opportunities for U.S. meat packers to meet one-on-one with members of the Japanese trade. This consumer has taken advantage of the event to purchase meat. (Meat Export Federation)

products and capabilities to interested industry members. Through elaborate trade show displays, companies displayed their products to the trade and consumers. MEF also staged the first U.S. Meat Month in Japan, providing numerous opportunities for U.S. meat packers to meet one-on-one with members of the Japanese trade.

Tadayoshi Watanabe of John Morrell & Company said MEF's program was a "good sales campaign of high grade. The program is a 10—100 percent." John Jay of Excel said, "MEF's approach is good. We're saying why our product is good, rather than why our competitor's product is bad."

In an independent evaluation of MEF's program, 75 percent of Japanese meat trade members said they had helped to improve the image of U.S. meat with consumers during the

U.S. meat-cooking seminars, like this one for Japanese consumers, was one of many highly successful activities of the Meat Export Federation. Other activities included television and print advertising, restaurant and retail promotions, and educational publications. (Meat Export Federation)

past year, and 100 percent said they believed that if quotas were liberalized, MEF programs would help improve U.S. meat sales in Japan.

It appears the Japanese industry was right. In August 1987, 5 months into MEF's campaign, the Japanese Government announced it would raise Japan's beef import quota an unprecedented 37,000 metric tons—a 21-percent increase. The increase would take place in Japanese fiscal year 1987, and approximately half of the increase was expected to be filled by U.S. beef.

Developing Markets for the Future

In the fast-paced world of the U.S. meat industry where entering a foreign market presents a series of formidable challenges, MEF is providing a valuable service. Through trade servicing, market development and market access, MEF is bringing buyer and seller together to help companies sell their products overseas today and in the years ahead.

Marketing Food Products Internationally—The Global Challenge

John C. Lenker, vice president, Pillsbury International, Minneapolis, MN

In the autumn of 1985, Bob Schreck, Pillsbury's director of international trading operations, was paging through a U.S. Government publication when something caught his eye. It was the name of a sheik from the Yemen Arab Republic, a nation of about 8 million people, slightly smaller than Minnesota, on the tip of the Arabian Peninsula. Schreck knew Yemen was a developing country with a low per capita income, but he also was aware that it had recently discovered oil and its economy was expanding dramatically. He called the sheik on the telephone and within two weeks the two were meeting at a New York City hotel.

By January 1986, at the sheik's invitation, Schreck was in Sana, Yemen's capital, to make Pillsbury International the first U.S. company to take advantage of Yemen's worldwide tender for flour. Since then, Pillsbury has shipped to Yemen more than 300,000 metric tons of flour (the equivalent of 66 million 10-pound bags of family flour) and significant quantities of wheat, rice, and sugar.

Export Strategy Works

The Yemen connection, even though a small part of Pillsbury's global marketing effort, is significant. It is an example of the early success of USDA's Export Enhancement Program and GSM 102-103 financing, which help American companies compete against European Common Market subsidies.

It also demonstrates how Pillsbury, despite its relatively small scale internationally, uses exports as one strategy to extend its presence into international markets, and develop brands with global potential. Over the past several decades, the Minneapolis-based food and restaurant company has used the strategy to create markets for high quality flour, expand Green Giant vegetables into almost 50 countries, and establish joint venture flour mills and flour-based businesses in developing nations.

The Personal Touch

As part of this strategy, Pillsbury's entry into the growing Yemen market was hardly happenstance. Schreck carefully researched tribal history and the culture of Yemen. Both parties sensed a commitment to mutual trust. Equally important, Schreck spoke for one of the world's oldest and largest food companies, with annual sales of more than $6 billion and a flour milling heritage spanning almost 120 years. Its experienced transportation, operations, and finance capabilities could be tapped to service the Yemen account and benefit both parties.

Despite those advantages, Pillsbury hit some bumps along the way. "We've had some glitches in financing, some delays in communication, and some issues regarding quality," said Schreck. "But in the end, it really gets down to the personal relationship. That has meant the difference."

Schreck also has used the personal touch to develop a smaller, but similar, flour export program in Zaire. His first contact with government officials led to a relationship with executives of UPAK Bakeries of Kinsasha, one of that African nation's largest bakeries. Using his experience in flour production, he spent 10 days at the bakery in December 1986 with a Pillsbury colleague to understand UPAK's system. Today Pillsbury supplies UPAK with 50,000 tons of custom-made flour annually, made specifically for the company's modern bakery equipment. This success, and others, helped make fiscal 1988 a record year at Pillsbury for bulk flour exports.

Pillsbury's Flour Export Legacy

Pillsbury began exporting flour to Europe in the early 1880's, shipping "Pillsbury's BEST" in barrels which today form the symbol of the company's widely known trademark. At that time, Pillsbury Mills was the world's largest flour miller. During the 1950's, it exported flour mostly to developing nations.

Some of those nations, to reduce costs by building their own mills, created joint ventures with Pillsbury. Using these joint ventures and other acquisitions made in the 1960's, Pillsbury turned its attention to developing markets for value-added food products. In the 1960's and 1970's, it entered niches in the European baked goods market by acquiring Gringoire Brossard, maker of premium cookies and cakes, and Green's, a leader in cake and dessert mixes in the United Kingdom. Tactical acquisitions were added and will continue to be added to extend these categories into a pan-European presence for Pillsbury.

Building a Global Brand: Green Giant

Today, Pillsbury International has identified at least two potential global brands in its broad portfolio of consumer food products: Green Giant, the world's largest processor and marketer of sweet corn; and Häagen-Dazs, the leading super premium ice cream in the United States.

When Pillsbury acquired the business in 1979, Green Giant already had developed an export network focused primarily in Europe and Latin America. Almost singlehandedly it had awakened foreign diets to the nutritional benefits and menu versatility of canned sweet corn.

Though grown as early as 2500 B.C. by Aztecs and Mayans and well established in the United States this century, sweet corn was indigenous to North America and virtually unknown 30 years ago in Europe. When Europe sought emergency relief after World War II, the United States responded with Marshall Plan shipments of animal feed corn. The program succeeded, but a generation of Europeans came to define "maize" as cornmeal and corn flour, not as sweet corn.

To develop the business, Green Giant had to change these negative perceptions, first among agents and the European grocery trade, then among consumers through product trial. Green Giant executives Bob Cosgrove and Gene Felton made a personal commitment to develop export markets in the early 1960's. They hired international staff specialists who studied worldwide potential and appointed Green Giant representatives, rather than export houses, for each major market to buy and resell on Green Giant's behalf. These Green Giant employees and their agents were fully devoted to getting the product on store shelves. Furthermore, they could assure their customers, as Pillsbury and Green Giant always have done, of consistent quality and dependable supply. Billed in England as "America's greatest selling corn," Green Giant conducted product demonstrations in British stores and supported sales with consumer premium promotions and U.S. television commercials with local sound tracks. The campaign was an immediate success. British consumers instantly associated the "green" in Green Giant with freshness and growth. By 1962, Green Giant products were in more than half the potential stores in southern England.

By the mid-1970's, exports of Green Giant canned sweet corn were rising at 36 percent a year. Imported sweet corn also became Green Giant's low-cost entry into the continental European vegetable market. A few years later, Green Giant used the same market development program in France, once again creating a significant, new vegetable category.

With business risk reduced by growing consumer acceptance, the second stage was ready, using local vegetables. To meet growing European demand and to reduce currency risk, Pillsbury also began producing Green Giant sweet corn at a joint venture facility, SERETRAM, in southwest France, with annual capacity of 2.8 million cases. Today, Green Giant sweet corn is number one in almost all of the markets where it competes in Europe, with sales approaching $100 million. In addition to canned sweet corn, Pillsbury has promising footholds in asparagus and frozen sweet corn. There is considerable room for growth. Sweet corn consumption in the United Kingdom and France is only one-fourth of that in the United States. Green Giant opportunities also exist in Latin America, especially Venezuela and Brazil, and in Mexico.

Pillsbury in the Orient

Pillsbury also sees substantial growth potential in Japan, where consumption of frozen foods was 8.4 kilos (4.2 pounds) in 1986, compared to 40 kilos (18.1 pounds) in the United States. Using $1.5 million in U.S. Targeted Export Assistance funds to support newspaper and magazine advertising, Pillsbury hopes to build its share of the market in Japan for Green Giant vegetables, especially canned corn, and polybags (plastic containers for "portion control") of frozen corn, peas, beans, cauliflower, and broccoli. Pillsbury also seeks a presence in Japan's neighboring markets—where premium quality vegetables can find a growing niche in South Korea, Taiwan, Hong Kong, and Singapore.

The company is also negotiating its first joint venture in The People's Republic of China, with a population that has the potential to become the world's largest market. The agreement could involve using fresh and canned asparagus from China and Pillsbury imports of Green Giant products, beginning with the traditional Green Giant entry vehicle, canned sweet corn. After North America and Europe, the Orient is becoming an important part of Green Giant's global marketing triad. Pillsbury's goal is to become the leading worldwide marketer of branded vegetables and to increase Green Giant's business outside North America to $500 million by 1992.

Häagen-Dazs: A World Brand?

Japan also has become the international launch pad for Pillsbury's other potential world brand: Häagen-Dazs ice cream. Acquired in 1983, Häagen-Dazs now has average annual volume growth of 17 percent, annual profit growth of 9 percent, and annual sales of more than $200 million.

Japan has become the international launch pad for Häagen-Dazs ice cream. (The Pillsbury Company)

The groundwork for Häagen-Dazs' entry into Japan was built on personal trust and contacts, developed by Hank Wendler, Häagen-Dazs director of business development in Japan. While with Carnation in the Orient in the mid-1980's, Wendler noticed in the *Japan Economic Journal* that Häagen-Dazs was discussing a joint venture with Suntory, a major Japanese corporation. "I knew I wanted to be part of the action," he said. "So I chased down an interview and by the time I was hired, Pillsbury had acquired Häagen-Dazs."

In 1985, Wendler made nine trips to Japan from the United States. He directed production and marketing teams and used kuchi-komi ("word of mouth") to draw attention to Häagen-Dazs' first shoppe in a high traffic area of Tokyo on a cold November day in 1984.

When the store opened, people stood in line 45 minutes to buy ice cream. Today almost 30 Häagen-Dazs shoppes are in Japan, many with annual sales of $1 million, and a Häagen-Dazs factory is in Gunma Prefecture, in the city of Takasaki northwest of Tokyo. Häagen-Dazs International also has entered Hong Kong, Singapore, Canada, West Germany, and Puerto Rico.

Focus on the 1990's

By focusing on a few, significant growth opportunities—such as Green Giant, Häagen-Dazs, value-added flour-based products in Europe and Latin America, and international trading activity—Pillsbury International is poised to double its current sales to $1.5 billion by the early 1990's.

Video Merchandising at Point of Sale

Roger J. Stroh, president, United Fresh Fruit and Vegetable Association, Alexandria, VA

Video merchandising is a hot, new sales tool which is dramatically increasing demand for fresh produce, meat, and seafood. Brief video messages about a featured fruit, vegetable, fish, or cut of meat are changing the way consumers shop and what they buy. In-store videos are educating consumers while dramatically boosting the sales of the spotlighted items.

Point-of-Purchase Videotapes Sell Product

According to the Point of Purchase Advertising Institute, about 80 percent of all buying decisions are made at point of purchase. This is a powerful reason for designing in-store merchandising programs which will inspire more customers to buy the featured items.

Because high-tech merchandising motivates more sales, the United Fresh Fruit and Vegetable Association, the National Live Stock and Meat Board, and the National Fisheries Institute have each developed an extensive library of point-of-purchase videotapes for merchandising in supermarket departments.

The success of these video programs is based on the premise that the more consumers know about these products, the more of them

Video merchandising is being used more and more in grocery stores to help customers in their buying. These shoppers have purchased pineapples with the help of a video display in the background that offers tips on preparing and serving this fruit. (United Fresh Fruit and Vegetable Association)

they will buy. Retail experiences over the past 3 years have indeed confirmed the hypothesis. Videotaped messages are particularly valuable for produce, meat, and seafood, since these items do not traditionally have labels describing their selection, care, preparation, or nutritional value.

The United Fresh Fruit and Vegetable Association, which pioneered the use of point-of-purchase videos in supermarkets, produced the FRESH TIP TAPE® series, currently consisting of 70 commodity titles. Each tape shows how to select and handle each fruit or vegetable, offers ideas regarding its preparation, and highlights its nutritional qualities—all in just 90 seconds. The same 90-second message is repeated over and over on an hour-long tape, which can be programmed to play as long as the retailer desires. As a result, produce shoppers walk away with plenty of information and often with the featured item in hand.

Interviews with produce customers have demonstrated that they appreciate information obtained from in-store videos, often crediting the tapes for their increased produce purchases. Customer surveys indicate that shoppers consider the point-of-purchase tapes a unique service—and one that influences their produce decisions.

Videotapes Boost Impulse Sales

Customers are not the only ones happy with video merchandising. Retailers report excellent product movement using point-of-purchase videotapes. Sales of familiar produce items have often doubled or tripled, while sales of specialty items have soared, in some cases 1,500 percent or more.

United's FRESH TIP TAPES have been responsible for boosting potato sales 300 to 400 percent, broccoli sales more than 500 percent, and pineapple sales more than 700 percent, all without adjusting price or promoting the item other than by featuring the relevant FRESH TIP video. Currently, 6,000 tapes are being used nationally, reflecting retailer satisfaction.

The National Live Stock and Meat Board's MEAT FEATURES® have also won enthusiastic response in the meat department. Like United's tapes, each tape concentrates on one specific item. Sixty-five different videos featuring specific cuts of beef, lamb, pork, veal, and deli meats have been produced within the past 2 years. Retailers across the country have purchased more than 7,000 tapes, showing tremendous increases in sales as a result. The most dramatic changes have been in specialty meat items, such as meat used in stir frying, showing sales increases of more than 330 percent.

Impact on Product Movement

Retail tests measuring product sales before use of the videotape, with it, and following its removal have shown the surprising impact of this program. For instance, in one supermarket test, kiwi sales increased 700 percent with the video. Three weeks after the tape was removed from the display, the store was still generating 300 percent sales compared to pre-tape sales figures.

That ripple effect has dramatic meaning for increasing product movement, as well as expanding consumer awareness and demand for produce, meat, seafood, or any other agricultural product. Consumers are learning from the in-store video merchandising system and, as a result, are buying more.

The formula for the success of video point-of-purchase merchandising has proven itself in department after department, store after store. It is successful because it provides many

Interactive video has added an exciting new dimension to shopping. Here, a demonstrator explains how the video can provide shoppers information on food, merchandise, and other commodities in the form of audio, full motion video. It requires some participation by the customer, who selects what information is to be presented. (United Fresh Fruit and Vegetable Association)

benefits for both store customers and supermarket retailers. The videotapes add an exciting, colorful dimension that consumers find fascinating, while they enhance the store's image and increase sales performance and profits. It is a retail formula that works, not only for consumers and retailers, but also for those who grow, ship, ranch, or fish, as well as brokers, wholesalers, and others all along the food distribution chain.

Interactive Video

A new and exciting technology that is emerging—called Interactive Video— will likely have a strong impact on point-of-purchase videos. Interactive video presents more information to the customer in the forms of audio, full motion video, computer graphics, and computer data. It requires a more active participation by the customer, who selects what information should be presented and in what sequence.

Consumer response to this new type of video, featuring fresh produce, was tested in a 4-week research study conducted in early 1988 by Infosmith for the United Fresh Fruit and Vegetable Association and Business Television, producer of the tapes.

Results indicated that when multiple items are featured on video, sales movement increases in the department. Produce sales generally rose 53 percent in stores featuring the new interactive video. By far, the biggest attraction to customers was the printing of recipes, which were used as shopping lists.

As the study indicated, interactive video, in addition to Fresh Tip Tapes, will have a strong impact on the in-store promotion of the future. Video merchandising will continue to educate consumers and increase sales for retailers. This is only the beginning.

"Jersey Fresh": A Fresh Idea in Farm Products Marketing

Arthur R. Brown, Jr., secretary, New Jersey Department of Agriculture, Trenton, NJ

New Jersey farm products have always enjoyed an excellent reputation, not only at home in the Garden State, but farther afield as well. With one of the most diverse agricultures in the Nation, New Jersey produces over 150 different agricultural commodities. While the famed Jersey tomato may be the most well known, Garden State farms actually grow everything from asparagus to zucchini.

With production worth about $600 million annually, agriculture also ranks as one of the State's largest industries. Fruit and vegetable crops account for about a third of this farm gate value, ranking New Jersey seventh in the Nation for production of fresh market vegetables. New Jersey also comes in second nationwide for production of blueberries, third for cranberries and peaches, fourth for asparagus, and fifth for sweet corn, summer potatoes, and tomatoes.

One critical key to this strong Garden State agriculture is freshness. New Jersey agriculture is faced with both the pros and cons of coexisting with the densest population in the Nation. But while growing urbanization presses Garden State agriculture to adapt, it also means that New Jersey sits in the middle of one of the ripest markets in the world. And it's that proximity that makes freshness a natural selling point.

Campaign Begins

This scenario, combined with a gradual loss of retail shelf space for New

FROM THE GARDEN STATE

Jersey agricultural products, was the backdrop for the 1984 birth of the "Jersey Fresh" campaign to advertise and promote New Jersey farm products in season. Recognizing agriculture's vital role in New Jersey's economic health, the Governor and the State legislature allocated $325,000 to the New Jersey Department of Agriculture for this campaign. The program had two prime objectives: to increase consumer awareness and to increase trade usage (the proportion of grocery store produce that comes from New Jersey) throughout the State and surrounding market areas.

Armed with professionally developed point-of-purchase materials and radio and billboard advertising, the department set out to inform consumers about the availability and freshness of "Jersey Fresh" farm products. Initially, radio and billboard provided the program's primary means of advertising. The department also established a "Jersey Fresh" matching funds program. By encouraging agricultural organizations to tie their own promotions to "Jersey Fresh," the impact of these program dollars was doubled.

The department's division of markets maintained regular contact with the retail sector, distributing "Jersey Fresh" ad slicks (which stores could use in advertising) and point-of-purchase materials to identify New Jersey produce. Food chains also were encouraged to add their store names to radio billboard ads identifying their retail outlets as sources for "Jersey Fresh" products.

Billed as one of the first programs of its kind, "Jersey Fresh" gave a star performance in its first year. Consumer awareness and trade usage made considerable gains—a fact substantiated by two Gallup surveys.

Comparison of a precampaign poll with one taken after the program's first year showed that consumer awareness of New Jersey farm products had doubled from 7 to 14 percent in just 1 year. From a precampaign level of 12 percent, trade usage jumped dramatically to 20 percent after the first year.

The "Jersey Fresh" success story spread quickly. As the program grew in prominence in agricultural marketing circles, other States began to adapt the "Jersey Fresh" model to their own situations.

Gains Continue in Second Year

Meanwhile, the New Jersey State Legislature, impressed with the program's significant 1-year gains, doubled the budget for the 1985 season. While that second season brought little change to the program's creative thrust, the intensity and reach of "Jersey Fresh" grew dramatically.

More chain food stores took advantage of the chance to add their names to "Jersey Fresh" radio and billboard ads, and took the initiative in featuring "Jersey Fresh" in a variety of ways. The logo appeared in chain ads, and many stores made "Jersey Fresh" point-of-purchase materials a regular part of their produce displays. Some chains even organized their own innovative "Jersey Fresh" promotions. These ranged from week-long features in print advertising to events bordering on full-fledged county fairs.

To complement trade activity, the department focused a major effort on consumer-oriented promotions— from tours to brochures to seasonal fairs. With free commodity samples, food preparation demonstrations, agricultural exhibits, entertainment, and contests, these promotions demonstrated the diversity of "Jersey Fresh" farm products in action.

The Philadelphia Zoo featured one of these "Jersey Fresh" events, combining a Halloween celebration with a focus on New Jersey's fall harvest. The zoo offered on-premises trick-or-treating, with a spotlight on New Jersey's fresh fall farm products.

Department personnel also organized a food communicator tour designed to send the "Jersey Fresh" message directly to the media. Food and agriculture writers from New Jersey and surrounding States boarded buses for a guided day-long farm tour highlighting specific New Jersey commodities. Both this and the zoo promotion have now become popular annual events.

National Agriculture Week was the focus of another "Jersey Fresh" special event, held week-long in a heavily-trafficked shopping mall. The department also developed "Jersey Fresh" recipe brochures, each featuring one major New Jersey farm product—such as eggplants, peaches, sweet potatoes, or apples—complete with consumer tips and a variety of recipes for that "Jersey Fresh" commodity.

Quality Grading Program Begun

That 1985 season saw an important expansion of the program's scope. In an effort to increase retail use and further enhance buyer confidence, the New Jersey Department of Agriculture developed a new marketing tool for the State's farmers—the "Jersey Fresh" Quality Grading Program.

To pack selected commodities under the "Jersey Fresh" Quality Grading Seal, growers agreed to be licensed and to follow department packing guidelines. Produce that qualifies for the "Jersey Fresh" Quality Grading Seal meets or exceeds the requirements for the top USDA grade for that commodity. Even in its first year, this voluntary program generated strong grower and buyer interest.

Initially, the program attracted 34 growers packing five commodities. Recognizing that Quality Grading promised buyers consistent high quality and uniform pack, growers saw that the program meant enhanced marketability—and increased profits—for their products.

Third Year—Looking for New Markets

At the end of that 1985 season, a Gallup poll once again showed "Jersey Fresh" continuing to make great strides, with consumer awareness rising to 17 percent. Recognizing the program's success, the State legislature approved $875,000 in "Jersey Fresh" funding for 1986.

Encouraged by survey results and continuing legislative support, the department began to look at opportunities to send the "Jersey Fresh" message outside the immediate region.

The introduction of two 30-second television commercials highlighted 1986, the program's third year. A generic message about the freshness and goodness of New Jersey farm products was followed by a 5-second tagline highlighting a specific commodity in season, along with the names of three food chains carrying the item.

Television now replaced radio as the primary means of advertising. "Jersey Fresh" commercials aired throughout New Jersey and the surrounding New York City and Philadelphia areas during the summer. This TV message also aired in Boston, marking the first real major expansion of "Jersey Fresh" outside the region.

Other 1986 additions to the program included new point-of-purchase materials, a stronger focus on extending the benefits of "Jersey Fresh" to direct marketers, and greater participation from agricultural groups.

To encourage that thoroughly broad-based participation, the department expanded its "Jersey Fresh" matching funds program. More than $200,000 was made available to interested agricultural organizations to promote New Jersey farm products. A regional peach festival in the Camden area, and a "Jersey Fresh" festival celebrating the State's agricultural diversity were financed with these funds. Both promotions have become major annual events that attract thousands of visitors.

The growth of the "Jersey Fresh" Quality Grading Program continued apace, too, with grower enrollment up 50 percent over 1985 and the list of eligible commodities growing to 15.

Fourth Year—"Demand the Freshest"

Once again, a Gallup poll at season's end showed "Jersey Fresh" maintaining a steady rise in trade usage and consumer awareness. Trade usage of New Jersey produce in grocery stores grew to 21 percent, while consumer awareness reached 23 percent. The State legislature matched the momentum by approving $1,275,000 in "Jersey Fresh" funding for 1987.

Encouraged by the continued climb in positive public response, the department set its sights on still higher accomplishments for the 1987 "Jersey Fresh" Program.

Until 1987, the general intent of "Jersey Fresh" had been to create consumer awareness through high visibility by billboard, radio, and television advertising, along with special promotions and the distribution of point-of-purchase materials. This effort was essentially soft-sell and educational in its consumer message, generally relying on tradition and the Garden State reputation for its impact. Ads primarily informed consumers about the availability, quality, and freshness of New Jersey grown farm products.

In 1987, this tone changed. The addition of a new slogan—"Demand the Freshest"—set the campaign's current, more aggressive tone. With "Jersey Fresh" recognition well established, the program was now ready to urge direct consumer action.

Recognizing that freshness tops the list of consumer priorities when buying produce, "Demand the Freshest—Jersey Fresh" said that consumers should not settle for just any product on the shelf. The slogan did two things: It urged consumers to demand the freshest product available, and it presented "Jersey Fresh" as the answer. Television ads, billboards, and new point-of-purchase materials reflected the "Demand the Freshest" theme, reinforcing the idea that "Jersey Fresh" was the product that best satisfied consumers' needs.

The program's fourth year included another notable addition. The department created a new television commercial, featuring the hearty endorsement of New Jersey Governor Thomas H. Kean. The audience for the "Jersey Fresh" message also grew in 1987 when the department extended the program's geographical reach to include the New England market area.

Chain store involvement reached an all-time high in 1987, with many chains organizing more individual promotions and routinely featuring "Jersey Fresh" in advertising. Department marketing personnel visited retail buyers throughout the East Coast and eastern Canada, making new contacts and distributing "Jersey Fresh" point-of-purchase materials and other buyer-related information.

These visits remain an important link of communication between the department and the retail stores. The chain store produce buyer learns up-to-date information about crop conditions and supplies, while the department sees firsthand how the program can be adjusted to meet specific, individual needs.

Grower and buyer enthusiasm for the "Jersey Fresh" Quality Grading Program continued to mount, with 115 growers enrolled in 1988. The list of farm products eligible for this marketing bonus continued to grow too, with 28 commodities approved for the program's 1988 season.

Summer 1987 also saw a high point in the excellent media coverage enjoyed by "Jersey Fresh," including Governor Kean's presentation of a basket of "Jersey Fresh" produce to President Reagan during a Garden State visit. An Associated Press laser photograph took the moment nationwide.

Other valuable national coverage included a feature spot on NBC's "Today" show, when Willard Scott, one of the country's most popular broadcasters, highlighted "Jersey Fresh" apples in season.

Looking Ahead

The 1988 season campaign theme, "Farm Fresh To You Each Morning," is featured in a new 30-second TV spot. The trademark of the "Farm Fresh" campaign is a sunrise farm silhouette, which can be seen on point-of-purchase materials including price cards, window signs, availability charts, and consumer recipe and information brochures.

One goal is the eventual merger of the "Jersey Fresh" promotional program with the "Jersey Fresh" Quality Grading Program, targeted for 1990. This merger will generate a single logo, recognized by retail stores and consumers alike as a promise of quality and consistency in New Jersey farm products. Use of the new, unified "Jersey Fresh" logo will therefore be tied to the grower's participation in the Quality Grading Program.

This merger is the next logical step in a program which has grown, in just 4 years, from an advertising logo to something much bigger. "Jersey Fresh" is now a clear forerunner of efforts designed to preserve a valuable, viable industry—and a way of life—for future generations in the Garden State.

Potatoes—Turnaround In Consumer Attitudes

Robert L. Mercer, president, The Potato Board, Denver, CO

Since 1972, the National Potato Promotion Board has been educating consumers on the high nutritional value and low calorie count of potatoes—with the goal of increasing per capita consumption while improving returns to the grower. We have experienced considerable success in meeting this goal. In 1972, per capita consumption of potatoes in the United States was 115 pounds a year. Most recent figures show annual consumption to be 120 pounds per person.

A major reason for this turnaround in consumption was a change in consumer attitudes toward potatoes. When the Board was formed, the image of the potato was not a good one. Sure, everyone loved the taste, but many thought the potato's nutritional value was low, and most were convinced that potatoes were fattening.

Nutrition Education

The first thing we did was to document the true nutritional value of the potato. Our experts conducted extensive tests and discovered an amazingly good nutrition story. Almost everyone was surprised. A medium-size potato contains only 110 calories, yet has 50 percent of USDA's recommended daily allowance (RDA) for vitamin C, high levels of potassium and fiber, and numerous other vitamins and minerals—resulting in a high nutrition/calorie ratio. In time, the potato became the first produce item with an approved nutrition label.

The Board's advertisements began telling the potato nutrition story to consumers. The initial ads were direct in combating the misconceptions about the potato's calorie count. Then, as the public began to get the message, the ads took on a different, softer tone. They also contained both calorie and nutrition information.

Our two most recent ads underscore the nutritional value of potatoes. One, with a variety of potatoes in an apothecary jar, states that potatoes contain a significant percentage of the RDA of many vitamins and minerals. The other shows a potato being painted green to remind consumers that it is, indeed, a vegetable.

Jane Brody, a syndicated columnist for the *New York Times,* has written about the nutritional value of the potato in her *Good Food Book.* Brody stated that the potato has "fewer calories than many foods people turn to when trying to lose weight." In addition, she pointed out that the potato is "low in sodium" and stated that "the potato is a nutrient bargain."

Public Relations

After developing the nutrition label and starting the ad campaign, we began working with dietitians, nutritionists, and teachers. These important groups were told the potato's story through ads in professional journals, presentations at conventions, and educational materials.

In addition, the potato's story was taken to newspapers and major national magazines. Articles on the potato's good nutrition, along with new (and fun) recipes, were regularly sent to newspaper food editors. And twice a year, Potato Board representatives met with key food editors to keep them thinking about potatoes.

On a segment of "Good Morning America," food commodity advertising was analyzed by consumer reporter John Stossel. "Three cheers for the potato industry," remarked Stossel. "They're nutritious, low in calories, and fat free. So, if those ads get us to eat more potatoes, good for the industry, and good for us."

Next Step—Retail Merchandising

To ensure that shoppers found an attractively displayed product in grocery stores, we started our merchandising program. We currently have four merchandisers who assist retailers in promoting and marketing potatoes around the country.

Potato Lover's Month

Along the way, we decided to add some fun to the promotion of potatoes and created Potato Lover's Month. Celebrated every February since 1978, Potato Lover's Month is observed in schools, retail stores, and the media.

Potato Lover's Month kits are used in schools to teach nutrition in an entertaining fashion. An annual contest provides cash awards for the most creative cafeteria promotions, and judging is not easy. Entries have involved entire communities—parents, newspapers, and sometimes even mayors have taken part. Some schools have held special potato days, put on plays about nutrition, and dressed everyone up as vegetables.

In grocery stores, potatoes are displayed and advertised around the Potato Lover's Month theme. The growing participation of major retail chains in the campaign has turned what was once a rather slow month for potato sales into one of the best.

In the media, hundreds of radio and television interviews are given— telling the potato's nutrition story in a light tone. Some television stations hold cooking demonstrations, some television crews visit potato farms, and everyone seems to have fun.

Kraft Salad Days

The first major retail push each potato crop year takes place in the fall when the largest percentage of the crop is harvested. The next big push comes in February, with Potato Lover's Month, and the third is Salad Days, from May through July.

The Salad Days commercial tie-in with Kraft Co. gives the Board an expanded advertising program, and keeps potatoes (and low-calorie potato salads) on consumers' minds through the summer months. The Kraft sales force, working with the Board's merchandisers, distributes beautiful materials and encourages their use in produce department displays.

Exports to Southeast Asia

The Board is always looking for new markets and new consumers for potatoes, and a search for export markets determined that Southeast Asia had the best potential. Reasons for the area's suitability include its increasing standard of living, the growing popularity of Western foods there, and its large tourist trade.

Currently, Japan is the largest importer of U.S. frozen potato products, but other Asian countries, such as Hong Kong, Singapore, Malaysia, Indonesia, and Taiwan, are also rapidly growing markets for U.S fries. The effort to develop these markets

Japan is the largest importer of U.S. frozen potato products, but other Asian countries are rapidly growing markets for U.S. fries too. This Japanese girl is enjoying U.S. fries from a fast food restaurant in Japan. (FAS)

received a shot in the arm in 1986 when USDA's Foreign Agricultural Service allocated $2 million to the Board's efforts. Since that time, this expanded program has resulted in significant sales increases.

In Japan, the Board launched a television advertising campaign stressing the high quality of the U.S. potato.

Tie-ins at restaurants and in grocery stores reached millions more, and awareness of U.S. potatoes and potato products soared. The other countries in the plan (Hong Kong, Singapore, Malaysia, Indonesia, and Taiwan) also are receiving increased promotional attention, resulting in creative tie-ins and increased sales. The expanded program is now in its third year, and is creating a large, loyal market for U.S. potatoes.

Gymnastic Sponsorship

One exciting new project is Potato Board sponsorship of the U.S. Women's National Gymnastic Team —the young women who are representing the United States at the 1988 Summer Olympics in South Korea.

This is a public relations sponsorship which involves working with the gymnasts to teach them about nutrition and have them become spokespersons for potatoes. The funds the Board is putting into the Gymnastics Federation allow the gymnasts to train as a team more frequently and to attend more international competitions.

The gymasts give frequent media interviews where they discuss potatoes, making the point that potatoes are nutritious complex carbohydrates containing few calories. National magazines run feature stories on the gymnasts and their training program (including, of course, how they eat). A shopping mall exhibit with the gymnastics theme will be displayed in 20 major cities—calling consumers' attention to the Board's sponsorship and the potato's good nutrition.

What's Next

In 1987, we started working on what we call our "position paper," a blueprint for the future. We had made great strides in improving public awareness of the potato's nutritional value and felt we needed to evaluate our position. The question was, should we continue with what we were doing or look for new challenges?

This process involved a thorough review of the past and an evaluation of our best promotion options. It later included consumer research on several possible campaign strategies: convenience, nutrition, taste, and fun. Also considered were the recommendations of industry leaders. The result of this study and introspection was the recommendation that future advertising stress the convenience of potatoes.

Today's lifestyles, with most household members working and everyone in a hurry, demand convenience foods. Our research indicated that a strategy highlighting convenience would be effective. And the need is there, as many consumers do not consider potatoes convenient.

So we believe we are only beginning our efforts to bring the good qualities of the potato to light. When we started 15 years ago, few thought we could make the potato a popular health food. In the 1990's we also intend to make it one of the most contemporary foods—in terms of convenience and trendiness.

Consumers Want Leaner Beef—and Get It

John J. Francis, vice president, beef marketing, Beef Industry Council, National Live Stock & Meat Board, Chicago, IL

The way beef is marketed today bears little resemblance to the marketing activities of 20 years ago.

More and more women are in the work force, so value-added convenience foods are increasingly important. Consumers have questioned traditional dietary regimens. Old values were rejected, and new lifestyles with increased dietary awareness and balance have appeared.

Also, per capita spending on beef dropped from 2.7 percent of disposable income in 1960 to 2.4 percent in 1968.

Consumer Challenges

Inflation caused consumers to ask why beef prices were continually increasing. In 1972, prices had reached their highest point in 20 years, and to the consumer, this seemed unreasonable.

The beef boycott of 1973, dietary debates, and increased consumption of poultry and fish served notice to the beef industry that a more meaningful dialogue with the consumer must be established.

If beef were to survive in the new marketplace, a method had to be developed to predict and prepare for consumer challenges. Several steps were initiated, and a long and intensive effort to show how beef could fit in with the modern consumer began.

Remaking Beef Cattle

The beef industry's ideal animal during the early 1950's was short-legged, short and deep in the body, and had a good deal of body fat. Market animals were bred to these proportions for good reason: They met consumer expectations. In fact, during the 1950's, consumers preferred beef with excess fat, and cuts without plentiful fat were considered inferior.

Consumer preference during the 1970's and 1980's, however, changed. Scientific cross-breeding of traditional breeds, along with the introduction of European breeds to the U.S. beef gene pool, enabled cattle producers to breed a leaner beef animal that was more acceptable to new consumer tastes. These animals were longer bodied, longer legged, more muscular, and less inclined to deposit fat than those of the 1950's. Fat content was further reduced through improved animal nutrition practices.

Retailers also came to recognize that the presence of excess fat was no longer desirable, and modified their trimming methods accordingly. Before 1986, most retailers trimmed outside fat to a maximum of one-half inch. Today, many meat cutters trim closer—to one-quarter inch or less. Beef, in almost every way, was remade to meet the changed expectations of today's consumers.

Market Development

One of the first things developed was a long-range plan to guide the industry to the 1990's and beyond. The long-range plan is updated yearly, and results to date have been highly positive.

The Beef Promotion and Research Act of 1985 enabled the beef industry to implement a national, legislated checkoff program to build consumer demand. Producers pay one dollar per head on beef cattle at slaughter. (Farmland Industries, Inc.)

Beef Promotion and Research Act

This 1985 Act enabled the beef industry to implement a national, legislated checkoff (assessment) program to build consumer demand and to realize its "dollar a head" checkoff goal. This program, which went into effect October 1, 1986, raised approximately $70 million in its first year of operation, about half of which was used by the State beef councils for in-state promotion efforts or reinvestment in the national program.

This new program builds on the existing promotion structures at the national and State level, but is overseen by a new organization, the Cattlemen's Beef Promotion and Research Board, or, as it is sometimes called, the Beef Board. Where funds were once minimal, the increased checkoff began to support a vast range of strategies and executions to market beef more successfully. It also allowed the industry to reposition beef in a "Beef is Back" campaign

which emphasized the increasing popularity of beef, successfully demonstrating how beef fits into today's consumer diet.

Execution of Long-Range Plan

To make it all happen, the Beef Industry Council and Beef Board established programs designed to enhance beef appeal and marketability to consumers. These programs build demand for beef by conveying positive industry messages through believable and influential public opinion leaders—especially the news media, educators, and health care professionals. Public relations efforts include press seminars stressing "beef is back," publications about beef and microwave cooking, and special events held to spread consumer awareness of the value of eating beef.

Research Programs

These programs discover new information about beef, including its value to health and nutrition, new products and technologies, and new value-added uses—all of which lead to a better future for marketing beef. In fact, research studies have helped to prove that beef is leaner, and lower in calories and cholesterol, than many consumers believed.

Promotion Programs

These programs carry the beef industry's message directly to consumers through the media, at the supermarket meat case, and in restaurants. The goal is to favorably influence consumer demand for beef, through messages that reinforce positive images of beef—its taste, convenience, versatility, and nutritional value.

Consumer advertising targets adults 25 to 54 years old, who have above average education and income. For the first time, a large and extensive mix of national advertising was used to spread a positive product image. With more than $30 million in support, this included network television, network radio, consumer magazines, and newspapers.

Advertising can improve attitudes about beef among light users with television, radio, and print ads. Beef magazine and newspaper ads address complex nutrition topics like iron and cholesterol, and tell consumers the real facts about beef.

Foodservice promotion focuses on restaurants and other away-from-home settings for meals. These programs encourage beef on the menu by focusing on light, healthful, and popular ethnic foods. Restaurant trade advertising, beef menu ideas, editorial support, distributor incentives, and merchandising support for school foodservice programs are some of the strategies and tactics used.

The aim of retail sales promotion is to influence purchases at the supermarket meat counter. Point-of-purchase materials are developed and then installed in major supermarkets. This program also includes consumer and trade incentives, in-store videos, and merchandising projects.

Program Evaluations

Overall, evaluations of each of these programs have been favorable, and the results suggest that the beef industry has indeed turned the corner, and will continue to increase its sales through marketing techniques discussed. For example: Walker Research, Inc. conducted a benchmark study in January 1987, just as the industry's new consumer marketing programs were reaching full swing, and again in June 1987. The Walker study found:

1. The number of Americans who believe beef fits into their lifestyles increased from 59 percent in January to 64 percent in June.

2. Those who believe beef is an important part of a well-balanced diet increased from 51 to 56 percent.

3. Those who say beef can fit into a reduced-fat diet increased from 32 to 38 percent.

4. In January, 8 percent said they were eating more beef, and in June, 13 percent said they had increased consumption.

The industry appears to be reversing the trend among consumers to reject beef as inappropriate for their times and lifestyles. Instrumental in this reversal has been the industry's change from a production-oriented to a consumer-oriented business. Many more changes are in store, as new beef products (many of which will be branded) are brought to market in the 1990's. But one thing seems certain. Beef is not only back, it's here to stay.

The Other White Meat®

*Charles R. Harness, director of industry information, National
Pork Producers Council, Des Moines, IA*

A well-planned and coordinated national marketing program to improve the sale of pork in the United States has changed consumer attitudes about this meat product. It began in November 1986 when the National Pork Board launched the National 100 Percent Legislative Pork Producers checkoff (this is an assessment on pork producers and importers). The Board (15 members nominated by producers and appointed by the Secretary of Agriculture) established a first-year industry budget of $22 million for promotion, research, and consumer education programs.

The money for these programs comes from checkoff funds collected on all U.S.-produced market hogs, feeder pigs, and breeding stock, as well as imported hogs and pork products. The rate is one-quarter of 1 percent of market value. The compliance rate averaged 98 percent during the Board's first year, and refund requests remained low, averaging about 10 percent of all checkoff funds collected during the year. Seventy cents of every producer checkoff dollar is being spent to help stimulate consumer demand for pork.

Campaign Theme: The Other White Meat®

The major thrust is a bold campaign begun in 1987 to reposition fresh pork in the minds of consumers as a lean, nutritious, and convenient product that is also versatile and fits right into the modern lifestyle. In consumer research conducted before the campaign started, over 40 percent of all consumers already subconsciously viewed fresh pork as a white meat. Pork was even defined as a white meat in Webster's dictionary. Extensive pretesting of the "White Meat" concept showed it to be a highly believable and extremely effective way to get the message about fresh pork across to consumers.

Campaign Changing Consumer Attitudes

Seven months into the campaign coordinated by the National Pork Producers Council (NPPC) an independent research company reported, "there is growing evidence that the 'White Meat' message is changing consumer attitudes about pork." In 7 short months, the "White Meat" campaign had established itself as one of the most effective food campaigns ever developed. It was helping to sell more pork.

20 TV Markets Targeted

The "White Meat" campaign targeted 20 major metropolitan population centers, and placed two 30-second television commercials on stations in these markets. One of the commercials featured classic dishes updated to include pork. The other featured lean, low-calorie pork.

Ads in 18 Magazines

The print campaign included 18 magazines selected from the women's service, lifestyle, and cuisine categories. The ads featured full-color photos of classic dishes, such as cacciatore, cordon bleu, a l'orange and

The major thrust of a promotion campaign begun in 1987, by the National Pork Producers Council, was to reposition fresh pork in the minds of consumers as a lean, nutritious, convenient, and versatile product. The campaign is helping increase the consumption of pork. (Norman E. Pruitt)

florentine, all made with fresh pork. All the ads included a coupon which readers could cut out and send in for copies of recipes. By the end of 1987, over 146,000 requests for free recipes had been received.

Nearly 85 Percent of Targeted Market Reached

The combined television and magazine "White Meat" campaign reached millions of Americans in 1987. The "White Meat" message reached nearly 85 percent of the projected target audience—women between the ages of 25 and 54 who are light-to-moderate users of pork. Awareness of pork as a "White Meat" increased 72 percent in these television markets during the first 7 months of the campaign. Even in markets where magazines were the only support, 35 percent of those surveyed 7 months into the campaign were aware of the pork industry's new promotion effort.

States Provide Additional Funds

The "White Meat" campaign received widespread industry support. Twenty State pork producer associations contributed $750,000 in State funds to further strenghten the national effort in target cities. The National Pork Board matched the additional State funds dollar for dollar.

A Coordinated National Marketing Program

The national media campaign was conducted in concert with other aspects of the marketing campaign program coordinated by NPPC. Four NPPC regional merchandisers helped to raise promotion funds by encouraging cooperative promotion efforts by packers and food retailers. The major objective was to devote more meat case space to fresh pork, and to encourage food retailers to feature pork more often in their own advertising. During 1987, the four regional merchandisers held numerous retail seminars and conducted special video training programs as well as a national store display contest. Over 20,000 retail food stores participated in one or more of the industry's cooperative programs during the year.

Peggy Fleming Serves as Industry Spokesperson

Olympic gold medalist Peggy Fleming became the official national spokesperson for America's pork producers in 1987. She made numerous appearances around the Nation on TV and radio programs, telling consumers how pork fits into her own personal lifestyle.

Merle Ellis Visits Food Editors

Merle Ellis, one of the Nation's best-known authorities on meat selection and cooking techniques, accompanied NPPC's own consumer affairs director in one-on-one meetings with the food staffs of such major magazines as *Good Housekeeping, Ladies Home Journal,* and *Weight Watchers.* They carried the message of today's leaner pork to food and nutrition professionals across the Nation, and in the process generated ideas for pork features in many of the magazines they visited.

Foodservice Industry Also Targeted

The campaign aimed at the giant foodservice industry tied in directly with the overall "White Meat" effort. Eye-catching color ads were placed in the foodservice industry's own leading magazines, showing foodservice operators how pork could be easily substituted for classic menus that traditionally feature other protein sources. Over 14,000 foodservice units representing more than 150,000 restaurants and institutions requested the recipes that accompanied the ads.

America's Cut™ Introduced

In 1987, America's pork producers became the first national commodity group to develop and trademark a standardized, premium meat cut and then market it nationally. In cooperation with eight State producer associations, NPPC introduced "America's Cut™" in July 1987. By the end of the year, it was being featured in 23,000 supermarkets and was available at 3,000 restaurants.

Health Professionals Get Special Messages

Health professionals are influential in advising consumers on their eating habits. The National Live Stock and Meat Board, using pork producer checkoff funds, provided the Nation's doctors and dietitians the latest nutritional information on pork during 1987. They held special seminars and placed advertising in publications read primarily by health professionals.

Goal Achieved

As the first year of the national legislative checkoff progressed, the news media and market analysts noted that a stronger demand for pork seemed to be developing. One publication, *Pork Pro Newsletter,* said that "a big share of the credit for the surge in pork demand must go to the 'Other White Meat' campaign."

By year's end, University of Missouri agriculture economist Glenn Grimes was saying, "The apparent increase in demand for pork put $500 million in U.S. pork producers' pockets during 1987 that wouldn't be there under normal conditions."

And Board president Virgil Rosendale said, "All segments of the pork industry have pulled together as a team to make sure the checkoff works, and that programs and projects undertaken with producer funds are run effectively and efficiently."

Dairy Farmers Are Pioneers in Promotion

Joseph J. Westwater, chief executive officer, National Dairy Promotion and Research Board, Arlington, VA

"During the last three years, 1984-1986, milk and dairy product consumption has increased about 10 percent, the largest and longest sustained consumption gain ever," states USDA's 1987 Report on the Dairy Promotion Campaign. The report adds, "While a number of economic and social factors have contributed to this gain and the exact influence of each factor cannot be measured, the National Dairy Promotion Program has played an important role."

As part of the Dairy and Tobacco Adjustment Act of 1983, Congress established the National Dairy Promotion and Research Board to carry out a coordinated program to maintain and expand domestic and foreign markets for U.S. fluid milk and dairy products.

Thirty-six dairy farmer leaders, representing milk producers throughout the United States, serve on the Board. They are selected by the Secretary of Agriculture from nominations submitted by dairy farmers and their organizations.

This dairy program calls for a mandatory assessment of 15 cents on each hundredweight of fluid milk marketed commercially in the 48 contiguous States. At current milk production levels, this generates about $200 million for the promotion and research program. Producers can receive credit of up to 10 cents a hundredweight for payments made to qualified State and regional promotion programs.

Here are some of the Board's promotional and research activities.

Advertising

Selling dairy products through advertising and promotion is a marketing challenge. Each product, and each campaign, has its own "marketing personality." The Board allocates about 80 percent of its financial resources to advertising.

By studying dairy consumption data and applying evaluation results, target audiences are pinpointed, strategies selected, and budgets allocated.

Six national advertising campaigns are working for America's dairy farmers. These include cheese, fluid milk, dairy calcium, butter, ice cream, and nonfat dry milk. These programs are coordinated with the American Dairy Association, C.O.W. (California, Oregon, and Washington) Dairymen, Inc., and State and regional promotion groups.

Cheese

About 30 percent of the Nation's milk production goes into cheese. Since it takes 10 pounds of milk to make a pound of cheese, the industry markets a lot of milk by selling cheese. And cheese is highly promotable.

The theme of the national cheese campaign is "Don't Forget the Cheese." Targeted at medium-to-light female cheese consumers 25-54 years old, the campaign offers straightforward ideas for adding cheese to various eating situations.

The advertising features a variety of domestic cheeses, offers many cheese uses, and reminds shoppers, "Don't Forget the Cheese." Both national network television and print advertising are used to communicate the cheese message.

Fluid Milk

Nearly 36 percent of the Nation's milk is consumed in fluid form. America's dairy farmers are investing a substantial part of their advertising dollars in these products.

As part of its strategy for promoting fluid milk, the Board has segmented its advertising effort. Campaigns are directed at the youth and young adult markets. The campaigns strive to position milk as a product that is healthy and fits into today's active lifestyles. Television viewers are reminded that milk is "America's Health Kick" and "Does a Body Good."

Although the dairy farming industry has advertised milk to children and adults for many years, the expanded national funding has enabled a much greater effort.

In addition, the National Dairy Board has identified a new target audience—tweens. These young people, 11-16 years old, consume over 25 percent of the fluid milk. Using the theme, "Milk, it does a body good," the advertising plays on peer acceptance and the dramatic growth changes experienced at that age.

Dairy Calcium

Since dairy products provide 76 percent of the calcium needed in our

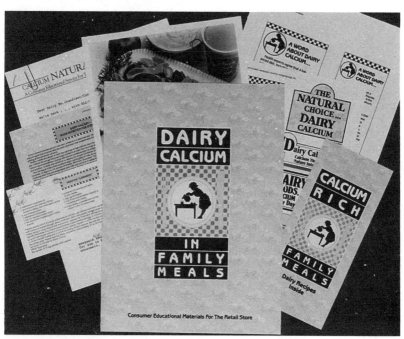

Dairy products provide 76 percent of the calcium needed in our diets, making it a natural for the dairy industry to promote their products. Publications such as these were produced by the National Dairy Board to promote dairy products as a source of calcium. (National Dairy Board)

diets, it is natural for the dairy industry to take marketing advantage of the situation. Research funded by dairy farmers, conducted over the years, has identified calcium in milk products as a help in preventing osteoporosis and perhaps other health problems.

To help offset increased advertising by the makers of calcium supplements, in 1984 the dairy calcium campaign positioned dairy as the preferred source of calcium. The theme adopted was "Dairy Calcium the Way Nature Intended."

Butter

Seventeen percent of the U.S. milk supply is turned into butter. This provides the industry with a challenging marketing opportunity.

The national butter campaign positions butter in a "light-hearted" manner against other spreads. Targeted at women 18-49, the main purchasers of butter in dual user households, commercials inform consumers that butter has the same number of calories as most other spreads—"36 per pat."

The "Give 'em all a little pat of butter" advertising plays up butter's superior taste and 100 percent natural dairy composition in an upbeat, contemporary way.

Ice Cream

Americans are consuming more and more ice cream. This tempting treat represents about 9 percent of the milk supply.

The Board has joined with the International Ice Cream Association and its members for major national promotions. Working together with the entire industry helps to sell more product.

The generic ice cream campaign is targeted at families, with emphasis on women 25-54. The 30-second and 15-second television commercials feature the product in a unique, fresh way. In support of the campaign, magazine ads are inserted in the grocery and restaurant trade press. The campaign runs during the peak ice cream consuming season. Branded ice cream manufacturers increase their advertising support during the campaign period.

Nonfat Dry Milk

The Board is working with trade-related organizations to promote nonfat dry milk. A series of print ads stresses the advantages of using this product. Nonfat dry milk is featured as a way to add calcium to frozen desserts, soup mixes, bakery products, and other prepared foods. Like the ice cream effort, the campaign includes additional branded support advertising to increase its impact.

Export and Military Sales

In efforts to develop programs designed to increase exports of U.S. dairy products, the Board invited various segments of the industry to submit proposals for innovative and feasible projects to develop or modify products that would increase consumption of U.S. dairy products in developing nations.

The Board compiled and published a booklet, "Export Programs of the U.S. Department of Agriculture—Dairy Applications," which is being distributed throughout the industry.

In the military market, point-of-sale materials were provided in more than 200 commissaries across the United States. With sales of over $6 billion annually, the military is the Nation's sixth largest retailer.

Nutrition Education

This program strives to position dairy as the best source of calcium and several other nutrients. Based on the most current nutrition research data, the Board develops and implements information campaigns and activities. From advertising in health journals to distributing consumer literature through supermarkets, the Board reaches millions of Americans with a positive health message about dairy products.

Nutrition Research

In 1984, the Board began funding a long-term nutrition research effort across the Nation. Today, this strong commitment continues with aggressive, market-oriented biomedical and nutrition research.

Proposed research projects are studied by an industry review committee, which develops a strategic plan for the industry's future nutrition research needs. The projects also are reviewed for scientific merit by a National Dairy Council committee of expert researchers. The Board's intention is to make certain that research funds are used in specific, efficient ways that will provide answers to better promote dairy products to the general public.

Through the Board, America's dairy farmers fund over 50 projects. New research is taking a more focused approach to ensure results that will benefit the dairy industry.

Although the focus has been on dairy calcium and its role throughout the human life cycle, researchers also are studying the importance of vitamin D. Researchers are finding that dairy products are part of the solution for many nutritionally related health concerns.

The Board recently established the National Dairy Board Institute for Nutrition and Cardiovascular Research at Oregon Health Sciences University. The Institute will become a prototype for future research efforts in other key areas including the role of fats in the diet. This area is and will continue to be a pressing research need for the industry.

The Board uses research findings to provide marketing strategies for promoting dairy products.

Through its combined research and public relations efforts, it works with a multitude of organizations and the mass media to communicate positive scientific results to consumers. This effort not only serves the dairy industry, but helps consumers improve their health by having a balanced diet.

Product Research

Through the Board's leadership, America's dairy farmers are making a long-term commitment to product research. Six dairy research centers, representing 12 universities, are funded jointly by the Board, State and regional dairy organizations, and universities. The "centers" program, in focusing on dairy product research, will go a long way in repositioning "dairy related" research at the top of the scientific priority list.

The dairy research center effort is one-half of the Board's commitment to new and improved dairy products. The other half includes several competitive research projects.

Competitive research covers a wide range of applied and basic projects. Topics range from the study of casein, a major component of milk, to the modification of starter cultures through genetic engineering. Food safety and quality also are given priority.

The combination of the "centers" and competitive projects provides the industry with a broad base of research resources.

Is it possible to manufacture cholesterol-free dairy products? What new generation of products and packages will the new research thrust provide? Will milk's component parts become competitive in the food manufacturing process? Today's dairy food scientists are working to find the answers to these questions. Their findings will have a significant impact on the dairy marketplace of tomorrow.

Evaluation

The Act under which the Board was established mandates the evaluation of its efforts. Even without this requirement, it makes sound business sense to constantly gauge the effectiveness of the promotion and research programs.

Among the major tools used to measure the effectiveness of the Board's advertising are the following: consumer attitude and awareness studies, consumption and sales analysis, and econometric analysis.

1. **Consumer attitude and awareness studies** are used to evaluate attitudes and awareness of advertising for dairy products. They are done on a continous basis for fluid milk, dairy product calcium, cheese, and butter.

While consumer attitude and awareness studies indicate what people think about advertising campaigns and products, they provide limited information about changes in sales trends.

2. **Consumption and Sales Analysis.** Since increased sales of dairy products is the objective of Board programs, a number of different instruments are used to monitor changes in consumption.

Perhaps the best of these measurements are those provided by USDA. Monthly fluid milk and milk for processing figures give a solid indication of consumption trends for all major dairy products. The most important evaluative tool is a measurement of consumption.

Additional information on in-home consumption of fluid milk, butter, cheese, and ice cream is purchased from commercial research firms. These services provide details on who consumes dairy products, how much they use, and other detailed information.

3. **Econometric Analysis.** This is a more sophisticated analysis of program effectiveness. It attempts to isolate one "advertising effect" from other factors that might increase or decrease sales.

Solid Support for Program

America's dairy farmers continue to be very supportive of their investment in promotion and research. In August 1985, a referendum required by law was conducted among dairy farmers to continue the 15 cents per hundredweight assessment for the expanded program. The farmers voted overwhelmingly—by 89.7 percent—to support the promotion of their products.

Today, dairy farmers rank 65th among the Nation's leading advertisers. The coordinated effort of the Board and the State and regional promotion groups has raised the industry to new levels of progressive market expansion.

The pioneer leadership of America's dairy farmers in expanded promotion and research is spreading to other commodities such as beef and pork. These promotion and research programs will go a long way in making American agriculture more competitive in today's marketplace.

Problems In Evaluating Generic Dairy Promotion Programs

Tom Cox, assistant professor, and Bob Wills, associate scientist, Department of Agricultural Economics, University of Wisconsin - Madison

Generic commodity promotion programs have gained considerable momentum in recent years.

In 1987, more than $400 million was spent to promote dairy products. More than half was spent by processors to promote their own brands. About $200 million was generic or commodity promotion, mostly financed by mandatory assessments on dairy farmers; a small amount came from voluntary contributions of processors or equipment suppliers.

In 1983, Congress authorized mandatory assessments for generic promotion and research under the Dairy and Tobacco Adjustment Act. The Dairy Promotion and Research Order authorized under that act assesses dairy farmers 15 cents per hundredweight. Five or ten cents of this assessment can be designated to go to qualified State or regional promotion programs. At the beginning of 1987, 84 State and local programs were qualified. Some of the State and

Since 1983, dairy farmers have been assessed 15 cents per hundredweight for their dairy herds' milk production. This money is used to promote dairy products, and in 1987 more than $400 million was spent on promotion. (Soil Conservation Service)

local money is spent directly for promotion, research, and education and some funds are pooled in broader national or regional promotion programs such as American Dairy Association promotions for the United Dairy Industry Association.

Evaluation of Promotion Programs Mandated

The 1983 act also mandated USDA evaluation of the national program in annual reports to Congress. Evaluation enables program managers to better allocate funds among promotional activities including research and education programs, media advertising, and trade promotions, as well as to allocate their promotion efforts effectively across geographic and demographic markets and over time. Moreover, dairy farmers need program evaluations to choose whether to give their "middle nickel" to the local or national promotion agencies.

Unfortunately, evaluations of promotion programs are difficult. The analytical framework and data gathering techniques need further development. Interactions with brand and generic advertising of other commodities, and interactions over time with price, income, and demographic factors, complicate the analysis. Also, there are a number of different promotion agencies with different objectives. Finally, most evaluations require much information about product movement, measures of promotion effort, and other factors that affect demand—and often this information is incomplete or does not exist.

Common Viewpoints About Promotion

Some agricultural producers express the opinion that "You have to promote product; everyone does it." A

related view is that generic commodity promotion programs are defensive measures against the heavy national and regional advertising of competing products. For example, dairy farmers seek to offset branded soft drink or branded and generic orange juice advertising with a generic promotion program that extols the virtues of fluid milk and milk products. Similarly, producers of competing foods such as eggs, poultry, pork, and beef may argue that they need a generic commodity promotion to maintain or increase their share of protein consumption. Practically everyone seems to believe that promotions will increase their sales.

Need For Program Evaluation

While the common wisdom that generic commodity promotion programs are useful may be valid, much is unknown. Most of these programs are under Federal or State legislation or both. Commodity producers and authorizing agencies want to know whether the promotion programs are "cost-effective" in the sense of generating a return on investment greater than or at least equal to the cost of the promotion program. A bigger question is whether generic promotion funds could be used better.

Diversity of Generic Promotion Programs

Evaluating the cost-effectiveness of generic promotion programs is difficult because of their incredible diversity. This diversity is reflected in *the range and types of commodities* from fluid milk as a natural source of calcium to Wisconsin cheese, *the range and types of institutional structures* from regional to national scope, and whether *authorization* is based on State or Federal legislation, or both.

Major Media Advertising for Seven Dairy Products, 1985-1986

	1985		1986	
	Generic	Brand	Generic	Brand
		$1,000		
Milk & Butter	$24,161.3	$ 11,388.8	$ 58,411.6	$ 10,713.3
Cheese	38,388.7	85,623.9	35,343.5	75,158.2
Ice cream (excluding fruit and juice popsicles	17.4	44,548.4	0	85,995.0
Cottage cheese & yogurt	16,845.5	49,097.1	23,009.2	52,624.6
Total	$79,412.9	$183,747.3	$116,764.3	$215,795.0

Source: Leading National Advertisers, Inc., *Class/-Company/Brand $*, New York, 1985 & 1986.

Retail and Trade Promotion Diversity

Sixteen domestic and two foreign sources spent $79 million in 1985 and $116 million in 1986 on generic dairy advertising. Generic advertisers included the American Dairy Association; the Southeast United Dairy Industry; the United Dairymen of Arizona; the Utah Dairy Commission; the California, Oregon, Washington Dairymen (COW); the Pennsylvania Dairy Association; the Wisconsin Dairy Board; and the National Dairy Promotion and Research Board. In contrast, roughly twice these amounts were spent on "brand" advertising of dairy products. While both types of media advertising target final consumers by using television, radio, newspapers, and magazines to "pull" product through retail outlets, generic dairy and brand advertising are likely to have distinct impacts.

Brand advertisers try to increase sales of their brand at the expense of competing producers. They may not increase overall sales of the product. Generic advertising attempts to increase overall sales but is indifferent as to the distribution of these sales among brands. The two types of advertising may interact. Finally, State and regional promotion programs may resemble brand advertising to the extent that they differentiate the product by its source.

In addition to media advertising, significant promotion expenditures are aimed at processors and distributors. A large portion of cheese consumption is attributed to increased away-from-home consumption of cheese on pizzas, salads, cheeseburgers, and the like. Other nonmedia efforts entice retailers to set up special displays or features for dairy products, to "push" the products toward consumers.

Diversity of Other Relevant Factors

So many factors affect consumption of dairy products that it is hard to isolate the effect of generic advertising. Geographic and media markets, competing advertising agencies and media campaigns, timing and media mix, Federal farm and food policy, prices (including those of competing and complementary food items), consumer incomes, socio-demographic and psychographic profiles of regional commodity markets—all alter the effectiveness of generic promotion programs. Evaluating the net impacts of specific regional or national promotion programs in the midst of all these other changes can be quite difficult.

In addition to commodity and institutional diversity, the objectives, administration, and activities of generic promotion programs often differ. Most commodity promotions encompass multiple activities in addition to consumer media advertising. For example, most generic promotion programs also support research and development, consumer and trade education, and trade promotion targeted toward processors, wholesalers, foodservice outlets, and retailers. These activities likely have different impacts than media advertising in terms of their duration, intensity, and measurement, which, in turn, will affect the time required for realizing and evaluating a return on promotion investment.

How Broad an Evaluation?

The more diverse the products, markets, activities, and objectives of the promotion, the more difficult it is to evaluate its performance. Conversely, the more narrowly geographic and product markets are defined (for example, cheese or fluid milk consumption in major metropolitan markets of New York State), and the fewer and more homogeneous the promotion programs are, the easier it is to evaluate their effectiveness. While not necessarily an easy task, it is easier to accurately measure changes in fluid milk and cheese consumption in a metropolitan market such as New York City or Albany than to do so for the whole United States. It is also somewhat easier to measure the relevant sources of change in consumption patterns for metropolitan markets than for the United States in aggregate. So, the narrower the market and the fewer the relevant sources of change in consumption patterns, the easier it is to measure the impact of these forces on consumption, and, hence, evaluate the effectiveness of promotion programs.

Most program evaluations of specific dairy products (such as cheese or fluid milk) in narrow geographic markets (such as cities) reveal positive net returns to promotion programs. For example, a recent study of fluid milk promotion in New York City from January 1980 to December 1984, done at Cornell University, estimates additional sales revenue of $1.50 for every $1 spent. The study also indicates that the optimal level of advertising (where marginal costs equal marginal benefits) would be about 65 percent of the amount actually spent during the study period.

Unfortunately, the narrow product and geographic scope of these results makes it difficult to generalize to the United States as a whole, because generic programs differ from one another, and because there are differences from city to city and from region to region in milk use patterns, retail prices, income levels, and demographics.

Inadequate Data To Evaluate

In contrast to brand advertising of specific products by particular firms, tracking product movement of generic commodities produced and marketed by multiple firms can be considerably more difficult. For example, a State generic dairy promotion board may wish to track the sales of dairy products produced by that State but sold in national markets by multiple distributors. Often, the State product is combined with products from other States and loses its unique identity before it is sold to consumers.

An additional evaluation difficulty concerns the trend toward away-from-home consumption that characterizes most food commodities. For example, most of the increase in U.S. cheese consumption has been in the Italian cheeses, mozzarella in particular. Most of this growth in consumption results from increased pizza consumption. Unfortunately, existing information about away-from-home consumption is often inadequate, or nonexistent, for evaluation purposes.

Inadequate Methodologies

Methodological issues about how to specify and measure the impacts of generic promotion programs need to be clarified. These issues include 1) the measurement of dynamic advertising sales response (lag effects and decay rates, threshold and saturation levels), 2) the measurement of cross-promotion effects (the interaction of generic and brand advertising and competing advertising messages), 3) the aggregation of multiple activities (such as research, education, trade promotion, and media consumer advertising) into comparable dollar measures for use in evaluation, and 4) incorporation of supply response into the evaluation methodology.

Considerable basic and applied research of this nature is required before our evaluation methodologies are adequate to resolve the complex issues about generic commodity programs.

Increasing expenditures on generic promotion of agricultural commodities increases the need for evaluation of these programs. Given the importance of accurate program evaluation, and the difficulties in promotion evaluation outlined, the need for a long-term commitment to improving data and research methodology is clear.

Consumers "Take Comfort in Cotton"

J. Nicholas Hahn, president and chief executive officer, Cotton Incorporated, New York, NY

With the transformation of the United States from a postwar economy into a thriving, affluent industrial society in the early 1960's, U.S. consumer expectations broadened and expanded. "New and improved" were catchwords to describe new consumer interests, including clothing. A family of synthetic fibers, developed at this time, became popular with the public. For the next 20 years these synthetic fibers ruled clothing, a pretender to king cotton's throne.

How Cotton Became King

In the decade following the development of Eli Whitney's saw gin in 1791, cotton replaced wool and linen as the chief fiber for U.S. clothing and forever changed textile production from a domestic chore to a highly profitable manufacturing industry.

By 1860 the United States was exporting nearly 1.2 billion pounds to England. In 1960 worldwide production of cotton had reached 25 billion pounds. In the United States, cotton accounted for 78 percent of all textile fibers sold at retail. There seemed to be no end in sight to the demand for cotton.

Synthetics and a Changing Consumer

After the close of World War II, synthetic fibers, primarily nylon and polyester, made steady gains in development and production. By

Following the development of Eli Whitney's saw gin in 1791, cotton became king of the textiles when it replaced wool and linen as the chief fiber for U.S. clothing. Cotton changed textile production from a domestic chore to a highly profitable manufacturing industry. (Soil Conservation Service)

1968 total worldwide production of nylon and polyester reached 3.2 billion and 2.5 billion pounds respectively. Production of cotton dropped to 22 billion pounds.

U.S. affluence and power had created a "push-button" consumer consciousness. Consumers demanded that their lives be made simpler and more carefree than they had been. All that remained for the synthetic fiber industry was to develop and market the right product.

In the High Plains of Texas, a coalition of growers began to detect that the old way of doing business had changed. Growing cotton fiber and delivering it to a selling point would no longer be sufficient to maintain profitability. Competition was rising in the form of a well-organized synthetic fiber industry exercising total control of its product from production through marketing. Without the variables of weather and pest control to consider, the synthetic fiber producer could manage supply and offer a product consistent in quality. Technology would even allow for specific fiber variants to be produced for individual end-products. Perhaps even more important, the synthetic fiber industry could offer technical and marketing support for its product from start to finish. U.S. cotton growers were dependent on third-party support—mills, manufacturers, and retailers—for marketing. If a textile mill required technical assistance in processing cotton, frequently the most accessible source for information was a regional synthetic fiber salesperson. The answer to most cotton production questions was simple—run uniform, strong synthetic fibers instead.

Growers realized that without a collective national marketing effort, consumer preference for their fiber would wane. Regional producer organizations called for a national effort. The ground-swell of popular support was sufficient to petition Congress into developing and passing the Research and Promotion Act of 1966.

Cotton Incorporated

Cotton Incorporated, formed in 1971, is a USDA-approved organization consisting of certified producers. It contracted with the USDA-approved Cotton Board established in 1966 to promote cotton. In the 1970's, Cotton Incorporated faced a steadily declining market share, virtually no product at retail, a consumer increasingly enamored of easy-care products, and a textile industry that had just about abandoned the production of cotton goods. Cotton Incorporated began with a basic marketing philosophy, unique to the textile industry at that time, to "appeal directly to the consumers and satisfy their needs."

A focal point of promotion was needed—a symbol that could serve as the basis of all advertisements, produce an identity for the fiber, attract instant attention at retail, and in one glance communicate comfort, quality, and cotton.

Seal of Cotton

In 1973, after several years of development, the Seal of Cotton was introduced. Cotton Incorporated felt that public awareness of the seal would be a barometer of advertising and merchandising success, and so tracking of consumer identification of the seal began. After 1 year of commercial television advertising, a survey was made of the seal and 11 other corporate symbols, such as the CBS eye, Shell Oil, and the Wrigley arrow. All words were removed from the symbols, and respondents were asked to identify what each represented. When the results were proportionally calculated to represent the population of U.S. adults, about 18 percent were able to identify the Seal of Cotton.

From the beginning, Cotton Incorporated was committed to television advertising. Television was the only medium that could cost effectively reach millions of consumers instantly and allow for sight, sound, and motion. Cotton Incorporated chose to target women aged 18-49, a demographic segment that accounted for 70 percent of all textile purchases. To reach them, advertising was concentrated in morning news shows and daytime soap operas. The fiber company's message was simple, "The more cotton, the better."

Advertising would serve to raise consumer awareness, but it could not spur purchases or increase cotton's market share if no product existed. The synthetic fiber industry had achieved sweeping success by providing easy-care, no-iron apparel and home fabrics. It was the right characteristic at the right time. For cotton to compete, it would have to offer the same performance.

"Easy-Care" Cotton Challenge

Work to find a cotton-polyester blend had been underway for several years in USDA and Cotton Incorporated textile research laboratories, but the breakthrough happened at Cotton Incorporated's Raleigh, NC, Research Center. Blended fabrics of 60 percent cotton and 40 percent polyester offered the comfort of cotton with a sufficient easy-care performance consumers expected. The new fabric was named NATURAL BLEND® and,

backed by strong marketing approach, Springs Mills introduced the fabric in 1974.

Finally, a competitive product existed. NATURAL BLEND fabrics reached retail with the introduction of a cotton-rich product by Manhattan Shirt in 1975. But cotton's share of the textile market continued to decline to an all-time low of 34 percent. The momentum built by the powerful synthetic industry was fed by polyester producers each spending substantial dollars on advertising and promotion.

"Baby Boomers" and Cotton

Seemingly far removed from Seventh Avenue and the textile industry, however, the tide was turning. The same affluent postwar economy that had created a market for easy-care polyester also had created the single largest consumer demographic segment in history: the baby boomers. These youthful consumers created a demand for cotton that began to turn the tide. With this growing demand for cotton products, king cotton began to reemerge as a competitive force in U.S. clothing and fashion. Cotton was beginning to win back the share of market it had earlier lost to the "easy-care" synthetics.

Demand for cotton began to grow steadily, as did consumer awareness of cotton. For example, in one year alone, from 1975 to 1976, consumer recognition of the Seal of Cotton jumped from 35 percent to 46 percent. Meanwhile, NATURAL BLEND continued to grow in popularity. Montgomery Ward introduced a cotton-rich shirt in 1976, followed by Sears and J.C. Penney in 1977. Cannon introduced the first NATURAL BLEND sheet in 1977 and switched its "Royal Classic" towel line from blends to 100 percent cotton, as West Point Pepperell did with three towel lines, because of consumer demand.

Success Builds

Success began to build, and synthetic fiber manufacturers took notice. In an effort to capture cotton's single largest market and the only product area that had withstood polyester's intrusion, a synthetic fiber manufacturer contracted with a major mill and apparel manufacturer to produce a blended denim jean. Cotton Incorporated responded quickly with a major media campaign on television, in newspapers, and in magazines to tout the advantages of 100-percent cotton denim jeans. Retailers and manufacturers lent their support, and plans for a major blended denim jean evaporated.

With sufficient product now becoming available at retail, Cotton Incorporated adopted a competitive positioning in its advertising—"Once you get a feel for cotton, you won't feel like anything else"—to entice consumers back with the comfort of cotton. Success continued throughout 1979 and 1980 as Fieldcrest and Sears offered NATURAL BLEND sheets, and later J. P. Stevens began production of a 100-percent no-iron sheet, based on Cotton Incorporated technology.

By 1983, cotton could register sufficient gains. The fiber's share of the total textile market climbed 5 percentage points above 1975 levels to 39 percent. Recognition of the Cotton Seal soared to 63 percent. The program was working, and consumers were growing disenchanted with synthetics. To sustain growth, Cotton Incorporated needed to document this attitudinal shift.

Cotton Revolution

The fiber company contracted with the Home Testing Institute to conduct an in-home survey of 1,700 families. The respondents were asked to check their closets for textile products they no longer used, not because of fashion or fit, but because of fabric-related failures. Overwhelmingly, consumers cited pilling, snagging, static electricity, yellowing, and inability of a fabric to breathe as reasons why they had discarded certain textile items. When this sampling was projected over the U.S. population, more than one billion textile products had been discarded because of fabric failures, primarily attributable to synthetic fibers.

The study prompted Cotton Incorporated to launch a major promotional campaign reeducating consumers on the definition of textile performance. The program, *True* Performance, centers on a retail identification program of hand-tags and labels. The system provides a convenient checklist of salient cotton characteristics at retail, making it easy for consumers to identify the natural fiber's advantages. The labels identify characteristics such as "breathable," "pill-free," "snag-free," "washable," "comfortable," and "static-free." Further studies found that the appearance of *True* Performance tags actually increased consumer buying intentions by 25 percent to 144 percent.

The program struck a responsive chord with the baby boom generation, which by 1984 had moved into a dominant position in the mainstream economy. Within 2 years, most major apparel manufacturers and retailers were participating actively in the program. Cotton's momentum, sparked by the introduction of NATURAL BLEND in 1974, was in full bloom.

In an effort to recapture the success that had come so easily in the early 1970's, the synthetic fiber industry banded together to form the Polyester Fashion Council. The Council's mission was to erase polyester's "tacky" image and reintroduce it as a "fashion" fiber. Top fashion designers were enlisted to produce high-end synthetic fiber fashions, and the

Council would later even petition the Federal Trade Commission to legally change the name "polyester." The request was denied for fear it would mislead consumers.

By 1986 cotton was once again in a dominant position. The fiber's share of the total textile market reached 44 percent. In apparel, cotton held a 43 percent share and in home fabrics, a 50 percent share. Cotton Seal recognition among U.S. adults climbed to 71 percent.

In less than 20 years, Cotton Incorporated accomplished what once seemed improbable. Through a coordinated system of research, marketing, merchandising, advertising, and promotions, cotton, once pegged as a warm weather fiber, was being sold for fall and winter. Denim jeans were transformed from utilitarian apparel into a fashion item. Ground was broken in categories such as nonwovens (personal hygiene products, mattress pads, etc.) and decorative products such as cotton window coverings, upholstery fabrics, and wall coverings.

It was apparent that consumers had come back to cotton. Cotton Incorporated mobilized to strengthen that position and ensure that consumers not only like cotton, but love it. Close tracking of the baby boomers was maintained throughout the 1980's, and as these consumers moved further into adulthood and started families, testing revealed attitudinal changes, especially in cotton's target audience of women aged 18-49.

Take Comfort in Cotton

With the multiple role demands of wife, mother, and employee, women were feeling the strains of their responsibility. Focus groups highlighted how women sought the "one quiet moment of the day" where they could pamper themselves. Overwhelmingly, these quiet moments involved cotton textiles—plush towels, cotton bathrobes, a favorite quilt, or comforting jeans and T-shirts.

Recognizing that a "New American Family" was evolving, Cotton Incorporated developed a new advertising campaign to mirror these strong feelings toward cotton. The campaign, dubbed "take comfort in cotton," reached national airwaves in 1987 by advertising on morning news shows, daytime television, and late night programs. Identification with its message brought consumers to a new level of preference for cotton.

New Cotton Sales

As 1987 came to a close, Cotton Incorporated realized its most successful year. Market share climbed to 49 percent, seal awareness held fast at 71 percent, and mill consumption of U.S. cotton hit levels not seen in 15 years. In its 17 years of operation, Cotton Incorporated generated more than $14 billion dollars of new cotton sales for the Nation's cotton growers on an investment of less than $300 million dollars. The natural fiber had reestablished itself as the primary fiber for domestic textile production.

Future Looks Promising

Heading into the 1990's, the future is promising. A new generation of teenagers is growing up in all-cotton jeans, cotton-rich fleece, knits, sheets, and towels. As fashion trends come in vogue, as textile developments reach fruition, and as demographic shifts influence the market, Cotton Incorporated will continue to change and adapt. Always stressing cotton's comfort and performance, Cotton Incorporated will base future marketing on the same sound principle it began with: Above all else, respond to the consumer, provide products to meet demand, and institute the programs that will foster the most profitable return to the Nation's cotton growers.

Louisiana, We're Really Cookin' Cajun

Larry Michaud, press secretary, Louisiana Department of Agriculture and Forestry, Baton Rouge, LA

The Cajun phenomenon is the marketer's dream come true. It has been an American classic: the rags-to-riches success story.

The success of Louisiana Cajun's marketing story has been part happy accident, part the cooking and promotional talents of Paul Prudhomme—and since his initial breakthrough, the cooking and showmanship of numerous other Louisiana chefs—part awareness by private and government leaders of a good business opportunity, and part recognition and appreciation by those outside Louisiana's borders of a heritage and cooking unique to America: Cajun food, as cooked by Cajuns, is delicious.

Origin of Louisiana Food

Prudhomme didn't start Cajun cooking, of course. That began 225 years ago in the swamps and bayous of south Louisiana as a small colony of exiled French families from Nova Scotia (then Acadia) known as Acadians—colloquially, Cajuns— struggled to make a new life in a strange land. But Prudhomme, directly descended from that group, did begin, and kept fueling, the madcap media blitz and promotional tours that catapulted Cajun to the forefront as the preeminent cooking craze of this decade.

Prudhomme consistently refers to his food as "Louisiana food." Although Louisiana food is best known as Cajun, it also includes its big-city first cousin, Creole, which has many of the melting pot influences of New Orleans with its French, Spanish, and African heritage.

Cajun is usually referred to as "poor country folks" fare, derived from the trapping, hunting, fishing, and small farming legacy of its forebears. Creole is a more sophisticated offering and usually includes some type of tomato portion. It results from the cooking styles of the commingled wealthy French and Spanish in New Orleans in the pre-Cajun era in Louisiana. Both include the "holy trinity" of finely chopped onions, celery, and green peppers.

Many have as their base stock the "roux." A roux is a thickening agent without which many Cajun/Creole dishes would be little more than a soup. Cajun cook Alton Pitre calls the roux a "controlled burning of flour and oil—equal parts of both." Although simple in concept, the roux is critical and if not stirred constantly and attended to with precision, it becomes a charred mess in the bottom of the skillet. To the base ingredients add wild game, the vast array of freshwater and marine seafood, seasonings, and vegetables available in Louisiana, and rice. The result is Cajun food in its many manifestations.

Cajun Chef Prudhomme Starts Craze

Although Prudhomme ticks off a series of events in the late 1970's and early 1980's as significant along the way to making Cajun a household word, for him it started years earlier. For 12 years Prudhomme tramped through the kitchens of America's restaurants. Along the way, he soaked up the food types, cooking styles, and food industry hype that were all to figure in what today is a multimillion-dollar food industry business for himself and his Louisiana Cajun contemporaries.

In 1982, he started his own line of products, "Cajun Magic." In 1983, he did blackened redfish for *New York Times* food critic Craig Claiborne's birthday party. There was a huge media turnout. Several chefs were cooking for the affair, but "All of a sudden this smell started coming from my side of the room. People started tasting blackened redfish and the whole attitude changed. It was the hit of the party."

Other Chefs Promote Cajun Cooking

Part of Louisiana's Cajun heritage is that cooking is not confined to the female in the household. Many Cajun men cook and cook well, and serve as role models for their sons, handing down the heritage through the generations. When Prudhomme broke through the State's boundaries, many excellent Cajun cooks and chefs were waiting for the opportunity to show their culinary art.

The common denominator of the most successful chefs is a willingness to take their cooking to the public. As roving ambassadors for the taste of Cajun they have covered the globe in the 1980's.

Paul Prudhomme didn't start Cajun cooking, but, as a descendent of those that did some 225 years ago, he has helped catapult Cajun to the forefront as the preeminent cooking craze of this decade. (Restaurants & Institutions Magazine)

Chef Buster Ambrosia was asked by the Louisiana Department of Agriculture to cook for the 1986 annual meeting of the Lions Club International in Taiwan. "We cooked for thousands of people—Lions Clubs from all over Europe, the Middle East, Far East, you name it. During our stay we prepared a total of 135 dishes. We took more than 2,000 pounds of spices, seasonings, sauces, and other ingredients as well as our crawfish, crabmeat, and red snapper and added them to some of the seafood they had over there. We introduced a cuisine to people from all over the world in that one spot. People had heard a lot about it, but they had never had a chance to taste it."

Currently scores of Louisiana chefs are making personal appearances across the country and around the world. John Folse is another of Louisiana's premier celebrity chefs who was permitted to open the only American restaurant in Moscow during the 1988 Reagan-Gorbachev summit talks and recently started a line of prepared Cajun products tailored to the European market. One of Folse's first big breaks came in 1985 when he was invited to Hollywood by 20th Century Fox to cook for a party for Cybill Shepherd. Since then, he has done additional Shepherd-instigated crawfish cookouts for some of Hollywood's biggest names. "And while we're cooking we also give them a little Cajun and Creole culture and history lesson."

One of the largest gatherings of Louisiana chefs to promote Cajun was at Bloomingdale's flagship store in Manhattan during June and July, 1986. Prudhomme, Folse, and seven other Louisiana chefs made personal appearances in a kickoff event which included much of the New York media.

The 2-month promotion, sponsored by the Louisiana Department of Agriculture, featured some three dozen Louisiana food manufacturers who, according to Glen Senk, operating vice president of Bloomingdale's, "otherwise would never have had the chance to reach this type of major national market."

Cookbooks a Marketing Tool

While personal appearances got the fledgling Cajun food industry off the ground, cookbooks are probably the single largest marketing factor keeping the food style before the public. Almost all of Louisiana's celebrity chefs have branched out into the cookbook business and acknowledge that selling cookbooks is a major business enterprise.

In January 1988, one Baton Rouge bookstore had 53 Louisiana cookbooks, many in their fifth or more printing. Some were multiple efforts by a single chef. Wilson had four; Prudhomme, two. *Chef Paul Prudhomme's Louisiana Kitchen* was in its 50th printing. The book has won a number of major awards in the cooking field and since its publication in 1984 has sold more than 700,000 copies. Three versions of "River Road," the No. 1 best selling community cookbook in the country published since 1959 by the Baton Rouge Junior League, were available, but most were a compilation of the cooking expertise and recipes of a single chef.

Cookbook sales not only reach the homemaker/cook, family, and friends, but also spawn media book reviews. Prudhomme says, "There was a span of about 3 years when it seemed like every writer who came to my restaurant or wrote about my book tried to write a better article about it than the guy before him."

Free Media Exposure

Aside from Wilson's appearances on PBS, cookbooks, and media accounts

One of the greatest marketers of Louisiana Cajun is Justin Wilson. In his folksy-Cajun country dialect in Tangipahoa Parish, Wilson reaches across America each week on public television with his show "Justin Wilson's Louisiana Cookin' Outdoors."(WLPB-TV, Baton Rouge, LA)

of personal appearances, countless other print and air time has been given to Cajun in the 1980's. As Prud-homme points out, people hurried to write or broadcast the cutest, most electrifying, best quotable quote extolling the virtues of Cajun. The reams of material range from Craig

Claiborne and Dan Rather to thousands of pieces in local media in the farthest reaches of America.

Food Shows

While Louisiana chefs have been the most visible component of Cajun, many behind-the-scenes efforts insure that Cajun continues to have staying power and makes the transition from temporary fad to permanent trend. Among these has been the work of the marketing staff of the Louisiana Department of Agriculture. Aside from hosting media promotional events, the marketing specialists have attended some 50 food shows all over the world in the 1980's selling Louisiana Cajun.

The major food buying decisions by the large restaurant and supermarket chains here and abroad are made at food shows, where those selling their products staff booths handing out literature, providing demonstrations, and taking orders from interested brokers.

The number of products available for sale at these food events has mushroomed in the last 6 years. The Louisiana Department of Commerce estimates that more than 100 new Louisiana companies in the 1980's were geared to the Cajun food market.

Pride in Cajun Culture

But the existence of a Cajun culture on which to predicate the Cajun food industry was in jeopardy only a few short generations ago. As recently as the 1930's and 1940's, Cajun children were caned at school for speaking their native Cajun French. The idea was to become American—speak English. Fortunately, there has been a renaissance of pride. They now take immense pride in their French heritage as seen in a revival of their language (a Cajun French dictionary was recently published for the first time) and their music.

Cajun music, Creole Zydeco, and new styles that blend the two, featuring the fiddle and accordion, are now being heard nationwide. Last year Cajun-Zydeco festivals drew huge crowds in Los Angeles and San Francisco.

Two of the top ten pop albums of 1987 featured a new musical hybrid fusing basic rock with authentic Cajun/Creole music. "The Lonesome Jubilee" album by John Cougar Mellencamp features accordion and fiddle on each track. And Paul Simon's Grammy-award winning pop album "Graceland" featured two Zydeco songs.

Jimmy Bulliard, Sr., founder of Cajun Chef Products in St. Martinville, recalls the furor in 1958 when he came out with his product line. "You should have seen the letter writing campaign people started to the local paper. People felt Cajun was degrading. 'Shame on us,' they said. They said we should call it Acadian or Creole, anything but Cajun."

Bulliard persevered with his "Cajun Chef" line of hot sauce, cayenne peppers, gumbo filé, pickled peppers, and others and is now one of the venerable ancestors of Cajun food. His product line has had a steady, gradual increase through the years. He markets through brokers and distributors while attending trade food shows sponsored by a specific grocery chain.

His concerns about long-term viability are echoed by a number of other Cajun food producers. "There are too many getting into it. Down the road, some of them are not going to be able to stay."

The elder in the Cajun-related Louisiana food business is B.F. Trappey's Sons, Inc., founded in 1898. Trappey's has for generations been known to Louisianians for their canned yams, cut okra and tomatoes, black-eyed peas, and red kidney bean products, and a selection of hot sauces and peppers.

Getting on the Cajun bandwagon, Jack Blendeman, president of the company, says that, although much of their product line is Cajun to the core in terms of ingredients, they only recently began marketing a specific line with the Cajun name titled Cajun Style Seafood Okra Gumbo, Cajun Style Okra Gumbo, and Cajun Style Chicken Sausage Gumbo.

He says of the impact of Cajun, "Our business is growing sustantially each week." Aside from food shows and work through distributors, his latest marketing angle is the U.S. military. Approached to develop a line to go to military commissaries, he points out that 53 percent of military personnel are from the South. He plans to make presentations of their products to individual military purchasing districts here and overseas.

New Companies

Although a number of companies have been in business for years, many more are recent creations to take advantage of the Cajun's newly found fame such as the Pizzolato family's business.

Ten years ago, Tony Pizzolato and his five sons were in the seafood business. "Tony's Seafood" was a small takeout seafood store in Baton Rouge. The five sons were on the road, each in his own truck, selling shrimp from the roadside in the Baton Rouge and Lafayette areas. After a heart attack sidelined the father, several of the sons came back to run the store while Tony recuperated. While convalescing, son Cliff says, "Dad began piddling around with some of the fish fry mixes he had been making for us at home for years and we began selling it through the store."

As requests for the fish fry mix mounted through word-of-mouth advertising, Tony decided to have art work done on a packaged product. And then the name changed.

"There was a Tony's Shoe Shop down the street and a Tony's Donut Shop across the way. And, besides,

Tony's sounded too much like pizza," the elder Pizzolato said. So they settled on the name "Louisiana Fish Fry Products, Ltd."—a name he now acknowledges has proved to be a stroke of genius.

"Anything with Louisiana or Cajun in it is going to sell these days," Cliff says. Now the Pizzolatos have seven salespersons on the road nationwide. Their products are selling in 34 States. Their most popular sellers are the Cajun Jambalaya Mix, Cajun Etoufee Mix, Cajun Gumbo Mix, Cajun Hush Puppy Mix, and Cajun Brown Gravy Mix. Last year the family bought the entire square block the original store was located on, and this year they have just completed the purchase of an adjoining square block needed to expand their manufacturing facilities.

"Business has increased between 50 and 75 percent each year since 1982," Cliff says. What marketing expertise do they use to launch a new line, now numbering some 15 products? "We put our latest product up against what we think is our major competitor," Cliff says. "We get at least 150 customers coming through the store to try each in a blind taste test. And we keep mixing and remixing it until we get at least 8 out of every 10 customers to say they like our version best."

Carroll Thomas is another descendent of the original Acadians. Although his product line numbers just two items, Cajun Power Garlic Sauce and Cajun Power Spicy Hot Sauce, they are selling from Alaska to Singapore to Europe.

"I've gone from zero business to distribution in 65 percent of the United States without spending a dollar on advertising," Thomas says. His break came when he was asked to do a cooking demonstration in Sante Fe for actress Jessica Lange. A local restaurant there kept a bottle of his garlic sauce on their tables where a California food critic for *Metropolitan Home* magazine tried it.

A story in the magazine praising the sauce led to "thousands and thousands of orders," which resulted in samples of the sauce being featured on the television series "Hour Magazine," where it was touted by the show host Gary Collins as "my all-time favorite."

"I chose the 'Cajun Power' name before Cajun really got out of the Cajun area and it's been dynamite. It's a case of we always knew how good our food was but we kept it to ourselves. Now everybody wants it."

Not All Success Stories

Not all of the Cajun entrepreneurs, however, have been fortunate enough to get that lucky break that brought their product to the attention of millions of American consumers.

Alton Pitre is one of the small Cajun entrepreneurs who, 4 years ago, started selling his own line of seasoning, "Pitre's Original Creole Seasoning."

Pitre, cooking since the age of 11 for his large family in Abbeville because, "Mama was more productive in the field with the farm chores than I was," says of his venture into the Cajun business, "It has been tough, real tough. I haven't lost any money on it, but I sure can't retire on it either."

He had made his seasoning for 15 years before putting it on the market. "The problem is that there are 15 to 20 similar seasonings on the shelves in Louisiana now. It's a situation of if they sell a case of mine it will be at the expense of someone else's product."

He is in one warehouse in Dallas and handled by four small distributors in Illinois as well as in several specialty shops in New Orleans. But, Pitre says, "It's hard to sell a one-product line. If the bigger stores are going to carry something, they want a complete line of products. They want to buy a complete package from one supplier. Less bookkeeping, less headaches all around."

Tourism Advertising Promotes Cajun Food

Figures on the dollar impact of Cajun outside the borders of the State are not available. Neither are the exact sales figures on Cajun food products. Bruce Morgan, director of promotions for the Louisiana Department of Culture, Recreation, and Tourism, with an annual budget of $4.6 million, is responsible for developing the advertising material and placing the advertising for the State's tourism industry. He says spending on foodservice in 1986 was in excess of $1 billion, or 27 percent of the tourist dollars spent in the State by the 13 million visitors that year.

Foodservice accounts for Louisiana's largest travel-related payroll, totalling $252 million or 35 percent of the State total. More than 37,000 Louisianians are employed in Louisiana restaurants.

Most of the State's tourism budget is aimed at paid advertising emphasizing Louisiana cuisine. The State promotes Cajun and Creole foods in publications nationwide. The primary slogan used in the paid tourism advertising indicates where Cajun food ranks in the things Louisiana has to offer: "Louisiana, We're Really Cookin'."

Part VII

Where to Get More Marketing Information

ABC 2

DEF 3

JKL 5

MNO 6

TUV 8

WXY 9

001000045172

U.S. Export Assistance Programs

Melvin E. Sims, general sales manager and associate administrator, Foreign Agricultural Service

After 6 straight years of decline, the volume of U.S. agricultural exports is rebounding. U.S. export assistance programs deserve credit for part of this improvement.

These programs serve many purposes. Not only do they facilitate market development, but they also help meet subsidized competition from other exporting nations and provide financing and food aid to needy countries. While some of these export assistance programs have a long history, others are relatively new, the result of recent legislation.

Regardless of when the programs were started, they all have a common goal—to boost U.S. agricultural exports, whether commercial or concessional. These export assistance programs also share a common administrator, USDA's Office of the General Sales Manager (OGSM). After the various programs receive the appropriate funding through Federal legislation, different divisions of the Foreign Agricultural Service (FAS) home office in Washington, DC, make the funds available to various U.S. organizations and industries that export U.S. agricultural goods.

The competition for world agricultural markets is becoming increasingly tight, and the United States must work diligently to regain, maintain, and expand its export markets. As U.S. agricultural exporting organizations learn about the various export assistance programs available to them, and in turn take advantage of these programs, more progress will be made in the growth of U.S. agricultural export markets.

Export Enhancement Program (EEP)

EEP is one of the newest of USDA's export assistance programs. First announced under the authority of the Commodity Credit Corporation (CCC) Charter Act on May 15, 1985, the EEP expands U.S. agricultural export markets and counters the subsidized exports of competitor countries. While the program is similar to the export subsidies of the European Economic Community (EEC), it is in fact more limited through targeting, protection of nonsubsidizers' interests, and meeting the world market price but not breaking it. Although the initial $1.5 billion in funds allocated by the Food Security Act of 1985 have since been depleted, the program has continued to operate under provisions of the CCC Charter Act.

Any overseas market in which U.S. exporters face subsidized competition from other suppliers is eligible for inclusion in the EEP. These markets are recommended by USDA program experts, members of the U.S. agricultural community, and foreign government officials. Similarly, any U.S. commodity is eligible for export under the program as long as 1) U.S. exports would increase above the level obtained without the program, 2) each proposed sale targets a specific market to challenge those competitors who overtly subsidize their exports, 3) the sale would result in a net plus to the overall economy, and 4) the sale would not increase the amount of allocated funds spent beyond what would have occurred without the program.

Once a sales initiative is announced, U.S. agricultural exporters in the private sector must contact prospective buyers in the eligible countries in order to negotiate prices, quantities, and other terms of sale. The exporter then submits a bid to USDA requesting a subsidy, or bonus, that would allow the sale at the price that had been agreed upon. USDA reviews all of the bids submitted for a particular sale. If they are responsive to the terms of the announcement and the selling price is at or above the prevailing world market price, the competitiveness of the requested bonus or subsidy is reviewed and either accepted or rejected. If a bid is accepted, the sale is complete, and the U.S. exporter receives the bonus in the form of generic certificates. The certificates are for a specified value that either the exporter or an assignee can redeem for a like quantity of designated commodities from the CCC inventory.

Commercial Export Credit Programs

In addition to the EEP, overseas markets for U.S. agricultural products are developed through the Export Credit Guarantee Program (GSM-102) and the Intermediate Credit Guarantee Program (GSM-103). These programs help U.S. firms export agricultural products to countries that would otherwise be financially unable to buy U.S. agricultural products.

First implemented in 1980, the GSM-102 Export Credit Guarantee Program replaced longstanding 6- to 36-month direct CCC credit sales, expanding export credit facilities for U.S. agricultural products. The objectives of the GSM-102 program are to 1) ensure that payments for foreign sales are as reliable as for domestic sales, 2) permit U.S. exporters to meet credit terms offered by foreign competitors, 3) substitute commercial dollar sales for sales under Public Law 480 (Food for Peace), 4) prevent the decline of established markets abroad, and 5) encourage new uses of U.S. agricultural products in importing countries.

The GMS-102 program not only promotes U.S. agricultural exports by allowing eligible countries to buy U.S. farm products on credit terms of 6 months up to 3 years, but it also guarantees repayment of these short-term loans. During fiscal year 1987, 26 countries had $3.8 billion available in short-term loan guarantees for a variety of commodities with an export value surpassing $2.6 billion.

The Intermediate Credit Guarantee Program (GSM-103) is an extension of the Export Credit Guarantee Program. It helps developing nations make the transition from concessional financing to cash purchasers. The GSM-103 program focuses on agricultural exports with long economic lifetimes, such as breeding livestock. Consequently, the loans need to cover a longer period, so they are made for more than 3 but no more than 10 years.

Targeted Export Assistance Program (TEA)

TEA, introduced in the Food Security Act of 1985, stimulates exports of U.S. agricultural products through market development targeted at countering or offsetting unfair foreign trade practices. The program encourages U.S. agricultural exports by distributing $110 million each fiscal year through 1988 in CCC funds or commodities to help participating producer organizations finance promotional activities for U.S. agricultural products adversely affected by unfair trade practices of foreign competitors or importers. In each of fiscal years 1989 and 1990, the legislation authorizes an increase in the program level to $325 million.

USDA annually announces the availability of the TEA Program in the Federal Register and the deadline for submitting applications to FAS. FAS reviews all the applications at one time and, with the approval of the Under Secretary for International Affairs and Commodity Programs, allocates TEA resources considering the following factors:

1. The existence of unfair foreign trade practice as defined by the General Agreement on Tariffs and Trade (GATT) and the extent to which it has adversely affected exports of the U.S. agricultural commodity or product,

2. The extent to which the applicant organization estimates that it, its members, or foreign third parties will be willing and able to contribute resources to the joint project,

3. The organization's prior export promotion experience and the adequacy of its administrative and personnel resources to plan and manage a program of the size requested,

4. The likelihood of success of the proposed project in terms of increasing U.S. exports or mitigating the unfair practice,

5. Whether the commodity is in adequate supply domestically, and

6. The willingness of the U.S. trade to follow up the promotion effort with aggressive selling of the commodity or product of the type, quality, and quantity desired by foreign customers.

Once the allocation has been announced, and TEA resources have been obligated in an agreement between the recipient and CCC, the nonprofit participant submits an annual activity plan to FAS for its approval. The activity plan describes the major impediments to increasing U.S. exports of the commodity in each of the markets in which the participant will be working, the proposed activities, the goals and benchmarks against which progress will be measured, and a budget that includes TEA resources and contributions from U.S. participants and foreign third parties. Only when FAS has approved the plan may the participant conduct activities and incur expenses to be reimbursed with TEA resources.

Public Law 480

Also known as the Food for Peace Program, Public Law 480 is one of the USDA's oldest export assistance programs, and it still accounts for several million tons of U.S. agricultural exports each year. Approved July 10, 1954, the program was originally designed to dispose of surplus commodities through their sale to friendly overseas nations, who paid for the products with local currencies. The program also provided for the donation of surplus commodities to other nations as necessitated by emergencies or disasters.

Today, Public Law 480 exports not only contribute to meeting the humanitarian food needs of the world through surplus donations, but they also lay the foundation for future U.S. commercial export markets and provide a catalyst for agricultural and economic growth in developing countries. Assistance is given under three titles.

Title 1

Sales are made to friendly countries under long-term concessional loans with terms of up to 40 years, a 10-year grace period, and low interest rates. These sales simultaneously promote U.S. agricultural exports while stimulating economic development in the recipient country. U.S. exports under title I have effectively encouraged foreign buyers to look to the United States for their commercial imports of agricultural products.

Title II

This title authorizes food donations to needy countries and also pays for the cost of shipping the exports. Food donations are made to alleviate famine and provide other urgent relief, to protect against malnutrition, and to provide nonprofit school lunch and preschool feeding programs overseas. Title II also allows for government-to-government donations and donations through international and U.S. voluntary agencies.

Title III

Also referred to as Food for Development, this title focuses on using Public Law 480 exports for economic development in countries with an annual per capita gross national product of $835 or less, which fulfills the criteria set forth by the International Development Association for development loans. Title III can be applied to title I in order to turn a loan into a grant.

If a country with approved development proposals uses the funds made from domestic sales of title I commodities for approved projects, the dollar equivalent of the title I loan is forgiven.

Local Currency Initiative

In addition to the Public Law 480 activities included in titles I, II, and III, the Food Security Act of 1985 started a new program called the Local Currency Initiative. Its purpose is to stimulate economic growth in the private sectors of recipient countries by selling U.S. farm products for local currency. The U.S. Government loans the currencies to private financial interme- diaries in the title I countries, who, in turn, relend to the local private sector.

Additional Information About Programs

To qualify for participation in EEP, contact the CCC Operations Division of the Office of the General Sales Manager. For infor- mation about GSM-102 and GSM-103 credit guarantee pro- grams, and P.L. 480 Program, contact the Office of the General Sales Manager.

To submit a TEA Program proposal or to find out the status of programs under consideration, contact the FAS Marketing Programs Staff.

Getting the Facts and Figures for Farming

Charles E. Caudill, administrator, National Agricultural Statistics Service

USDA's Agricultural Statistics Board meets monthly in Washington, DC, behind locked doors, unable to leave their guarded quarters, and with phones disconnected. The Board reviews the results of well-defined surveys of the Nation's agricultural sector and prepares the official facts and figures that will influence America's biggest business. Only authorized individuals may enter the Board's area during a full-scale lockup, and no one leaves until the report is released at the set time of 3:00 p.m.

Tools for Decisions

The released estimates are tools to help farmers and ranchers work out their planting, breeding, feeding, storing, purchasing, and marketing plans. Exactly how the data may be used depends on the user and the marketing move planned. A farmer may decide to cut hog production or switch from corn to soybeans, or feed more cattle. A shipper may order more or fewer boxcars.

These official estimates are the meeting ground for producers and those they deal with across the agricultural network. Producers can't operate independent from other market factors. They are affected by the transactions of commodity buyers and speculators, program adjustments by legislators, and decisions by chemical and equipment manufacturers, transportation firms, lending institutions, and so on. University, government, and private economists use the estimates to predict supply and demand conditions farmers are likely to encounter.

Without the Board's evaluations of agriculture, farmers and others would have to rely on information furnished by companies and commodity interests with sufficient resources to generate their own estimates.

Neither Bull Nor Bear

Some farmers feel that these official crop and livestock reports depress market prices and that they would be better off without them. But realistically, it is the supply actually entering the market in relation to existing demand that controls the price. Studies have found that farm product prices are as likely to rise as fall following release of a USDA statistical report. Simply abandoning crop estimates could not help the producer. It is impossible to conceal for long an unusually large or short potential supply because too many buyers would know it from their own private sources.

The Board's special security conditions are imposed because many agricultural commodities are heavily traded on the futures market, and anyone with advance USDA information would have an unfair advantage. No one outside the Board has access to the data before release, nor does anyone influence its decisions.

The Board annually issues several hundred reports covering 120 crops and 45 livestock and related products, plus summaries of prices, labor, farm numbers, and other topics. The Board—a part of USDA's National Agricultural Statistics Service (NASS)—also publishes local and regional information through 44 field offices serving all States. Together, these continuing series of reports help maintain an orderly association between the production and marketing elements of agriculture. The information is readily available to the public, being released at a scheduled date and time to assure equal access.

Data Sources

Sample surveys provide the information for most of the estimates. What is happening with the total group can be accurately inferred from contacts with a scientifically selected portion of the producers. This method yields reliable results and is far cheaper and quicker than attempting to make a complete count.

Survey contacts are made by mail, telephone, personal interviews, and in-the-field counts and measurements of growing crops. In some instances, farmers living in randomly selected land segments are asked for information about their crops, livestock, and other items. The total acreage in these segments is less than 1 percent of all the land area in the 48 contiguous States, but well-designed survey techniques assure that these segments represent the Nation's agriculture.

A significant point about these surveys is that producer participation is always voluntary. There are no penalties for noncooperation, nor is anyone paid to report. The survey program has operated this way since Congress gave the Patent Office $1,000 in 1839 to "collect statistics and distribute seeds." Any information a farmer gives in a survey is strictly confidential. The survey responses are used only to form State and national estimates.

Much of the input for yield estimates of major crops comes from on-the-spot examination of crops in the field. In a recent season, sample plots were set up in 1,900 typical corn fields in 10 major corn-producing States, over 1,900 soybean fields in 15 States, over 2,500 winter wheat fields in 17 States, and 1,400 cotton fields in 6 States.

The sample units are quite small; for corn, a two-row section 15 feet long; for wheat, three drill rows 21.6 inches long; for soybeans, a two-row section 3 feet long; and for cotton, a double row section 10 feet long. Monthly during the growing season, field workers visit the units to count and measure plants and immature fruit. These measurements are translated into yield forecasts by mathematical models. At maturity, the crop in the sample plots is carefully harvested and sent to a laboratory for weighing and moisture determination.

From Soup to Nuts

Crop reports estimate the acreages that farmers intend to plant in the coming season, the acres planted and harvested, production and disposition of the crop, and remaining stocks. Forecasts of yield for major crops are issued monthly during the growing season. Estimates of grain stored on farms come from survey responses by farmers. For grain stored off farms, data is collected from mills and elevators, oilseed processors, and USDA's Agricultural Stabilization and Conservation Service. The program for livestock, dairy, and poultry covers a wide variety of items ranging from eggs in incubators through ice cream manufacturing. Each month, the Board reports the prices received by farmers, and ratios commonly used to evaluate the purchasing power of farm commodities. Other reports deal with such items as cold storage holdings, mink, honey, floriculture, and the weather.

Why's and Wherefore's

Why do farmers, buyers, processors, and many others take the time and trouble to provide information on production, supplies, prices, and marketing plans? Check these questions and answers for the reasons.

How Do These Estimates Help?
Farm organizations use them for planning programs; so do legislators. Extension economists and private farm management consultants use them as a basis for advising farmers. Agricultural industries, farm supply and service companies, transportation and processing firms, bankers, and credit associations use them, too.

Advance indications of supplies also avoid severe price adjustments that might otherwise result at harvest-time when crops actually hit the market. Without the advance indications, the uncertainty itself would be enough to require additional precautions by food marketers and suppliers that would add considerably to their costs and yield lower prices for producers.

Do Farmers Give Honest Answers to Survey Questions?
Virtually all the farmers who cooperate on these surveys answer the questions the best they can. They recognize that the final estimates can be no better than the raw data they provide.

Aren't the Estimates Always Changing?

Forecasts of such things as farrowing plans and planting intentions certainly will change when the pigs are born or the crop is in the ground. Monthly crop yield forecasts reflect the effects of recent weather and other factors on production. The idea is to keep estimates current, not hold on to out-of-date information.

Why Must Some People Report So Often?

NASS surveys use a sample of just a few carefully selected producers representing all farmers and ranchers. The sample is changed periodically to include different land area and farmers. However, larger producers may be included more often because their operations have a greater impact on the total situation.

Detailing One Survey

Each June, NASS conducts a major survey where farmers are visited by field interviewers—enumerators—for a firsthand account of agricultural activities..

The midyear survey collects data on crop acreages, grain stocks, number of farms and land in farms, livestock inventories, pigs farrowed, economic data, and other agricultural items for State, regional, and national estimates.

Enumerators use aerial photographs to account precisely for land within the boundaries of the selected area segments. After locating each appropriate farmer, the enumerator explains the purpose and importance of the survey and asks a specific series of questions. All survey answers are carefully recorded. The completed questionnaires are sent to State offices where they are checked for completeness and consistency for use in making the estimates.

A number of quality controls in data collection maintain the integrity of the survey. These include careful selection and training of about 2,000 part-time enumerators, use of detailed instruction manuals, close field supervision, built-in questionnaire checks, comparison of reported acreages with those measured on the aerial photographs, and visual checks of some segments by supervisors.

Sampling errors for major agricultural items from the midyear survey average about 4 to 8 percent on a State basis, about 2 to 3 percent on a regional level, and about 1 to 2 percent for U.S. totals. A sampling error of 2 percent means that chances are about 19 out of 20 that the estimate is within 4 percent of the result that would be obtained if the same procedure were used to survey the entire population rather than just a sample.

Credibility and Law

A number is no better than its reputation. Users must have confidence in the timeliness and reliability of the data and in the integrity of the issuing organization. Farmers, business people, and Government officials make decisions involving billions of dollars a year on the basis of agricultural estimates.

The overriding need for integrity, reliability, and impartiality in agricultural estimates is reflected in the laws, regulations, and procedures that govern the work of NASS.

Five titles and 17 separate sections of the U.S. Code are specifically addressed to issuing crop and livestock estimates. They govern such major operations as security procedures, confidentiality of reported data, and the exact timing for release of major reports.

The law also specifies penalties that can be imposed upon employees. Any employee disclosing any data or crop information before official release, or engaging in trading on the commodity markets, is subject to a $10,000 fine and 10 years in prison. Intentionally issuing false information may mean a $5,000 fine and 5 years in prison.

Continuous Suport for Data Collection

The public, through congressional appropriation, has seen fit to continuously support this Federal statistical program for 125 years. Almost as continuously, the data accuracy has been improved. While the accuracy of today's estimates is considered to be generally adequate, there is a growing need for it to improve even more, according to both data users and providers. This is increasingly apparent as more and more marketing decisions are based on information provided in NASS reports. NASS will continue doing its best to meet such needs, while being as prudent as possible in spending taxpayers' money.

A complete catalog of national crop, livestock, and price reports is available from the Agricultural Statistics Board, Room 5829-South, U.S. Department of Agriculture, Washington, D.C. 20250.

For information about individual State estimates, contact the appropriate State Statistical Office.

Alabama
Box 1071
Montgomery 36192

Alaska
Box 799
Palmer 99645

Arizona
201 E. Indianola
Suite 250
Phoenix 85012

Arkansas
Box 3197
Little Rock 72203

California
Box 1258
Sacramento 95806

Colorado
Box 17066
Denver 80217

Florida
1222 Woodward St.
Orlando 32803

Georgia
Stephens Fed. Bldg.
Suite 320
Athens 30613

Hawaii
Box 22159
Honolulu 96822

Idaho
Box 1699
Boise 83701

Illinois
Box 19283
Springfield 62794

Indiana
Agricultural Administration Bldg.
Purdue University
West Lafayette 47907

Iowa
833 Fed. Bldg.
210 Walnut St.
Suite 833
Des Moines 50309

Kansas
444 S.E. Quincy St.
Suite 290
Topeka 66683

Kentucky
Box 1120
Louisville 40201

Louisiana
Box 5524
Alexandria 71307

Maryland-Delaware
50 Harry S Truman
 Parkway, Suite 202
Annapolis 21401

Michigan
Box 20008
Lansing 48901

Minnesota
Box 7068
St. Paul 55107

Mississippi
Box 980
Jackson 39205

Missouri
Box L
Columbia 65205

Montana
Box 4369
Helena 59604

Nebraska
Box 81069
Lincoln 68501

Nevada
Box 8880
Reno 89507

New England
Box 1444
Concord, NH 03301

New Jersey
CN-330 New Warren St.
Room 204
Trenton 08625

New Mexico
Box 1809
Las Cruces 88004

New York
Dept. of Agriculture and Markets
1 Winners Circle
Albany 12235

North Carolina
Box 27767
Raleigh 27611

North Dakota
Box 3166
Fargo 58102

Ohio
Room 608 New Fed. Bldg.
200 N. High St.
Columbus 43215

Oklahoma
2800 N. Lincoln Blvd.
Oklahoma City 73105

Oregon
1735 Fed. Bldg.
1220 S.W. 3rd Ave.
Room 1735
Portland 97204

Pennsylvania
2301 N. Cameron St.
Room G-19
Harrisburg 17110

South Carolina
Box 1911
Columbia 29202

South Dakota
Box V
Sioux Falls 57117

Tennessee
Box 41505
Nashville 37204

Texas
Box 70
Austin 78767

Utah
Box 25007
Salt Lake City 84125

Virginia
Box 1659
Richmond 23213

Washington
Box 609
Olympia 98507

West Virginia
State Dept. of Agriculture
Charleston 25305

Wisconsin
Box 9160
Madison 53715

Wyoming
Box 1148
Cheyenne 82003

From NAL: Everything You Want To Know About Agricultural Marketing

Robert W. Butler, information specialist, Collection Development Office, National Agricultural Library, Beltsville, MD

A rich source for information on agricultural marketing, as well as other agricultural topics, the National Agricultural Library (NAL) is the library for USDA and the agricultural library for the Nation. NAL is one of three national libraries; the others are the National Library of Medicine, in Bethesda, MD, and the Library of Congress, in Washington, DC.

From its beginning in 1862 the NAL has built up a collection of 2 million books, journals, reports, and other materials on agriculture. It maintains an international publications exchange program with foreign governments, universities, and industries in 140 countries. Its collecting area includes all aspects of agricultural markets and marketing—and always has. The NAL also prepares an index to agricultural literature, the AGRICOLA data base, with 2,500,000 citations to journal articles, books, reports, proceedings, and other materials.

Recognizing the current need for a well-informed agricultural marketing community, NAL makes available its wealth of resources directly through many services and media, including 12 specialized information centers.

Information Center for Agricultural Trade and Marketing

As one of the newest, this Center focuses on agribusiness, countertrade (barter), exports, and trade development. The agricultural trade and marketing issue has become a global one, with new emphasis on trade development in Third World countries and foreign marketing through U.S. farming cooperatives. The Center was formed in response to the concern of policymakers, agricultural experts, farmers, and consumers about such issues as U.S. export decline, implications of world events, and shifting global trends.

Using the enormous resources of the NAL, the Center's staff members organize and disseminate information to interested users. They facilitate communication and cooperation among USDA, private institutions and organizations, and users who have similar or allied interests.

The Center and NAL continue to ensure that all relevant agricultural trade and marketing literature is indexed and accessible worldwide through the AGRICOLA data base and other appropriate bibliographic services.

Other Information Centers

Other subject-oriented centers provide access to indepth information on aquaculture, alternative farming systems, animal welfare, biotechnology, critical agricultural materials, family, fiber, food and nutrition, food irradiation, horticulture, and rural information.

Reference Services

Both the staff of the specialized information centers and the reference staff of NAL assist in finding information. For service you may phone, write, or visit NAL. For those not in the Washington, DC area, first try the local land-grant university or USDA field library.

At NAL, staff assist by accessing the agricultural literature, identifying current research conducted by USDA agencies, or referring to experts or organizations in the field. The Agricultural Trade and Marketing Information Center provides a list of organizations with its "Directory of Export Assistance." Staff also can provide bibliographies on topics such as "Aquaculture: development plans and marketing, 1970-86" (NAL QB87-48); "Floricultural marketing, 1970-86" (NAL QB87-56); "Marketing of horticultural products, 1979-Apr 87" (NAL QB87-63); "Australian and New Zealand agricultural markets, 1979-Mar 87" (NAL QB87-60).

Computerized Data bases

Information center staff, as well as reference staff, both use computerized data bases indexing the agricultural literature, especially AGRICOLA and AGRIS.

AGRICOLA Data Base

AGRICOLA (AGRICultural OnLine Access) is a bibliographic data base consisting of records for literature citations of journal articles, monographs, theses, patents, software, audiovisual materials, and technical reports relating to all aspects of agriculture. From its beginning in 1970 to 1984, AGRICOLA was primarily an index to the collection of the NAL. Since then it has been expanded to include other material. For these materials, the source library owning the publication is identified. NAL staff and its cooperators regularly scan more than 5,000 incoming journal titles for input to the data base. The data base now contains over 2.5 million records, 81,000 of which are concerned with agricultural trade and marketing.

AGRIS Data Base

This data base, most useful for information on agricultural subjects, is coordinated and prepared by the United Nations Food and Agriculture Organization (FAO). AGRIS is composed of bibliographic records for the worldwide literature of the agricultural sciences and technology. National and multinational centers in different parts of the world prepare the records for journal articles, books, reports, and conference papers. The AGRIS data base mounted online in the United States, in the DIALOG system, excludes all items published in the United States and submitted to AGRIS by NAL, since these are in the AGRICOLA data base. The complete AGRIS data base, available outside North America, lacks some of the records provided by NAL, particularly in the "nonconventional" or nonresearch literature.

Others
Many other data bases deal with agriculture. A list of 15 data bases about agribusiness, exports, imports, markets, and trade information resources is available from the Agricultural Trade and Marketing Information Center.

Document Delivery

The materials are available on interlibrary loan through the nationwide library system connecting local public, business, government, university, and other libraries to the NAL. If items are not available at a local library, its staff will assist in obtaining them. Photocopies of NAL articles are available for a fee; loans of materials are made only through another library. If the material requested is not available at NAL, information on alternate locations often is provided.

NAL also provides full document delivery service to USDA employees, either directly or through the network of State land-grant universities.

New Technologies

To enhance its ability to provide information, NAL is exploring ways to store and disseminate information more effectively.

Text Digitizing Project
NAL and 42 land-grant university libraries are cooperating to test methods of transferring full text and images from printed form into digital form, automatically indexing the text. The indexed full text can then be transferred to a CD-ROM laser disc. Because much of U.S. and world literature on agriculture and its applications remains difficult to access because of the cost of indepth indexing and abstracting by humans, this project will provide for the use of the CD-ROM discs as a storage and dissemination medium that allows searching of the full text. The data base can be retained in a standard format and used in other ways in the future. Much of the world's literature is printed on acidic paper, which eventually will disintegrate. This technology promises preservation in a more stable medium.

Full Text on Optical Disc

In cooperation with land-grant universities, Extension, and other institutions, NAL is evaluating the use of 12" laser discs as a means for storing, retrieving, and disseminating information from agricultural publications. This approach uses videodisc and optical digital technologies to capture both full text and illustrations. A cooperative project for storing and disseminating USDA, Extension, and other Federal publications, now in its second phase, has expanded from 3 to 15 participating institutions. This project identifies problems in converting data in various formats to a single format used in creating the discs.

Scanning Device

NAL and the University of California at Los Angeles are cooperating to investigate the status of handheld scanning devices (the "magic wand"), which can be used for library applications to speed data entry and coding in the cataloging and indexing processes. NAL hopes to have experimental workstations employing state-of-the-art technology installed in 1989.

Interactive Training

NAL, in cooperation with the University of Maryland, has developed AGRICOLearn, an interactive laser disc course for instruction in searching the AGRICOLA online data base. The computer-based course is a stand-alone, one-on-one system to

The National Agricultural Library, in cooperation with other institutions, is evaluating the use of 12-inch laser discs as a means for storing, retrieving and disseminating information from agricultural publications. A 12-inch disc and a smaller one, which resemble phonograph records, are at the left. (William E. Carnahan)

serve as an alternative to the current instructor-led courses. The system includes an IBM XT/AT or compatible computer with a laser disc player and a touch monitor. The course provides learners at various levels with an understanding of and ability to search the AGRICOLA data base online through two data base services—DIALOG and BRS. It also provides an overall understanding of online data base searching. The combinations of video, graphics, voice, and text make it not only effective for instruction, but enjoyable too.

Photo Collection on Laser Disc

A cooperative project to explore use of laser videodisc technology as a storage medium for photo collections was recently completed. A portion of the Forest Service photo collection, one of the largest on the subject of forestry, has been placed on videodisc and joined with a computer-searchable index. This system is available to various Forest Service regional offices and land-grant institutions for evaluation. Another project will explore the effectiveness of digitizing photographs and storing them on the newer Write Once Read Many (WORM) laser disc, also with a word-searchable index. This type of disc allows frequent addition of images and data to keep the system up to date. Current photographs in the USDA photo library and other USDA photos will be the source materials for this project.

Through these technologies and others yet to be explored, NAL and its specialized information centers strive to fulfill their mission to acquire and deliver information on agricultural marketing or any aspect of agriculture.

Cooperation

The technology projects described require the cooperation of both public and private institutions. Likewise, NAL cooperates with land-grant institutions and other USDA agencies in providing information services and publications to users throughout the country. It collaborates in cataloging and indexing projects nationally and internationally. In these ways NAL continues to strengthen information activities for the entire agricultural community.

By concentrating attention on priority topics, such as agricultural marketing, by identifying new means for information delivery, and by working closely with other information facilities in the field, NAL is developing a national system for agriculture that will effectively make available needed information.

Agricultural Marketing Service—Its Programs and Services

Information staff, Agricultural Marketing Service

For 75 years USDA's Agricultural Marketing Service (AMS) has been providing a vast array of marketing programs, marketing services, and regulatory functions to U.S. agriculture. AMS assists in the complex process of moving food and fiber products from producer to consumer. Its programs and services promote an efficient, effective, and equitable agricultural marketing system.

AMS Marketing Programs

Food Purchasing

AMS purchases food for distribution to schools, institutions, and other eligible outlets by USDA's Food and Nutrition Service. They include perishable products in temporary surplus and foods that specifically help schools meet nutritional requirements of the program. Food customarily purchased by AMS includes meat and meat products, poultry and poultry products, egg products, fish, and processed and fresh fruits and vegetables.

Government Food Quality Assurance Program

AMS has developed uniform and simplified specifications, such as Commercial Item Descriptions, to allow the needs of many Federal agencies to be met by current food industry production practices. User agencies include military installations, Veterans' Administration hospitals, schools, correctional institutions, and other Federal foodservice programs.

Grade Standards

AMS maintains grade standards for cotton, dairy products, fruits, beef, veal, calf, lamb, pork, mohair, poultry, rabbits, shell eggs, tobacco, vegetables, and wool. The standards describe the entire range of quality for each product and are the basis for the quality grades.

AMS Marketing Services

Grading and Acceptance Services

Grading services for the products mentioned under "Grade Standards" are available on request for a fee paid by the users.

Grading provides buyers and sellers with an impartial appraisal of the quality of the commodities being sold, and assists farmers in receiving fair prices for their products.

Market News Service
Market news reporters gather data by visits to trading points and by telephone on qualities and quantities of products sold, prices paid, demand, movement, and trends. AMS uses satellite communication, earth stations, and microcomputers to disseminate 700 to 900 market news messages and reports daily, which are made available to the agricultural industry as well as the print and electronic news media. Automatic telephone recordings also are employed to provide current market information. Market news services are operated cooperatively with State Departments of Agriculture.

Market Research and Development
AMS researchers explore new techniques and methods for improving marketing, including handling, processing, packaging, storage, and distribution of agricultural products. Researchers also work with local governments and food industry groups to identify existing problems, to design improved facilities, and to assist in the development of modern, efficient wholesale food distribution centers and farmers' markets. AMS supports marketing studies at the State level through a matching funds grant program.

AMS Regulatory Functions

Commodity Research and Promotion Programs
Commodity research and promotion programs enable farmers to solve production and marketing problems; finance their own coordinated programs of research; create producer and consumer education; and develop promotion programs to improve, maintain, and develop markets for their commodities. Research and promotion programs have been authorized by Congress for beef, cotton, dairy products, eggs, floral products, honey, lamb, mohair, pork, potatoes, watermelon, and wool. AMS monitors the activities of all Federal research and promotion programs; most programs are administered by boards appointed by the Secretary of Agriculture.

Fair Trade Practices
Assurance of dependable supplies, reasonable prices, and protection against unfair business practices is important to producers, marketers, and consumers alike. To promote fair play in marketing, AMS administers four major regulatory laws: the Perishable Agricultural Commodities Act (PACA), the Federal Seed Act, the Plant Variety Protection Act, and the Agricultural Fair Practices Act.

Marketing Agreements and Orders

Marketing agreements and orders are designed to help stabilize markets for a number of farm commodities, chiefly milk, fruits, vegetables, and certain specialty crops like nuts, raisins, and dates. These programs are initiated and designed by farmers and administered by AMS. A marketing order may be issued by the Secretary of Agriculture only after public hearings, and after producers vote at least two-thirds approval through a referendum.

Egg Products Inspection and Shell Egg Surveillance

Mandatory inspection is continuous in all plants processing liquid, frozen, and dried egg products to ensure that products reaching the consumer are wholesome and unadulterated. The disposition of certain types of undergrade shell eggs that are potential health hazards is also controlled.

For Further Information

To obtain additional information on AMS marketing programs and services and to find out how to reach the office that can help you with these programs and services, contact AMS Information Staff, Room 3510-S, P.O. Box 96456, Washington, DC 20090-6456.

How to Find Marketing Information You Can Use

Ovid Bay, director of information & communications, retired, Extension Service

Contact Your State Department of Agriculture

Each State has a Department of Agriculture, which is located in the State capitol (except in Indiana it is at Purdue University, in Alaska at Palmer, and in New Mexico at Las Cruces). Several departments assist in developing new markets and new marketing approaches for existing markets. They can tell you about marketing regulations, and they collect and disseminate marketing information.

To locate your State Department of Agriculture, check under State offices if they are listed in your telephone book. Or call your State capitol office, which may be an 800 number.

Contact Your Local Cooperative Extension Service

Your State Cooperative Extension Service at your land-grant university has a local office in each county to provide objective, university-based research information on agriculture, home economics, 4-H and youth, and rural development.

Extension agents provide answers to specific questions about production and marketing, farm and home management, nutrition, consumer queries, and related questions.

To locate your local Extension Service office, check the telephone book under county government. Extension is listed under various headings such as "Extension Service," "Cooperative Extension Service," or "Your State University Extension Service."

The State Extension Information Office is located at the land-grant university (except in Arkansas, where it is located at Little Rock).

Contact a Trade Association or Farm Organization

Most commodity groups or associations provide marketing and promotional expertise, and news about their commodity. These are some of the major associations and farm organizations:

American Association of Nurserymen
1250 Eye Street, N.W., Suite 500
Washington, DC 20005

American Bakers Association
1111 - 14th Street, N.W., Suite 300
Washington, DC 20005

American Cotton Shippers Association
1725 K Street, N.W., Suite 1210
Washington, DC 20006

American Dairy Products Institute
130 North Franklin
Chicago, IL 60606

American Farm Bureau Federation
600 Maryland Avenue, S.W., Suite 800
Washington, DC 20024

American Feed Industries Association
1701 North Fort Myer Drive
Arlington, VA 22209

American Frozen Food Institute
1764 Old Meadow Road, Suite 350
McLean, VA 22102

American Goat Society
Rt. 2, Box 112
De Leon, TX 76444

American Meat Institute
1700 North Moore Street
Arlington, VA 22209

American Plywood Association
7011 South 19th, P.O. Box 11700
Tacoma, WA 98411

American Quarter Horse Association
2701 1-40 East, Box 18519
Amarillo, TX 79160

American Rabbit Breeders Association
1925 South Main St., Box 426
Bloomington, IL 61701

American Seed Trade Association
1030 15th St., N.W.
Washington, DC 20005

American Sheep Producers Council
200 Clayton Street
Denver, CO 80206

American Soybean Association
600 Maryland Avenue, S.W.
Washington, DC 20024

Burley and Dark Leaf Tobacco
    Export Association
1100 17th St., N.W., Suite 902
Washington, DC 20036

California Avocado Commission
17620 Fitch, 2nd Floor
Irvine, CA 92714

California Cling Peach Advisory
    Board,
P.O. Box 7111
San Francisco, CA 94120

California Pistachio Commission
5114 East Clinton Way
Suite 113
Fresno, CA 93727

California Raisin Advisory Board
P.O. Box 5335
Fresno, CA 93755

California Table Grape Commission
P.O. Box 5498
Fresno, CA 93755

Corn Refiners Association
1001 Connecticut Avenue
Washington, DC 20036

Cotton Council International
1030 - 15th Street, N.W.
Suite 700, Executive Building
Washington, DC 20005

Farm and Industrial Equipment
    Institute
410 N. Michigan Ave., Suite 680
Chicago, IL 60611

Florida Department of Citrus
1115 East Memorial Boulevard
P.O. Box 148
Lakeland, FL

Flue-Cured Tobacco Cooperative
    Stabilization Corporation
Box 12600
Raleigh, NC 27605

Food Marketing Institute
1750 K St., N.W., Suite 700
Washington, DC 20006

Grocery Manufacturers of America
1010 Wisconsin Avenue, N.W.
Washington, DC 20007

Independent Bakers Association
Box 3731
Washington, DC 20007

International Apple Institute
6707 Dominion Drive, Box 1137
McLean, VA 22101

International Ice Cream Association
888 16th St., N.W.
Washington, DC 20006

Millers National Federation
600 Maryland Ave., S.W., Suite 305
Washington, DC 20024

Minnesota Grain Exchange
Minneapolis, MN

National Ag Chemicals Association
1155 - 15th St., N.W., Suite 900
Washington, DC 20005

National Association of
    Conservation Districts
1025 Vermont Ave., N.W., Suite 730
Washington, DC 20005

National Association of Meat
    Purveyors
8365-B Greensboro Drive
McLean, VA 22101

National Association of
    Wheat Growers
415 Second St., N.E., Suite 300
Washington, DC 20002

National Broiler Council
1155 - 15th St., N.W., Suite 614
Washington, DC 20004

National Cattlemen's Association
1301 Pennsylvania Ave., N.W.
Suite 300
Washington, DC 20004

National Cheese Institute
699 Prince Street, Box 20047
Alexandria, VA 22320

National Corn Growers Association
201 Massachusetts Ave., N.E.
Suite C-4
Washington, DC 20002

National Cotton Council of America
1030 - 15th St., N.W., Suite 700
Washington, DC 20005

National Council of Commercial Plant
    Breeders
1030 - 15th St., N.E., Suite 964
Washington, DC 20005

National Council of Farmer
    Cooperatives
50 F St., N.W., Suite 900
Washington, DC 20001

National Dairy Promotion Board
2111 Wilson Blvd., Suite 600
Arlington, VA 22201

National Farmers Organization
Corning, IA 50841

National Farmers Union
600 Maryland Ave., S.W., Suite 202
Washington, DC 20024

National Food Processors Association
1401 New York Ave., N.W.
Washington, DC 20005

National Forest Products Association
1250 Connecticut Ave., N.W., Suite 700
Washington, DC 20005

National Grange
1626 H Street, N.W.
Washington, DC 20006

National Hay Association, Inc.
P.O. Box 99
Ellensburg, WA 98926

National Milk Producers Federation
1840 Wilson Blvd.
Arlington, VA 22201

National Pecan Marketing Council
741 Piedmont Ave., N.E.
Atlanta, GA 30308

National Potato Promotion Board
1385 South Colorado Blvd.
#512
Denver, CO 80222

National Pork Producers Council
1015 - 15th St., N.W., Suite 200
Washington, DC 20005

National Turkey Federation
11319 Sunset Hills Road
Reston, VA 22090

North American Blueberry Council
P.O. Box 166
Marmora, NJ 08223

North American Export Grain
    Association
1747 Pennsylvania Ave., N.W.
Suite 1175
Washington, DC 20006

Northern Hardwood and Pine
    Manufacturers Association
P.O. Box 1124
Green Bay, WI 54305

Northwest Cherry Growers
1005 Tieton Drive
Yakima, WA 98902

Northwest Horticultural Council
P.O. Box 570
Yakima, WA 98907

Nursery Marketing Council
1250 Eye St., N.W., Suite 500
Washington, DC 20005

Oregon-Washington-California
    Pear Bureau
Woodlark Building
Portland, OR 97205

Papaya Administrative Committee
First Insurance Building
1100 Ward Avenue, Rm. 860
Honolulu, HI 96814

Protein Grain Products
    International
6707 Old Dominion Drive
Suite 240
McLean, VA 22101

Rice Council for Market
    Development
P.O. Box 740123
Houston, TX 77274

Rice Millers Association
1235 Jefferson Davis Hwy., Suite 302
Arlington, VA 22202

Southern Forest Products Association
P.O. Box 52468
New Orleans, LA 70152

Sugar Association
1511 K St., N.W.
Washington, DC 20005

The Fertilizer Institute
1015 - 18th St., N.W., Suite 11
Washington, DC 20036

Tobacco Associates
1101 - 17th St., N.W.
Washington, DC 20036

United Egg Producers
3951 Snapfinger Parkway, Suite 580
Decatur, GA 30035

United Fresh Fruit & Vegetable
    Association
727 North Washington St.
Alexandria, VA 22314

United States Beet Sugar Association
1156 - 15th St., N.W.
Washington, DC 20005

U.S. Brewers Association
1750 K St., N.W.
Washington, DC 20006

U.S. Chamber of Commerce
1615 H St., N.W.
Washington, DC 20062

U.S. Feed Grains Council
1400 K St., N.W., Suite 1200
Washington, DC 20005

U.S. Meat Export Federation
3333 Quebec St., Suite 7200
Stapleton Plaza
Denver, CO 80207-2391

U.S. Wheat Associates, Inc.
1620 I St., N.W., Suite 801
Washington, DC 20006

USA Dry Pea and Lentil Council, Inc.
Stateline Office
P.O. Box 8566
Moscow, ID 83843

Washington State Apple Commission
P.O. Box 18
Wenatchee, WA 98801

Western Wood Products Association
1500 Yeon Building
Portland, OR 97204

Wine Institute
165 Post Street
San Francisco, CA 94109

Index

A&P stores, 123, 198
A. C. Nielsen Co., 98
A. Flavus, 183
Acquired immune deficiency
  syndrome, 168
ADAPT (Agricultural
  Diversification Adds
  Profit Today) conferences,
  112-115
Advertising, 4, 23, 27, 152;
  brand, 45, 132, 169, 278-280;
  cooperative, 175; cost of
  51-52, 147; cotton, 282-285;
  dairy, 271; generic, 44-49,
  236, 278-280; "Jersey Fresh"
  campaign, 256-260; national,
  98, 267; "Other white meat,"
  268-270; point of sale, 188;
  potato, 261-264. *See also*
  Brand identification;
  Promotion
Advertising Age, 160
Afghanistan, 142
Aflatoxin, 183-184
Agents: foreign sales, 240-243;
  marketing, 14-15
Agribusiness, global, 18-24
AGRICOLA, 306, 307, 309-310
Agricultural Act (1949), 67
Agricultural Fair Practices Act,
  312
Agricultural Marketing Service
  (AMS), 160, 199, 311-313
Agricultural Research Service
  (ARS), 116-119, 141-144;
  demonstration projects,
  155-158; European
  Marketing Research Center,
  213-216; Northern Regional
  Research Laboratory, Peoria,
  Il., 216
Agricultural Stabilization and
  Conservation Service, 301
Agricultural Statistics Board.
  See National Agricultural
  Statistics Service
Agriculture, Department of. *See*
  USDA
Agriculture, Secretary of, 160,
  312, 313
AGRIS, 307-308
Agway, Inc., 210
Ainsworth, Gary, 119
Akiyama, Dr. Dean, 231
Albemarle Cotton
  Cooperative, 212
Alfalfa sprouts, 137
Algeria, 66
Almonds, Japanese market for,
  169-172
Ambrosia, Buster, 288

American Dairy Association,
  47, 271, 277, 278
American Egg Board, 161, 162
American Farm Bureau
  Federation, 210
American Newspaper
  Publishers Association, 233
American Soybean Association,
  216, 230-233
Anderson Clayton, 11
Animal and Plant Health
  Inspection Service, 216
Aquaculture, in Southeast Asia,
  231-232
Arbitrage, 38
Argentina, 68
Arizona, 156; migration to, 7
Army Corps of Engineers, U.S.,
  119
Artichokes, Jerusalem, 137
Asparagus, 237-238
Assessments. *See* Checkoffs
Associated Milk Producers,
  Inc., 210
Association of South East Asian
  Nations (ASEAN), 245
Australia, 19, 20, 68, 169,
  237, 238
B. F. Trappey's Sons, Inc., 290
Babb, Emerson M., 50
Baby boom, 6, 86
Baby boomers 77, 89, 283-285
Bacillus thuringiensis, 219
Bailey's Irish Cream, 19
Bangladesh, 64, 66
Bassin, Susan B., 187
Bay, Ovid, 314
Beans, snap, 142
Becker, Mark, 114
Beef: advertising of, 48;
  branded, 28, 133-136;
  consumption by women, 71,
  72; lean, 28, 265-267; pro-
  motion of, 28, 244-248; vacuum
  packaging of, 134. *See also*
  Cattlemen's Beef Promotion
  and Research Board
Beef Board. *See* Cattlemen's
  Beef Promotion and
  Research Board
Beef Industry Council, 48,
  161-162, 266
Beef Promotion and Research
  Act (1985), 161, 266
Beef industry, 133, 136,
  265-267
Beef livers, 246
Beef surimi, 160, 162
Behr, Robert M., 47, 95, 222
Belgium, 100, 232, 245
Bell, James B., 199
Ben & Jerry's ice cream, 28,
  145-148
Bennett, Wayne, 230
Berries, 142-143, 212, 236

Bigg's hypermarket, 124
Bildner, Allen, 120
Biotechnology, 18, 23, 57, 163
Blendeman, Jack, 290-291
Block, John R., 166
Bloomingdale's, 288
Blue Diamond Growers Inc.,
  169-172; 208
Boards, commodity. *See*
  Commodity Research and
  Promotion Boards
Boehm, William T., 76
Bolivia, 66
Boyle, J. Patrick, 159
Brand Advertising Rebate
  Program, 45. *See also* Florida
  Department of Citrus
Brand identification, 51, 133,
  187; WUSATA programs,
  237-239. *See also* Advertising
Brazil, 66, 68, 98, 251
Brody, Jane, 261
Brooks, Howard J., 141
Brown, Arthur R., Jr., 256
Brunei, 245-246
Bulliard, Jimmy, Sr., 290
Bullock, Tom, 149, 209
Bureau of Labor Statistics, 120
Burger King, 87
Bushman, Don, 230
Business Television, 255
Butler, Robert W., 306
Butter, 273, 278
Cajun cooking, 88, 287-292
Calcium, dairy, 48, 272-274
California, 124, 126-127, 156;
  citrus breeding, 144; export
  crops, 214, 215; lettuce
  varieties, 142; tomatoes,
  144, 173, 175, 178;
  University of, 138, 143, 309
California, Oregon, and
  Washington Dairymen, Inc.,
  271, 278
California Proposition 65, 79
California Prune Board, 223
Campbell Soup Company,
  101-104, 109, 119, 121, 123;
  plastic packaging by, 109
Canada, 68, 100, 103, 155, 197,
  210; teletype network in,
  199; U.S. marketing in, 169,
  252, 259
Canary Islands, the, 246
Cannon, 283
Caplan, Frieda, 137
Caplan, Karen, 137
Capps, Oral, Jr., 203
Cargill, Inc., 20
Carrots, 119, 142
Carryout food. *See* "Takeout"
  food
Catfish, 115, 119, 212
Cattle, beef, 62, 133-136, 265

Cattlemen's Beef Board. *See*
Cattlemen's Beef Promotion
and Research Board
Cattlemen's Beef Promotion
and Research Board, 48,
161-162, 266-267
Caudill, Charles E., 299
Census Bureau, 83, 120
Certified Grocers, 198
Chamber of Commerce, 83, 85
Charecogn, Inc., 204
Checkoffs, 45-46, 160, 266,
268, 271, 275, 276
Cheese, 48, 71, 72, 271-272,
278
*Chef Paul Prodbomme's
Louisiana Kitchen,* 288
Chicken, 129-132
Chile, 68, 142
China, 66, 143, 230-231, 251
Cholesterol, 23, 61, 100, 121,
142; research on, 160, 163,
267. *See also* Fat, animal
CIP Forest Products, 156
Citrus fruit, 144; advertising of,
47
Claiborne, Craig, 287, 289
Clamato juice, 107
Coca Cola, 109
Coca Cola Bottlers, 171-172
Cohen, Ben, 145-148
Collins, Gary, 292
Colombia, 66, 68
Colorado, 114, 115, 238, 244
Combination stores, 9, 78
Commodity Credit
Corporation (CCC), 64, 67,
180, 294, 296, 298
Commodity options market,
34, 42-43
Commodity Research and
Promotion Boards, 160-163.
See also individual
Boards; Promotion;
Research
Computerized marketing
systems, 200. *See also*
Marketing, electronic
Computers: home, 207; 220;
National Agricultural Library
use of, 306-310; in pest
control, 220; scanning by, 78,
167, 204, use by farmers, 177,
180; *See also* Information
technology; Marketing,
electronic
ConAgra, Inc., 21, 122
Consumer research, 190. *See
also* Research
Consumers: changes in
perceptions of, 28, 222-225,
261-264, 268-270; changing
shopping habits of, 7, 100,
187; demands of, 26-27, 86,
99-104, 124, 196-197,

265-267; in Japan, 93-94,
134; trends in behavior, 57,
61, 159-160
Container trains, double-
stacked, 192
Continuing Survey of Food
Intakes by Individuals
(CSFII), 70, 71
Convenience foods, 121-124,
126
Convenience packaging, 26,
122
Convenience shopping, 9, 96,
100, 104, 120-124, 196-198
Convenience stores (C-stores),
10, 89, 196-197
Cookbooks, Cajun recipes, 288
Cooperative Extension Service,
85, 179, 217
Cooperative Farmers Night
Market, 174, 178
Cooperative marketing,
174-175, 208-212
Cooperative State Research
Service, 155
Cooperatives, farmer, 38, 39,
63, 208-212; regional, 210;
interregional, 210-211
Cooperator Program, 48
Corbin, Sidney, 115
Corn: feed, 250; grading
standards for, 185; growing,
154, 179-181; income from,
153; industrial, 229; plastics
from, 158; research on, 185;
sweet, 142, 238, 250-251;
varieties of, 116-117
Cornelius, James C., 32
Cornell University, 279
Cosgrove, Bob, 250
Cotton, 160, 200, 281-285. *See
also* Cotton Board
Cotton Board, 161, 162, 282
Cotton, Incorporated, 161, 162,
282-285
Coupons, 52; scanning of,
205-206
Cox, Tom, 276
CRAN · RASPBERRY, 152
Crawfish, 115 ,224
Credit sales programs. *See*
Export assistance programs
Creole cooking. *See* Cajun
cooking
Cumberland Farm Products,
Inc., 212
Dairy and Tobacco Adjustment
Act (1983), 47, 161, 271, 276
Dairy promotion programs, 48,
271-275, 276-280. *See also*
National Dairy Promotion
and Research Board
Danish Butter Cookies, 19
Davis, Robert, 217
Davis, William L., 222

Debbie Fields' cookies, 88
Defense Department, 156
Delivery, home. *See* Home
delivery
Denmark, 19, 100, 232, 238
Denton, Arnold E., 99
Department of Agriculture. *See*
USDA
Dik, David, 199
Dinsmore, Steve, 149-151
Distribution, food: changes in,
21, 77, 197; competition in,
196-198; convenience in,
196-198
Distribution system, food, 3, 4,
5; changes in, 21, 77, 167,
196-198; costs of, 191; in
Japan, 91, 169-172; new
overseas channels of, 237
Diversification, crop, 116-119;
product, 51, 112-115
Dominican Republic, 66
Dominick's, 198
Domino's Pizza, 89
Drive-thru, 89
Durstewitz, Jeff, 28, 145
Eagle, 198
Eastern U.S. Agricultural and
Food Export Council, Inc.,
234
Eckel, Keith, 178
Eggs, 28, 71, 72, 75, 160. *See
also* American Egg Board
Egypt, 66
El Salvador, 66
Electronic marketing. *See*
Marketing, electronic
Ellis, Merle, 177
England, 19, 100, 236. *See also*
Great Britain; United
Kingdom
Environment, concerns about,
24
Environmental Protection
Agency, 217-218
Europe, 143, 233, 238, 250;
exports to, 97, 169, 215, 216
European Community. *See*
European Economic
Community
European Economic
Community (EEC), 68, 227,
294
European Marketing Research
Center. *See* Agricultural
Research Service
Excel Corporation, 133-136,
245, 247
Export assistance programs,
294-298
Export Credit Guarantee
Program (GSM 102), 64-65,
249, 295-296, 298

Export Enhancement Program (EEP), 66, 227-228, 249, 294-295
Export Incentive Program, 48. *See* Targeted Export Assistance Program
Export management companies, 240-243
Export Product Review Program, 94. *See also* Foreign Agricultural Service
Export Programs of the U.S. Department of Agriculture —Dairy Applications, 273
Exporters. *See* Markets, developing overseas
Extension Service, 176-177, 210, 314
Farm organizations, 63, 314-318. *See also* Cooperatives
Farmers' markets, 39
Farmers Union Grain Terminal Association. *See* Harvest States Cooperatives
Farmland Industries, Inc., 210
Fast food industry, 8, 15, 75, 86-87, 196; restaurants, 123; stores, 15, 223
Fat, animal, 26-27, 112, 126
Federal Agricultural Marketing Agreement Act (1937), 47
Federal Grain Inspection Service, 186, 216
Federal Seed Act, 312
Federal Trade Commission, 285
Feed grains, 226-229
Felton, Gene, 250
Ferguson, Kristin S., 128
Ferris, John (Jake) N., 37, 179
Fieldcrest, 284
Fielding, William G., 133
Firestone Tire and Rubber Company, 156
Fish and Wildlife Service, U.S., 119
Fitzpatrick, Martin F., Jr., 191
Fleming, Peggy, 270
Florida, 7, 47, 123, 144, 173, 215
Florida Citrus Commission, 95
Florida Department of Citrus (FDOC), 46, 95-98, 222; Brand Advertising Rebate Program, 45
Flour, 250
Flowers, 112-113
Folse, John, 288
Foo Meng Hian, 245
Food and Drug Administration, 25, 163
Food and Nutrition Service, 311

Food consumption: away-from-home-eating, 7, 8, 11, 15, 75, 280; changes in, 61; of women, 70-75. *See also* Health, concerns about
Food for Development. *See* Public Law 480
Food for Peace Program. *See* Public Law 480
Food for Progress Program, 65
Food industry, 15, 196-198
Food manufacturing, 10, 111, 54-55
Food marketing. *See* Marketing
Food marketing industry, 6-11. *See also* Marketing
Food Marketing Industry Speaks, 123, 124
Food Marketing Institute, 79, 120-121, 123, 124, 198
Food quality, 25-30, 311
Food safety, 62, 79
Food Security Act (1985), 48, 61, 64-65, 68, 294, 296, 298
FOODEX Show, Tokyo, 237
Foodservice industry, 15, 54-55, 86-90, 270
Foreign Agricultural Service (FAS), 213, 215, 234-235, 263; Export Product Review Program, 94; promotion programs of, 5, 48-49, 97, 232-233, 294, 296-298. *See also* Targeted Export Assistance Program
Forker, Olan D., 44
Forward contracting, 32, 34, 40, 62
France: promoting U.S. products in, 222, 232, 236, 238, 251; hypermarkets in, 124
Francis, John J., 265
Freese, Betsy, 114
Frieda's Finest/Produce Specialties, Inc., 137-140
Friedman, Martin, 105, 159
Fruit: breeding varieties of, 141-144; computerized marketing system for, 200; consumption by women, 70, 71, 72, 74, 75; citrus, 144; growing, 173-175; marketing, 212, 223, 236; U.S. exports, 97, 216, 236
Futures market, 32, 34, 39, 41-42, 62, 180-181
Garden State. *See* New Jersey
Garlic, 237, 238
General Agreement on Tariffs and Trade, 64, 68, 196
General Foods, 109
General Sales Manager, Office of, 64, 294-298. *See also*

Export Enhancement Program (EEP)
Gerber baby food, 119
German Oil Millers Association, 232
Germany, Federal Republic of, 100, 169, 222, 232, 236, 252
Ghana, 66
Giant Food Inc., 4, 123
Gila River Indian Community, 156
Godiva chocolate, 104
Gold Kist, Inc., 210
Goldberg, Ray, A., 18
Good, Darrel, 40, 179
Good Food Book, 261
Good Housekeeping, 270
Government programs, 61, 63; aiding private sector, 227-229, 232-233; policies, 61; working with private sector, 155. *See also* USDA
Grade standards. *See* Standards
Grain: consumption by women, 70, 71, 72, 74; marketing of, in Illinois, 179-181; quality of, 182-186
Grand Union, 123
Grapefruit, 144, 215; promotion of, 97, 222
Grapes, 144
Great Britain, 232. *See also* England and United Kingdom
Great Depression, 8-9, 11
Green Giant vegetables, 249-252
Green, Judy, 80
Greenfield, Jerry, 145-148
Grimes, Glenn, 270
Growmark, Inc., 210
GSM 102-103. *See* Export Credit Guarantee Program; Intermediate Credit Guarantee Program
Guatemala, 66
Guavas, 137; juice of, 151
Guayule, 155, 156
Häagen-Dazs, 250, 251-252
Hahn, J. Nicholas, 281
Hale, Buddy, 114
Hallberg, Milton C., 12
Harness, Charles R., 268
Harvest States Cooperatives, 210
Hawaii, 151, 153-154
Hawthorne, Winnie, 115
Health, concerns about, 24, 126, 160, 183-184, 196, 207, 223, 265-267; Japanese health standards for processed pork, 92
Health and Human Services, Department of, 207
Healy, Tom, 245

Hedging, 32-33, 41-43, 180
Henry, Troy, 119
Hevea brasiliensis, 156
Hinsch, R. Tom, 213
Hog industry, 30
Holland. *See* Netherlands, the
Home delivery, 88, 89, 99
Home Testing Institute, 284
Honey, 160, 208. *See also*
  National Honey Board
Hong Kong, 100, 234, 238,
  251, 252, 262-263
Hopkins, Congressman Larry,
  153
Hormel, 109
Howard, Phillip, 119
Hungary, 68
Hybrid striped bass, 155,
  157-158
Hypermarkets, 9, 124, 196-197
Iacocca, Lee, 113
Ice cream, 28; promotion of,
  145-148, 273, 278
Ice Cream Manufacturers
  Association, 45, 278
Illinois, 40, 114, 123, 179-181,
  216
Illinois Cooperative Extension
  Service, 179
Incomes, increasing, 6-7, 111
India, 66, 142
Indiana, 114
Indonesia, 68, 245, 262-263
Information systems, 63, 195,
  206. *See also* Computers;
  Marketing, electronic;
  Information technology
Information technology, 22,
  23, 168
Infosmith, 255
Ingalsbe, Gene, 208
Insects, in exported fruit, 215;
  in grain, 184-185. *See also*
  Pest management
Interactive video, 255
Intermediate Credit Guarantee
  Program (GSM-103), 64-65,
  249, 295-296, 298
International Ice Cream
  Association, 273
Iowa, 115, 125-126, 127;
  State University of, 94
Iraq, 64, 65, 66
Irradiation. *See* Pest
  management
Israel, 66
Italy, 100, 222, 232
J. C. Penney, 203, 283
J. P. Stevens, 284
Jager, Lisa, 244
Jamaica, 66
Japan, 100, 210, 223-224, 236;
  distribution system, 91,
169-172; fast food industry
  in, 223; market for U.S.
  products: almonds, 169-172;
  asparagus, 237; feed grains,
  227; fruit, 236; fruit juices,
  239; ice cream, 251; meat,
  244-248; potatoes, 223,
  262-263; soups, 102, 104;
  soybeans, 230; specialty
  foods, 234; vegetables, 251;
  wines, 237; wood products,
  224-225
Japan Economic Journal, 252
Japan External Trade
  Organization, 92, 93
Japan Meat Processors
  Association, 94
Japan, Ministry of Health &
  Welfare, 92
Japan, Ministry of
  Construction, 225
Japanese Agricultural Standard
  (JAS), 92-93
Jay, John, 247
Jefferson, Thomas, 115
Jersey Fresh Campaign. *See*
  New Jersey Department of
  Agriculture
Jewell, 198
John Morrell & Company, 247
Jordan, 66
Jurchak, Tom, 173
Just-In-Time deliveries, 167,
  192
Kansas, 115, 154; State
  University, 136
Kaplan, Janet Kim, 116
Kean, Thomas H., Governor,
  259
Kenaf, 155-156
Kenaf International, 156
Kentucky, 153, 212
Kentucky Fried Chicken, 87
King-Casey study, 188
King Ranch, 113
Kings Super Markets, 123
Kiwifruit, 137, 214
Klein, Bill, 179-181
Klein, Debbie, 179-181
Knipe, C. Lynn, 91
Korea, Republic of, 65-66,
  234, 236-237, 251
Kraft Co., 262
Kroc, Ray, 86
Kroger Company, 133, 198,
  203, 204
Krumme, Richard, 112
Labeling, products for Japan,
  92-94
Lackawanna County, PA,
  173-178
Ladies Home Journal, 270
Land-grant universities, 210,
  217, 307, 308, 309, 310, 314;
  research in guayule, 156
Land O'Lakes, Inc., 208, 210
Lange, Jessica, 291
Laser discs, 309, 310
Lea & Perrins, 109
Leath, Mack N., 40, 182
LeComte, A., 93
Legislation: Agricultural Act
  (1949), 67; Agricultural Fair
  Practices Act, 312; Beef
  Promotion and Research Act
  (1985), 161, 266; Dairy and
  Tobacco Adjustment Act,
  (1983), 47; Federal
  Agricultural Marketing
  Agreement Act (1937), 47;
  Federal Seed Act, 312; Food
  Security Act (1985), 48, 61,
  64-65, 68, 294, 296, 298;
  Perishable Agricultural
  Commodities Act, 312; Plant
  Variety Protection Act, 312;
  Public Law 480, 64-65, 67,
  297-298; Research and
  Promotion Act (1966), 282
Lenker, John C., 249
Lentils, 222-223
Lifestyles, changing, 3, 6,
  76-79, 86, 96, 100, 120,
  136, 264
Local Currency Initiative, 298
Lorio, Wendell J., 119
Louis Rich Company, 125-127
Louisiana: Cajun cooking in,
  286-292; source of crawfish,
  224; hypermarket in, 124
Louisiana Department of
  Agriculture, 288, 290
Louisiana Department of
  Commerce, 290
Louisiana Department of
  Culture, Recreation, &
  Tourism, 292
M. Chrysops, 158
Maas, David, 115
Macher, Ron, 115
McDonald's, 86, 87
McLane Company, 196
McLane, Drayton, Jr., 196
Malaysia, 68; food promotion
  in, 234, 236-237, 238, 239,
  245, 262-263
Manchester, Alden C., 6
Mangoes, 137
Manhattan Shirt, 283
Marcin, Ginny, 99
Margin calls, 42
Market, commodity options,
  42-43
Market research. *See* Research,
  market
Marketing: challenges in, 2-5;
  changes in, 6-11, 18-24,
  196-198; competition in,
  173-178; 196-198; costs of,

15-17, 62; electronic, 34, 199-202; plan for, 35-36, 43, 180; specialized functions of, 12-17; target, 78, 271-272, 283-285; test, 27, 84-85, 107-109, 140, 152. *See also* Advertising; Agents; Markets; Promotion

Marketing alternatives, 32-34, 37-42, 60-61, 116-119, 153-158

Marketing information, 25-30, 63, 75, 314-318

Marketing strategies: cooperative, 174-175, 208-212; developing, 32-36, 60, 95; firms, 4, 50-57; farmer groups, 44-49; growth, 129-132, 146-148; individual farmers, 37-43; international, 64-68

Markets: changes in, 6, 18-24, 58-63; competing for overseas, 57, 226-229; developing overseas, 91-94, 169-172, 222-225, 230-233, 240-243, 244-248, 249-252, 294-298; foodservice, 128-132; military, 273, 291. *See also* Marketing; Marketing strategies

Maryland, 114, 157-158; University of, 309

Mauna La'i guava juice, 151

Mayer, Leo V., 64

Mayer, Steven D., 86

Meat, 62; consumption by women, 71, 72, 74; low-fat, 112. *See also* Beef; Chicken; Pork; Turkey

Mellencamp, John Cougar, 290

Mergers, of food manufacturing companies, 11; wholesalers, 10

Mercer, Robert L., 261

Metropolitan Home magazine, 292

Mexico, 65, 66, 251

Michaud, Larry, 88, 286

Microwave ovens, 26, 100, 120, 122, 126, 196; impact of, 109; new products for, 121, 159; packaging for, 188

Mid-America International Agri-Trade Council, 234

Mid-American Dairymen, Inc., 210

Migration, 173

Milk, 7, 10, 48, 178, 272, 277-279; consumption by women, 70, 71, 72, 74, 75; low-fat, 27, 110; sold in convenience stores, 10

Minnesota Corn Processors, Inc., 212

Missouri, 115, 216; University of, 179

Mold contamination, 183-185

Monaghan, Tom, 89

Montgomery Ward, 283

Morgan, Bruce, 292

Morocco, 64, 66

Morone saxatalis, 158

Moshfegh, Alanna J., 70

Mott's, 107

Murphy, Kevin, 152

Mushrooms, 104, 114-115, 137, 138, 212

Mycotoxins, 183

National Agricultural Library, 306-310

National Agricultural Statistics Service (NASS), 299-303

National-American Wholesale Grocers' Association, 168, 197

National Association of State Departments of Agriculture, 238

National Consumer Retail Beef Study, 134

National Dairy Board. *See* National Dairy Promotion & Research Board

National Dairy Board Institute for Nutrition & Cardiovascular Research, 274

National Dairy Promotion & Research Board, 45, 47, 161, 163, 271-275, 278

National Dairy Promotion Board. *See* National Dairy Promotion & Research Board

National Electronic Marketing Association, 200, 201, 202

National Farmers Union, 210

National Fisheries Institute, 253

National Grocers Association, 205

National Honey Board, 161, 162

National Institutes of Health, 24

National Live Stock and Meat Board, 253-254, 270

National Pork Board, 48, 161, 163, 268, 269

National Pork Producers' Council, 48, 161, 268

National Potato Promotion Board, 261-264

National Tea, 198

Nationwide Food Consumption Surveys (NFCS), 70, 71, 75

Nebraska, 154

Nestle, 11

Netherlands, the, 104, 213, 222, 238

New Jersey, 256-260

New Jersey Department of Agriculture, 256-260

New Mexico, 156, 238

New Product News, 105, 159-160

New York Times, 261, 287

New Zealand, 19, 68

Niche marketing, 53, 85, 114, 125, 198. *See also* Research, market

North Carolina, 133, 212

North Dakota, 113

North Yemen, 246

Nutrition, research, 274; education, 273-274, information, 207. *See also* Health, concerns about

Nuts, 144; almonds, 169-172; peanuts, 216; pecans, 238

Nylon, 281

O'Connell, Paul F., 153

Ocean Spray Cranberries, Inc., 149-152, 208

Office of the General Sales Manager. *See* General Sales Manager, Office of

Ohio, 124

Ohio State University, 134

Oilseeds, 66

Oklahoma, 116-119, 127

Oklahoma State University, 116, 118

Oklahoma State Government, 117

Onions, 142

Options, 41, 62, 181. *See also* Commodity options market

Oranges, 144; juice of, 45, 95-98

Ore-Ida, 223

Oregon, 114, 124

Oregon Health Sciences University, 274

Oscar Mayer Foods, 126-127

Packaging: convenience, 122; for at-home storage, 188; new, 23-24, 152, 209, 214-215, 236; plastic, 109; protective, 219; redesigning, 138-139; testing market for, 190; vacuum, 134; value-added, 187-190

Packing and processing, changes in, 168, 177

Pakistan, 66

Parthenium argentatum, 156

Patent Office, 300

Patrons of Husbandry (Grange), 210

Payne, Walt, 169, 208
Peaches, 143-144
Pennsylvania, 124, 144;
  Lackawanna County,
  173-178
Pennsylvania Dairy
  Association, 278
Pennsylvania Department of
  Agriculture, 178
Pennsylvania Farmers
  Association, 178
Pennsylvania State
  University, 176, 178
People's Republic of China.
  See China.
Pepperidge Farm cookies, 104
Perez, Jerry, 246
Perishable Agricultural
  Commodities Act, 312
Pest management, 217-220. See
  also Insects; Pesticides
Pesticides, 62, 79, 176, 220
Pheromones, 217, 220
Philippines, the, 68, 245
Pillsbury International, 249-252
Pink Grapefruit Juice Cocktail,
  152
Pitre, Alton, 286, 292
Pizza, 105-107, 278, 280
Pizzolato, Cliff, 291
Pizzolato, Tony, 291
Plant Variety Protection
  Act, 312
Point of Purchase Advertising
  Institute, 187, 253
Poland, 66
Polyester, 281, 283, 284-285
Polyester Fashion Council, 284
Pomegranates, 137
Population, U.S., aging of, 11,
  76-77, 89; growth of, 6;
  migration of, 7, 173;
  obtaining information
  about, 82
Pork, "America's Cut," 163;
  consumption by women, 71,
  72; promotion of, 28;
  selling in Japan, 91-94; the
  other white meat, 28, 48,
  268-270. See also
  National Pork Board
Pork Pro Newsletter, 270
Potato Board, 160-161. See also
  National Potato Promotion
  Board
Potatoes, 141, 223, 261-264.
  See also Potato Board
Prego spaghetti sauce, 102
Prices, food, 3, 53
Produce Specialties, Inc., 137
Product design, 24
Product diversification, 51,
  112-115
Product life cycle, 128-129

Product positioning, 22,
  105-106, 149, 151
Product quality, 26-27
Product standards, 21-22
Productivity, in food industry,
  58-60; 166-168
products, new, 105; costs of
  developing, 27-28;
  developing, 149-152, 153,
  160, 159-163; introducing,
  163, 223-225; inventing and
  testing, 27-28, 100-102,
  105-110, 152
Promotion, 51-52; almonds,
  170-172; beef, 28; Cajun
  cooking, 287-292; citrus, 47,
  97-98, 222; by cooperatives,
  175; cost of, 27; cotton,
  281-285; coupon, 52, 98;
  foodservice, 132; generic
  dairy, 271-275; 276-280;
  ice cream, 145-148;
  merchandising, 5, 23, 52,
  236; New Jersey products,
  256-260; pork, 28, 268-270;
  potatoes, 262-264; price, 5;
  prunes, 223; soybeans,
  230-233; specialty produce,
  139; turkey, 127; by regional
  trade associations, 234-239
Prudhomme, Paul, 88, 286-289
Pruitt, Bobby, 118
Prunes, 223
Public Law 480, 64-65, 67,
  297-298
Public relations activities,
  5, 98, 146-148, 261-262, 264
Publix Super Markets, 123
Puerto Rico, 252
Purcell, Wayne D., 199
Quaker, 11
Quality, consumers seeking,
  100, 110; of grain, 182-185;
  communicating information
  about, 25-30; of product, 62.
  See also Health; Food
  quality; Food safety
Quick service restaurants, 88.
  See also Fast food
  industry
Rackstraw, Kevin, 226
Radio Corporation of America,
  204
Rand Corporation, 120
Rasmussen, Gordon, 213
Rather, Dan, 289
Reagan, Ronald, 68, 259
Redark Development
  Authority, 116, 118, 119
Redfish, blackened, 88, 287
Regional trade associations,
  234-239
Research and Promotion Act
  (1966), 282

Research: consumer, 134, 190;
  cooperative, 210, 212; by
  farmer, 80-85; market, 95,
  98, 207, 213-216, 312;
  product, 149-152, 155,
  274-275, 283. See also
  individual commodity
  research and promotion
  boards
Restaurant Business magazine,
  121
Restaurants, 15, 75, 86-90, 121,
  123, 196, 197; quick service,
  128-129
Retailers, leadership role of,
  21; scanning by, 203-207
Reynolds, Bruce J., 240
Rhodes, V. James, 25
Rice, 66
Riceland Foods, 208
Richards, J. Wilfred, 175
Ricker, Harold S., 203
River Road, 288
Rosendale, Virgil, 270
Rubber, 156
Safeway stores, gourmet, 123,
  197
St. Marys Woolens, 115
Salad bars, 26, 88, 89, 196;
  crops for, 112
Sampson, Bob, 40, 179
Saudi Arabia, 66, 227-228, 246
Scanner checkout systems, 78,
  121, 139, 203-207
Scanners, electronic, 78, 121,
  167, 309
Schreck, Bob, 249-250
Schuck, Nancy Grudens, 80
Schuelke, Barbara A., 125
Schur, Sylvia, 105
Scott, Willard, 259
Sears, Jerry, 118
Sears, 283, 284
Selling Areas Marketing, Inc./
  Burke, 121
Seng, P. M., 92
Seng, Phil, 245
Senk, Glen, 288
Shepherd, Cybill, 288
Shopping á la Carte, 121, 123
Shopping, one-stop, 9, 120,
  124. See also Convenience
  shopping
Shopping, from home, 207
Siebert, Jerry, 58
Simon, Paul, 290
Sims, Laura S., 70
Sims, Melvin E., 294
Singapore, 245, 251, 252,
  262-263
Sioux Honey Association, 208
"60 Minutes," 79
Smith, Rick,
South Carolina, 115, 126, 142
South Dakota, 115

South Korea. *See* Korea,
Republic of
South Central Agricultural
Research Laboratory, 118
Southeast United Dairy
Industry, 278
Southern States Cooperative,
Inc., 210
Southern U.S. Trade
Association, 234
Soviet Ministry of Agriculture,
GOSAGROPROM, 232
Soviet Union, 218, 232, 233,
288; exports to, 66, 169
Soybean oil inks, 233
Soybeans, 158, 179-181, 216,
230-233; grading standards
for, 185
Spaghetti squash, 137, 138
Spain, 222-223, 227, 232
Specialty produce, 137-140
Spring Mills, 283
Sri Lanka, 66
Standards: Japanese
Agricultural, 92-93;
manufacturers' product,
21-22; need for grading,
185; U.S., 25-26, 62, 311-312
State Departments of
Agriculture, 83, 213, 234,
238, 314
State Agricultural Experiment
Stations, 155
Steve's Homemade Ice Cream,
122
Store Consolidation, 22-23
Store design, 23-24
Stores, grocery, 8-10, 22, 53,
167, 253-255, 257. *See also*
Supermarkets
Stossel, John, 262
Strategy, marketing. *See*
Marketing Strategy
Stroh, Roger J., 253
Successful Farming magazine,
112
Sudan, 66
Sugar, 153-154
Sugar snap peas, 137
Sunchokes (Jerusalem
artichokes), 137
Sunkist, 208-209
Suntory, 252
Supermarkets, 9, 26, 110, 173,
174, 267, 270; beef in,
133-134; challenges for,
76-79; installing fast food
operations, 89; in Japan,
223-224, 236; packaging for,
187-188; scanning checkout
systems in, 203-207;
shopping convenience of,
26, 120-124, 196-198. *See
also* Stores, grocery

Superstore, 9
Superwarehouse store, 9
Swanson brand, 103
Sweden, 100, 224
Switzerland, 66, 238
Tadayoshi Watanabe, 247
Taiwan, 222, 234, 251, 262-263
"Takeout" food, 88, 89, 106,
120-121, 123
Target marketing, 78, 271-272,
283-285
Targeted Export Assistance
Program (TEA), 46, 48, 61,
62, 66-67, 97, 162, 227-228,
232, 237-239, 246, 251,
296-297
Taylor, Glen, 118
Tea, herbal, exports of, 238
Teleauctions, 199, 201
TELECOT, 200
Teletype auctions, 201
Technologies, 57; developing
promising, 153-158; for pest
management, 217-220. *See
also* Information
technology; Marketing,
electronic
Test marketing, 27, 84-85,
107-109, 140, 152
Texas, 113, 156, 199
Texas A&M University, 231
Thialand, 68, 236, 245
*The Food Marketing Industry
Speaks,* 123, 124
Thomas, Carroll, 291
Three Rivers Produce, 117-118
Tobacco, 153
Tomatoes, 142; growing of,
173-178; in Lackawanna
County, 173; need for
quality, 112
Torgerson, Randall E., 208
Trade associations, 62,
314-318; regional, 234-239
Trade negotiations, 64, 68
Trains, container, 192-194;
unit, 194-195
Transportation, food, 38, 135,
191-195
Tree Top, 208
*Trends: Consumer Attitudes
and the Supermarket,* 120,
122
Tunisia, 66
Turkey, 66
Tyson Foods, Inc., 129-132
Uniliver, 11
U.S.S.R. *See* Soviet Union
Unit trains, 194-195
United Dairy Industry
Association, 277
United Dairymen of Arizona,
278

United Fresh Fruit and
Vegetable Association,
253-255
United Kingdom, 99, 222, 229,
238, 250; exports to, 102,
223, 251
United Nations Food and
Agriculture Organization,
307
USDA, 163, 178, 181, 204, 207,
210, 212, 273, 275, 292. *See
also* Agricultural Marketing
Service; Agricultural
Research Service;
Agricultural Stabilization and
Conservation Service;
Agricultural Statistics Board;
Commodity Credit
Corporation; Cooperative
Extension Service;
Cooperative State Research
Service; Extension Service;
Federal Grain Inspection
Service; Food and Nutrition
Service; Foreign Agricultural
Service; General Sales
Manager, Office of; National
Agricultural Library; National
Agricultural Statistics
Service
U.S. Feed Grains Council
(USFGC), 227
U.S. Fish and Wildlife Service,
119
U.S. Meat Export Federation
(MEF), 244-248
U.S. Women's National
Gymnastic Team, 264
Universal product code, 22,
139, 198, 203-207
Uruguay, 112
Uruguay Round, 64, 68
Utah Dairy Commission, 278
Value-added products, 100,
125-127
Variable levy system, 91-92
Venezuela, 251
Vegetables: consumption of,
by women, 70, 71, 72, 74;
computerized marketing
system for, 200; exports of,
216; growing, 173-178, 212;
varieties of, 141-142
Vegetable oils, 66
Vermont, 145-148
Video auctions, 200
Video merchandising, 253-255
Videotapes, 134, 253-255
Virginia, 199, 212
Virginia-Carolina Peanut
Farmers Cooperative, 212
Vitamin A, 142
Vitamin C, 151, 261
Vitamin D, 274

Watkins, Congressman Wes, 118
Walker Research, Inc., 267
Wall Street Journal, 79
Wann, E. Van, 116-119
Ward, Ronald W., 44
Washington State, 237
Watermelons, 142, 216
Weight Watchers, 270
Welch's, 208
Wendler, Hank, 252
West Germany. *See* Germany, Federal Republic of
West Point Pepperell, 283

Western U.S. Agricultural Trade Association (WUSATA), 234-239
Westwater, Joseph J., 271
Whatley, Booker T., 115
Wheat, 66, 154, 186
Wheatgrass, 138
White Wine Worcestershire Sauce, 109
Wholesale club outlets, 10
Wholesaling, food, 10, specialization in, 10
Wills, Bob, 276
Wilson, Ewen M., 2

Wilson, Justin, 288-289
Wisconsin Dairy Board, 278
Women: food consumption of, 70-75; targeting, 283-285. *See also* Work force, women in
Wood products, 224-225
Work force, women in, 3, 7, 76, 79, 86, 99, 120, 133
World Food Program, 67
Yemen Arab Republic, 66, 249
Youde, James, 234
Zaire, 250
Zerk, Willem, 244

Credits

The Yearbook Committee helped choose this book's contents—identifying authors and topics, recruiting authors, and editing chapters. Committee members, from the U.S. Department of Agriculture, are:

Gene Ingalsbe
  Agricultural Cooperative Service
George L. Clarke
  Agricultural Marketing Service
Sean Adams and Hubert Kelley (retired)
  Agricultural Research Service
Benjamin R. Blankenship, Jr.
  Economics Management Staff
Alden C. Manchester
  Economic Research Service
Ovid Bay (retired)
  Extension Service
Lynn K. Goldsbrough and Geraldine Schumacher
  Foreign Agricultural Service

In addition, Dave Holder of the Extension Service, Lee Schrader of Purdue University, Don Fersh and William T. Manley (retired) of the Agricultural Marketing Service, John Lee and Les Myers of the Economic Research Service, and Stan Prochaska of the Office of Information contributed to the Committee's work.

The Production Team in USDA's Office of Information included:

Art Director: Vincent Hughes, Design Division
Copy Editor: Grace Krumwiede, consultant to the Special
  Programs Division
Photo Editor: William E. Carnahan, consultant to the Special
  Programs Division
Illustrator: Richard Barnes, Design Division
Design and Production: Gene Hansen Creative Services, Inc.,
  consultant to the Design Division
Printing Coordinator: Warren Bell, Printing Division

U.S. GOVERNMENT PRINTING OFFICE:1988 0—187-237:QL2

For sale by the Superintendent of Documents, U.S. Government Printing Office
Washington, D.C. 20402

LC88-600562